W9-AQN-922

MODERN GENETICS

MODERN

GENETICS

HAIG P. PAPAZIAN

W · W · NORTON & COMPANY · INC ·
NEW YORK

Library of Congress Catalog Card No. 66-18629

PRINTED IN THE UNITED STATES OF AMERICA

2 3 4 5 6 7 8 9 0

Contents

List of Plates

BETWEEN PAGES 172 AND 173

List of Figures

LIST OF FIGURES

List of Tables

List of Appendixes

Preface ♀/♂

Attitudes to science vary from time to time and from country to country. In a recently published *Dictionary of American Proverbs* I find six entries under the title "Science." They are peculiarly depressing. Here is a sample:

"Science is a cemetery of dead ideas."

"Science is madness, if good sense does not cure it."

"Much science, much sorrow."

The present volume has not been written with the intention of exemplifying this attitude. Quite the contrary; it has been written with the feeling that science is interesting. It has not been written as a textbook to help students achieve higher grades; neither has it been written to improve the intellectual status of ambitious adults. Its purpose is rather to provide the agile mind with a substitute for crossword puzzles while commuting in the train. A pencil and sheet of paper will be found helpful companions.

Since intellectual agility is so often paralyzed prematurely during college or soon afterward, young readers may well enjoy this volume more than their seniors. Bertrand Russell tells a story about his boyhood to the effect that he got so excited on reading Kepler's laws governing the motions of the planets that a doctor had to be called to calm him down. Genetics is exciting, and it is so, like Kepler's laws or the atomic theory, because of its simple logical structure.

The beauty of a scientific theory is not enhanced by glamorous presentation nor by an attempt to amaze the reader with size or complexity. The essential virtues of the game of chess are not enhanced by ornate embellishment of the men or the board; in fact, a beginner would do well to learn the game with the plainest pieces.

Max Beerbohm once started a radio broadcast with the words "Ladies and gentlemen, I am afraid my subject is rather an exciting one and as I don't like excitement, I shall approach it in a gentle, timid, roundabout way." Space will not allow our subject to be approached in a roundabout way, but it will be approached gently. All avenues of the subject cannot be explored, but the structure of the science of genetics as it stands today can be presented without omitting any essential part because of fear that the reader will not be intelligent enough to follow.

Emphasis will be on the development of ideas in pure genetics. This does not mean that there are no interesting aspects of applied genetics. Genetics as a science is having an effect on crop production and animal husbandry, but on the whole, applied genetics has not changed our lives in the same way that physics or chemistry has. A country can outlaw genetics teaching with relative impunity, as indeed some contemporary civilized countries have done.

The political and philosophical impact of genetics, on the other hand, has been great. The theory of evolution caused social upheavals approaching revolutionary dimensions in Anglo-Saxon countries toward the end of the last century. More recently, hot arguments and terrible political action have centered around the concept of race. Finally, eugenics, which is concerned with improving our breed, involves genetics. There are advocates of negative eugenics who would discourage or prevent persons with obvious hereditary defects from having children, and there are the more ambitious who look forward to the day when human beings can be changed by genetic techniques into what they consider to be more desirable animals. The geneticist can contribute to these arguments by predicting what the results of a certain course of action are likely to be, but whether it is wise to take such action is a matter on which the geneticist's opinion has no special weight.

In the same way, the geneticist may enlarge our understanding of the more immediate question of the effects of nuclear-weapon testing and the possible use of nuclear bombs in little or great wars. The effects of man-made radiation will be discussed in later chapters.

The reader who approaches the subject for the first time should read the chapters consecutively. The story unfolds in a logical sequence, and one cannot appreciate a part of it without knowing what went before.

Part Two includes the revolutionary work done in the last twelve years. Most of this has been confirmed by workers in various laboratories throughout the world and can be considered already well established. Some topics which occupy the minds of research workers today have also been included, and these will be recognized by the added effort and concentration required to read the sections devoted to them. In order to alleviate mental strain, the more difficult chapters and passages have been interspersed with somewhat relaxing ones.

In general, successive chapters require increasing concentration on the part of the reader. Chapter XIX, in particular, makes use of simple algebra, and those who have no taste for mathematics can omit the offensive parts without losing the main stream of the argument.

Readers who know a thing or two should be warned that

many generalizations are made, especially in the early chapters, that do not tell the whole truth. The story would be intolerably dull and confusing if every statement were hedged by exceptions in order to comply with the rigorous truth. Rigor may be of the essence in some mathematical fields, but it has not always produced the best biology.

To those who approach the subject with a fresh and innocent mind, unfamiliar words may be an embarrassment. Just as in a novel one may have to interrupt one's reading to look back and identify Lady Drayford or Talbot, so here one may forget what transfer RNA, chromosomes, or alleles are. In many plays the characters and their relations are identified in the program, and in a similar spirit, technical terms are described here in the glossary.

New Haven
June, 1965

MODERN GENETICS

Part One ♀/♂

I Some Branches of the Science and an Introduction to Genetic Jargon

The branch of biology known as genetics began in 1900. This statement may surprise the reader, and rightly; I can think of no other science whose beginning can be so precisely pinpointed. In that year three men, working independently in three separate countries, rediscovered the work of Gregor Mendel, an Austrian monk. Mendel's most important paper had been published in 1866, but was ignored by the scientific community for thirty-four years. Mendel's laws laid the foundations of genetics in much the same way that the atomic theory laid the foundations of modern chemistry at the beginning of the nineteenth century. The astonishing genius of Mendel, and the reason why his theories were not appreciated for so long and then were rather suddenly developed by so many, provide much thought for the historian of science.

During the last fifty years or so, many avenues of research have been explored and an imposing edifice of related theories has been developed. It is my belief that the nice development of genetics has had two causes. First is the fact that the fundamental theories are universal; they apply to all life on earth and indeed may be included in a definition of life. Second, these theories are simple and, ex post facto, obvious, as becomes all great scientific theories. It is hoped that the reader will be persuaded to appreciate this point as he digests the later chapters.

The subject matter of genetics falls naturally into three parts. The first part, which can be called classical genetics, is concerned with laws governing the inheritance of various characters, such as blue eyes or hemophilia, from parent to offspring; in other words, the distribution of hereditary units or genes among progeny of a cross. This represents a completion of Mendel's fundamental theories, a filling in of details around his discoveries.

The second and third parts are more recent branches of genetics. The second part is concerned with the chemical nature of genes and the way in which they act. A new and profitable name for this work has been coined: molecular biology. The study of the way in which genes act merges into the subject of embryology, the study of the development of an individual from egg to adult. The process of differentiation involved here—the development of all the different kinds of cells and tissues and organs—is very little understood at present, but some genetic notions, especially those derived recently from work on bacteria and viruses, do offer some promising leads, as will be explained in Chapter XIII.

The third part of our subject and of this book is concerned with evolution, or the change in populations of individuals over long periods of time. The detailed study of this field involves rather heavy mathematics, but the main conclusions and an outline of the methods used will be described here without assuming any mathematical dexterity on the part of the reader. A French mathematician once said that one does not learn mathematics, one grows used to it. The same applies more or less to other fields of science. It is hoped that the reader will grow used to the language of genetics as the story is read.

As a preview of the subject matter, let us consider the question of sex. There are two sexes, male and female, and they occur in roughly equal numbers. What causes this? The answer, which was one of the early achievements of a Mendelian approach, is that there are two kinds of sperm: one kind produces male babies and the other, female.

Sperm produced by the father and eggs produced by the mother are single cells, and are called gametes. After an egg has been fertilized by a sperm it is called a zygote; this is also a single cell originally. The zygote subsequently divides into more and more cells until an embryo and finally a baby is formed. Inside the egg cell and inside the sperm there are objects which are called chromosomes. These can be seen with a microscope, but only at certain times and when properly colored. One of the chromosomes in the egg is called a sex chromosome and is designated X. Only about half of the sperm cells have an X chromosome; the others have a different sex chromosome, called *Y*.

When a sperm carrying an X chromosome fertilizes an egg, the zygote will have two X chromosomes: XX. When a *Y*-carrying sperm fertilizes an egg, the zygote will have XY chromosomes. Zygotes with XX develop into females, and all the cells of a woman have XX chromosomes. Zygotes with XY develop into males, and all cells of a man have XY chromosomes. When a mother forms eggs in her ovaries, the two XX chromosomes become separated and each egg has just one X. When the father forms sperm in his testicles, the XY chromosomes are separated and go into separate sperm; thus about half of the sperm cells have an X and half have a Y chromosome. The process can be shown in a diagram (Fig. 1).

In this brief account of sex determination in mammals

FIGURE 1

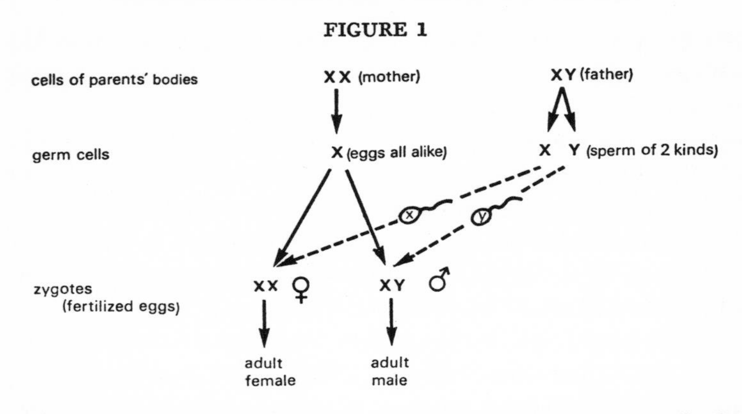

we have introduced the terms *cell, gamete, zygote,* and *chromosome*. Other genetic terms that will be used frequently are described below and can also be referred to in the glossary.

Chromosomes are subdivided into smaller units, called genes, which determine characters in somewhat the same way as the X and Y chromosomes determine sex. Each gamete —sperm or egg—contains only half as many chromosomes as any other cell of the body; germ cells are consequently said to be haploid, and all the other body cells are said to be diploid.

When cells of the body divide, their chromosomes also divide; this process of chromosome division is called mitosis. When germ cells are formed and the number of chromosomes is halved, a special kind of division of chromosomes takes place; this special division is called meiosis, in contrast to mitosis.

The kind of chromosomes a person has is called his genotype, and the appearance of a person is called his phenotype. Thus, men have the genotype XY and the phenotype male. Women have the genotype XX and the phenotype female. The designation of the phenotype may seem superfluous, but consider the case where sex is reversed by sex hormones or other treatment or accident. It is claimed that such reversals have occurred in poultry and, in a more ambiguous way, in humans. Then a person who had the genotype XX and should normally be a female, might through some agent such as hormones acquire the appearance or phenotype of a male. If this phenotype were so perfectly male that he could mate with a normal female and produce children, one would expect all his children to be females: since his genotype was XX, all his sperm would carry X, and none could carry Y. He would thus form only female-producing sperm.

A gene sometimes changes abruptly to another kind of gene and thus gives rise to a new character, blue eyes or hemophilia perhaps. This change in a gene is called mutation; it can be made more frequent by exposure to X-rays or various chemicals. When mutation occurs by itself, it is called spontaneous mutation; when it is deliberately caused by radiation or other treatment, it is called induced mutation. A cell that has mutated is called a mutant.

II *Stepping Stones: A Few Interesting but Untenable Ideas*

Before two cardinal facts, now familiar to all students, were firmly established, a great deal of thought and speculation from ancient times well into the eighteenth century was spent. The first of these facts is that all animals and plants come from similar animals or plants. No maggot, ant, or, as we can say today, bacterium or virus, ever—as was one thought—arises spontaneously from putrifying garbage or other nonliving matter. Some forms of life, such as the amoeba, may multiply by merely dividing into two equal halves, but most species arise from a small part of the parent, the egg. It is true that an ostrich egg or a coconut cannot be called small, but if these are examined closely it is found that the important part is in reality minute and is surrounded by a large amount of food to nourish the young growing embryo of bird or tree.

The second fact is that in those animals and plants which, like ourselves, reproduce sexually, the father through his sperm makes a contribution equal to that of the mother. The proper experiment to prove that sperm particles were the fertilizing elements was performed by the Abbé Spallanzani in the second half of the eighteenth century. He first demonstrated, very simply and directly, that some material contribution from the male was necessary. He covered male frogs and toads with silk knickers and found that the eggs of their female companions were then sterile. In order to go one step further and determine whether the sperm cells or the accompanying fluid was the essential ingredient, he strained off the sperm with filter paper and found that the fluid alone could not fertilize.

Spallanzani's experiments were conducted very much in the manner that we would follow today. However, he himself was not convinced by the experimental facts and clung in vain to his a priori belief that sperm had no important role.

If a new individual starts life as a single egg cell and a single sperm cell, there must be something in these microscopic bodies that says "man with blue eyes, long nose, and bald patch on his head"; or "female fly with apricot eye and forked bristles on her back."

In the middle of the eighteenth century the prevalent idea was that each egg contained a very small man or woman, complete in all characteristic details, which would grow by expansion into an adult. This "encapsulation" theory involved the further assumption that each egg in the ovary of the minute woman contained an even smaller woman—ad infinitum. In the words of Henry Baker (1754)

> Each seed includes a Plant: that Plant again,
> Has other Seeds, which other Plants contain:
> Those other Plants have all their Seeds; and, Those,
> More Plants, again, successively inclose.
>
> Thus, ev'ry single Berry that we find,
> Has, really, in itself whole Forests of its Kind.
> Empire and Wealth one Acorn may dispense,
> By Fleets to sail a thousand Ages hence:

Each Myrtle-Seed includes a thousand Groves,
Where future Bards may warble forth their Loves.
So ADAM Loins contain'd his large Posterity,
All People that have been, and all that e'er shall be.

Amazing Thought! what Mortal can conceive
Such wond'rous Smallness!—Yet we must believe
What Reason tells: for Reason's piercing Eye
Discerns those Truths our Senses can't descry.

Today we would reverse the conclusion and say that our senses discern the truth with which reason must comply.

Among those who believed in the encapsulation theory there was some argument as to whether it was the egg or the sperm which contained a preformed man. Belief so dominated the senses that some microscopists of the time described the miniature men in sperm, the so-called homunculi. It is clear that this theory does not stand up to precise reasoning. The head of a man's sperm is about 5/1,000 of a millimeter long, or about 1/320,000 of a man's height. The size of the sperm inside the little man in this sperm would be only 1.5×10^{-8} mm. long, less than one Angstrom unit (Å), which is the radius of a hydrogen atom. I will not labor the point further by calculating the size of the third generation! Again, one must consider the fact, evident from common experience, that children inherit from both father and mother; therefore both sperm and egg would have to contain a homunculus. Perhaps the egg would contain a little woman homunculus; somehow the two would fuse and a perfect man or woman having a recognizable likeness to both parents would be the result.

The encapsulation or Chinese-boxes theory was an attempt, although weak, at a theory of heredity.

The next idea to consider is pangenesis, proposed by Charles Darwin. This is worthy of attention in spite of its wrongness because it was a step in the right direction and because an understanding of it will lead to better appreciation of the Mendelian theory. Albeit very dear to Darwin, it was only an idea and he fully realized, and regretted, that no supporting evidence was forthcoming.

In the 1872 edition of the *Origin of Species* he describes his idea as follows: "According to this hypothesis, every unit or cell of the body throws off gemmules or undeveloped atoms, which are transmitted to the offspring of both sexes, and are multiplied by self-division."

One reason that Darwin liked this hypothesis was that it could explain the inheritance of acquired characters. If, for instance, a gunman exercised the trigger finger of his hand to such an extent that the muscles grew unusually large and strong, then the gemmules in that finger would increase by self-division and more of them would be in that gunman's sperm to be passed on to his children. They would thus inherit the characteristic strong finger acquired by their father.

Darwin was wrong in believing that acquired characters were inherited and wrong to think that the presence of this type of inheritance would support his theory of evolution. Actually his theory of evolution can be much better understood in terms of the mutation theory of variation, of which more will be said later.

A well-conducted experiment which helped to dispose of the theory of pangenesis was carried out by a distinguished cousin of Darwin's, Francis Galton. His account of this work is worth quoting at length.

> According to Darwin's theory, every element of the body throws off gemmules, each of which can reproduce itself, and a combination of these gemmules forms a sexual element. If so, I argued, the blood which conveys these gemmules to the places where they are developed, whether to repair an injured part or to the sexual organs, must be full of them. They would presumably live in the blood for a considerable time. There-

fore, if the blood of an animal of one species were largely replaced by that of another, some effect ought to be produced on its subsequent offspring. For example, the dash of bull-dog tenacity that is now given to a breed of greyhounds by a single cross with a bull-dog, the first generation corresponding to a mulatto, the second to a quadroon, the third to an octoroon, and so on, might be given at once by transfusion. Bleeding is the simplest of operations, and I know that transfusion had been performed on a large scale; therefore I set about making minute inquiries.

These took a long time, and required much consideration. At length I determined upon trying the experiment on the well-known breed of rabbits called silver greys, of which pure breeds were obtainable, and to exchange much of their blood for that of the common lop-eared rabbit; afterwards to breed from pairs of silver greys in each of which alien blood had been largely transfused. This was done in 1871 on a considerable scale. I soon succeeded in establishing a vigorous cross-circulation that lasted several minutes between rabbits of different breeds, as described in the *Proceedings of the Royal Society*, 1871 [25]. The experiments were thorough, and misfortunes very rare. It was astonishing to see how quickly the rabbits recovered after the effect of the anaesthetic had passed away. It often happened that their spirits and sexual aptitudes were in no way dashed by an operation which only a few minutes before had changed nearly one half of the blood that was in their bodies. (*Memories of My Life*, 1908)

The results were completely negative.

Charles Darwin did not give up the idea of pangenesis because of this experiment. He held that gemmules might still exist but not circulate in the blood. This is fair enough; many a theory though basically true must be modified in its details as more facts come to light. A theory must be given up when the strain of modifications becomes unbearable and especially when another theory is proposed which appears simpler. Darwin's pangenesis had to be given up, but his theory of evolution, modified as regards the inheritance of acquired characters, was almost universally adopted in its basic notions.

An element in the pangenesis hypothesis which is of special interest is its proposal of a particulate unit of heredity. This means that the characteristics of father and mother are not blended like colored inks to form a child intermediate between his parents, but that instead each character is represented by a particle, the gemmule, which cannot be divided into smaller particles. It is more like a set of colored marbles from one parent being mixed with another set from the other parent to form the set which will determine what the child will be like. In the next chapter we will see how this idea lies at the root of the Mendelian theory.

III *Genetic Particles: The Bead Game*

In a sense Darwin tried to include too much in his theory of pangenesis. He attempted to explain not only heredity, but how growth and differentiation of the body and its parts were related to the germ cells—sperm and eggs. Mendel's success lay in the fact that he concentrated on heredity alone; he conducted well-planned experiments to analyze the inheritance of distinct, clearly recognizable characters from parent to offspring. He performed his experiments with garden peas, but today the same type of experiments can be performed with simpler microscopic organisms, and the theory can be best introduced with an example from one of these.

Chlamydomonas is a small, green, one-celled plant that swims about in ponds by means of two thin flagella. Its food requirements, like those of most green plants, are simple. A few inorganic salts, water, air, and light suffice. Like men and beasts, not all *Chlamydomonas* individuals are perfect. A defect of *Chlamydomonas* which is occasionally found is paralysis of the flagella; the paralyzed *Chlamydomonas* cannot swim. In a small jar of still water they remain near the bottom, and incidentally, this fact has been utilized in an ingenious method of isolating rare paralyzed mutants among many millions of normal, wild-type cells. This method consists simply of putting an ultraviolet light directly above a jar full of *Chlamydomonas* in a nutrient solution. Ultraviolet rays, unlike X-rays, do not penetrate more than a millimeter or so through water. In a strong enough dose they kill all cells. Thus the *Chlamydomonas* well below the surface of the water are safe, but all those that swim to the top are killed. After sufficient time, most of the cells that can swim have been killed and a large proportion of the cells still alive are the paralyzed variants. This type of procedure is known as an enrichment or selective technique; the principle of killing off, by one method or another, most of a large number of individuals one doesn't want in order to be able to isolate the rare individual one does want is of widespread importance in microbiology.

Chlamydomonas has two sexes, which are called the (+) sex and the (—) sex. They look identical although they must have some physiological differences. When a (+) and a (—) strain are mated, the whole body acts as an egg or sperm, and following fusion, a thick-walled zygote is formed which can resist cold and other abuses much better than the vegetative cells (Figs. 2, 10). In appropriate conditions the zygote germinates to form four cells. It is a rule that the zygote of all simple organisms divides initially into four cells; this cluster will here be referred to as a quad. If a paralyzed *Chlamydomonas* is crossed with a wild type, and if we separate the four cells of the resulting quad and grow them, by asexual reproduction, into four cultures in separate tubes, we will find that exactly two of these cultures consist of paralyzed cells and two of wild-type cells. Further crosses can be made between paralyzed and wild-type cells from this so-called F_1 generation, by mating them either with each other, producing an F_2 generation, or back to cells from one of the parent cultures, pro-

FIGURE 2

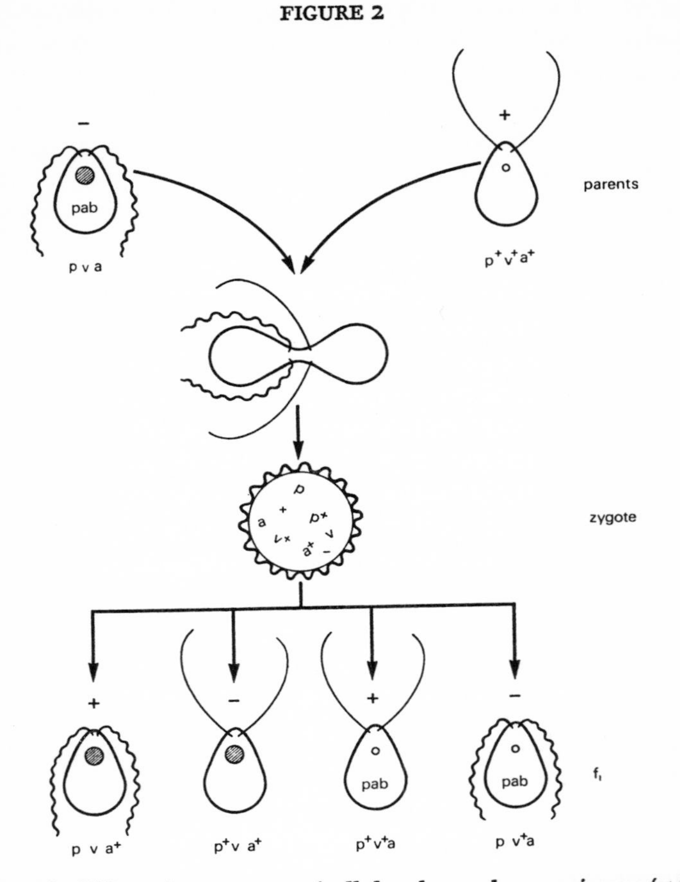

A *Cross in* Chlamydomonas, *a unicellular alga under 10 microns* (*1/100 mm.*) *long*. The top line represents the two parents, (+) and (–); the symbols for their genes are written underneath. These two cells mate to produce a zygote, in which the characters for flagella, extra volutin, and pab are not distinguishable. It germinates to produce four cells, which may have the combinations shown in the bottom line.

ducing a backcross. The result is always the same: when a paralyzed and a wild-type cell combine, exactly two cells of the quad are paralyzed and two are of the wild type.

The Mendelian theory explains these results by proposing the existence of an invisible particle, called a gene, which determines whether the flagella are paralyzed or not. Every individual has just one of this particular gene: either the wild-type gene, p^+, or the gene determining paralysis, p (+ is generally used in genetics to denote the wild, *i.e.* more normal, type). These genes divide in step with the cells during vegetative growth, thus insuring that all cells contain just one representative of this particular kind of gene controlling paralysis.

When a cell containing p^+ is mated to one containing p, the resulting zygote contains two genes, p^+ and p. In the zygote the genes divide once, producing a total of four genes, two p^+ and two p genes. Finally, when the zygote divides into four cells, one gene goes into each cell. The two cells that get a p^+ gene will swim normally, and each will divide asexually to fill a test-tube with Chlamydomonads that swim normally; the two cells that get the p gene will each reproduce to fill a test-tube with Chlamydomonads that are paralyzed. Mendel knew nothing about the nature of genes, but he established the essential point that they act like discrete particles which are remarkably stable. They can pass through many generations and many different crosses unchanged. A cell containing a gene p which has gone through a hundred crosses to the wild type is still just as paralyzed as was the original mutant.

The way in which alternative genes controlling a character unite in the zygote and are distributed to progeny constitutes Mendel's first law, the law of segregation.

A good scientist, like a good general, exploits any promising breach with the utmost vigor. The natural next step in the present case is to cross two parents that differ not in one, but in several characteristics.

Two other characters which have been found in *Chlamydomonas* are an abnormally large amount of the oily substance, volutin, which can be seen in the cell, and the inability to grow unless para-aminobenzoic acid is added to the medium. Para-aminobenzoic acid, or "pab," is related to folic acid, a vitamin the lack of which in humans produces some kinds of anemia. Probably all *Chlamydomonas*, and indeed all living cells, need pab, but the wild-type *Chlamydomonas* can manufacture its own. When there is a defect somewhere along the line of chemical synthesis leading to pab, then the cell will not live and grow unless pab is obtained from outside, from the medium.

A cross made between a cell having all three peculiarities —paralysis (p), extra volutin (v), and the need for pab (a)— and a wild type (p^+, v^+, a^+) will beget some zygotes which germinate to produce two $p\ v\ a$ individuals and two $p^+\ v^+\ a^+$ individuals, exactly like their parents. But there will also be some individuals unlike either parent. Some quads will be as follows: $p\ v\ a^+$, $p^+\ v^+\ a$, $p\ v^+\ a$, $p^+\ v\ a^+$ (Fig. 2). None of these are like the parents; although they have the parental characters, they have them in new combinations. Notice that each character, as was the case in the simple p x p^+ cross, is found in exactly two cells of the quad. Other zygotes would produce other combinations of these three characters. If we do not trouble to isolate the four cells of each quad, but just make a mass mating of hundreds of $p\ v\ a$ with $p^+\ v^+\ a^+$ cells, let the zygotes all germinate together on one Petri dish, and then after some growth isolate about 1,000 single cells and examine them, we will find that we have all the possible combinations of characters. Since there are three characters, each with two alternatives, there are 2^3, or 8, different combinations (Table 1).

TABLE 1

+ + +	$p\ v\ a$
+ v +	p + a
p + +	+ $v\ a$
+ + a	$p\ v$ +

The + signifies p^+, v^+, or a^+ according to its position.

Not only would these eight types be found, but they would be found in equal numbers; there would be about 125 of each. If one were to take three baskets, the first containing an equal number of large and small red marbles, the second an equal number of large and small blue marbles, and the third an equal number of large and small white marbles, and if one picked out 1,000 groups of three, each group consisting of one marble chosen at random from each basket, there would be about 125 of each of the eight possible combinations of colored marbles (Table 2).

TABLE 2

RBW	rbw	R = big red
RbW	rBw	r = little red
rBW	Rbw	B = big blue
RBw	rbW	b = little blue
		W = big white
		w = little white

The fact that different genes go to progeny independently, like the marbles, is known as Mendel's law of independent assortment. Two of each particular kind of gene go into the zygote and divide once; then each of the four of one kind goes to a separate cell. If this were not so, some cells among progeny would not have an exact set of genes, one for each character, but might have two for some characters, say p^+ and p for flagella, and none for another, perhaps volutin.

Each character has a gene which can exist in alternate states—p or p^+, a or a^+, v or v^+. The alternate states of a gene are called alleles. We know now that a gene can have more than two alleles, but since life on earth is biparental, any particular zygote does not normally contain more than two alleles of a gene.

An example of a gene with a very large number of alleles is the gene controlling the sex of mushrooms. Mushrooms, or Basidiomycetes, are the highest of the three major groups of fungi. They are composed of branched filaments which grow throughout the soil and then coalesce in a compact mass to form the fruiting body or mushroom as we know it. Most Basidiomycetes have to go through a sexual process before forming a fruiting body. Their peculiarity lies in the fact that there are, in some of the simpler species, about a hundred different sexes. As in *Chlamydomonas* the sex of a particular plant cannot be recognized by inspection, but only by its mating behavior.

If a large number of spores of a particular mushroom, say *Coprinus* (the ink cap), are grown separately and then mated with each other in all combinations, it will be found that the mushrooms can be divided into a number of sexes such that two individuals of the same sex cannot mate and produce offspring, but any two individuals of different sexes can do so. The progeny of a single fruiting body consists of only two sex types because sex is controlled by one gene with many alleles, the zygote and fruiting body can contain only two of these. Another fruiting body might have two different alleles and produce two different sexes.

A familiar gene with three alleles is that controlling the A, B, O, and AB blood groups in man, described in Chapter VI.

One of the men who rediscovered the laws of Mendel was William Bateson, an Englishman. In the year 1900, on the way to deliver a lecture before the Royal Horticultural Society, he read Mendel's work and suddenly appreciated its significance, in conjunction with his own work. He revised his lecture in the train and was the first in his country to introduce Mendel's laws. Bateson continued his researches—in the face of considerable opposition, we must honestly add—and discovered an important exception to Mendel's law of independent assortment. He discovered the exception, but it was left to Thomas Hunt Morgan and his collaborators at Columbia University in New York to provide the theory of linkage which so nicely accounts for it. Bateson worked with garden peas and chickens; Morgan worked with the fruit or vinegar fly, *Drosophila*. These organisms are complicated in being diploid, as is man, but the principle involved will be described in the next chapter by reference again to *Chlamydomonas*.

IV *Linkage: The Exceptions That Improved the Rule*

Bateson discovered that some pairs of characters do not assort independently. If an organism with two characters, a and b, is crossed with a wild type, $a^+ b^+$, the four possible types of progeny, $a\ b$, $a^+ b^+$, $a\ b^+$, and $a^+ b$, are not always obtained with equal frequency. If a large number of individuals are crossed and 1,000 progeny collected at random, instead of 250 of each type, there may be 400 of $a\ b$, 400 of $a^+ b^+$, and only 100 each of $a\ b^+$ and $a^+ b$. The parental combinations $a\ b$ and $a^+ b^+$ of these two characters appear to stick together. The degree of sticking together is known as linkage and is usually expressed as the percentage of recombinations; in this example the recombinants are $a\ b^+$ and $a^+ b$, and the percentage of recombination is $\frac{100 + 100}{1000} \times 100 = 20$ per cent.

For the same two characters the degree of recombination is found to be always the same, but for various pairs of characters it can vary from just above zero to 50 per cent. If it is really zero, then the two characters must be thought of as only one or at least as being controlled by only one gene. If it is 50 per cent, then assortment is independent: there is no linkage. If the cross is made with the characters described above in different combinations—a^+ b with a b^+—then the progeny will consist of about 400 of a^+ b, 400 of a b^+, 100 of a b, and 100 of a^+b^+, again showing 20 per cent recombination. In this case the recombinants are a b and a^+ b^+. Notice that the two parental types are equal in number, with 400 of each and the two recombinant types are equal, with 100 of each. This is always more or less true unless some other factor intervenes, such as lower viability of the double mutant.

Bateson was worried by this awkward exception to Mendel's law of independent assortment. The only explanation that occurred to him was that genes together in their parental combination multiply at a faster rate, in our example four times as fast as when in a new combination. This was a messy theory, and as more facts came to light it had to give way to the neat theory of Morgan and his associates.

We have already mentioned, at the end of the last chapter, the group of geneticists centered around Morgan at Columbia University. During the first three decades of this century, they did an enormous amount of work with a number of mutants in *Drosophila*. They made a major contribution to the solid basis on which the science of genetics now rests. Many of the older geneticists today owe their inspiration to contact with the Columbia group some forty years ago. Some of these geneticists are named in Appendix 4.

It was important that many workers should concentrate on the same organism, and *Drosophila* was a favorable choice. It looks very much like a common housefly, but it is less than half as large and the wild type has bright-red eyes. It was first used for genetic experiments by W. E. Castle at the Bussey Institute, Harvard University. He recognized the value of its small size and ease of breeding in the laboratory, but did most of his later work with mammals. Many mutant types of *Drosophila,* having eyes of different colors and wings and bristles of varying structure, can readily be obtained. Other genetic virtues of this fly, more sophisticated and unexpected, were to be discovered later and will be described in a subsequent chapter.

The experiments with *Drosophila,* along with other work, showed that the set of characters of an organism could be divided into subsets of linkage groups. Gene *a* might be linked to *b, b* to *c, c* to *d,* and *d* to *e,* but all of these would assort independently when crossed with *f, g,* . . ., *z.* The genes *a, b, c, d,* and *e* would then form a linkage group. This does not mean that each of the genes in a linkage group is directly linked to each of the others; *a* might not, for instance, be linked to *e,* but it might be linked to some gene which was linked to another gene which was linked to *e.* There is a chain of linkage connecting all the genes of a linkage group.

The Columbia school proposed that linkage was due to the fact that genes were not loose like marbles in a bag, but were joined to each other rather like beads on a string. Each linkage group could be represented by a string of beads. The separate strings assorted independently, but beads on the same string stuck together unless there was a break in the string. The theory also proposed that when there was a break, there was a rejoining with the string that came from the other parent.

Thus, if the two horizontal lines on the left (Fig. 3) represent

FIGURE 3

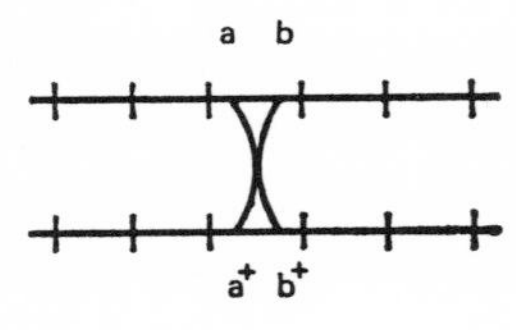

paternal and maternal linkage groups containing genes *a* and *b* and a^+ and b^+ respectively, and if there is a break in the two linkage groups between *a* and *b* with a rejoining the other way around, then the result will be as shown on the right. If such breaks occur in 20 per cent of the zygotes, then 20 per cent of the progeny will be *a* b^+ and a^+ *b*, or recombinants.

The fly *Drosophila melanogaster* has four linkage groups; Mendel's garden peas have seven; man, we conclude from a different kind of evidence, has twenty-three.

A linkage group is worth studying in greater detail. Different pairs of characters in a linkage group show different linkage values, or degrees of linkage. These values, when analyzed, make sense. It is found that if linkage values are taken to represent distances along a line, then these distances are additive. That is to say, if the percentage of recombination between *a* and *b* is 5 per cent and the percentage of recombination between *b* and *c* is 8 per cent, then that between *a* and *c* will be found to be about 13 per cent. All genes in a linkage group can be arranged in a linear order, following this principle. The limit to the amount of recombination is 50 per cent; however far apart two genes are, they will not show more than 50 per cent recombination, and in fact, low percentages are more reliable than high ones as indicators of relative gene position. These facts fit well with the idea of a linear array of genes, like beads on a string. The farther apart the genes, the more likely it is that there will be a break and rejoining somewhere between them, assuming always that breaks can occur anywhere along the line with equal and independent probability. Two breaks in the same nucleus will cancel each other out, and that is why genes that are very far apart, with many breaks between them, may show 50 per cent, but never more than 50 per cent, recombination.

Crosses of organisms differing in three linked characters fit with the theory. If a linkage group *a b c* is crossed with

TABLE 3

Type of Offspring	*No. of Each Type*	*Percentage*	*Where Cross-over Occurred*
$a^+b^+c^+$	315		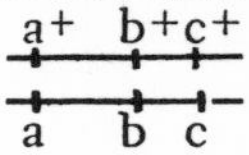 a+ b+c+
abc	315		a b c
a^+bc	100	20	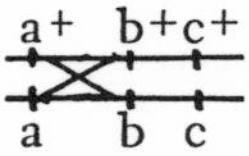 a+ b+c+
ab^+c^+	100		a b c
abc^+	75	15	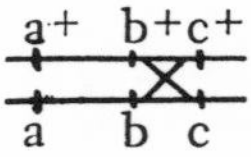 a+ b+c+
a^+b^+c	75		a b c
ab^+c	10	2	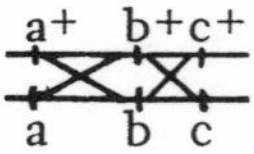 a+ b+c+
a^+bc^+	10		a b c
	1000		

$a^+ b^+ c^+$, 1,000 progeny may have the types[1] shown in Table 3.

If the same three genes had been taken two at a time in three separate crosses the results would have been about as listed in Table 4.

TABLE 4

Parents	*Percentage Recombinants Among Progeny*	
$ab \times a^+b^+$	22	(ab^+ and a^+b)
$bc \times b^+c^+$	17	(bc^+ and b^+c)
$ac \times a^+c^+$	35	(ac^+ and a^+c)

The map for these three genes would be a ←22→ b ←17→ c (←35→).

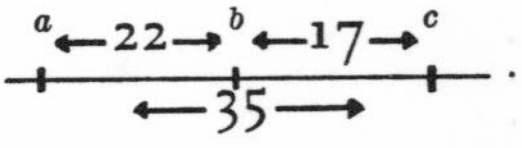

[1] Two complications that will become apparent in later chapters have been neglected here. One is the fact that four strands of genes are involved at the time of crossing-over not two; the other is that in diploid organisms what really should be determined is the genotype of the F_1 gametes resulting from a cross; this is done by backcrossing the F_1 individual to a fly that is recessive for all characters concerned.

Note that the summing of these values is only approximate, for $22 + 17 \neq 35$. This is because there were 2 per cent double cross-overs and in these *a* and *c* come out in their parental combinations. The occurrence of double cross-overs can only be detected when there is a third gene in the cross, lying between the other two.

Going back to the results of the three-point cross, in the first two types no recombination has occurred. In the next two there has been a break, or cross-over, between *a* and *b* in 20 per cent of the zygotes; in the third, 15 per cent crossing-over between *b* and *c*. The fourth pair represents zygotes in which there were two cross-overs in the same nucleus; there were 2 per cent of these double cross-overs.

Data of this sort can be analyzed further. Theoretically there should be over 3 per cent double cross-overs because if cross-overs are independent of each other, the simultaneous occurrence of two cross-overs should be the product of the probabilities of each separate event. If percentages are converted to probabilities by dividing by 100, we have $.22 \times .17 = .0374$ as the product of separate probabilities; this is 3.7 per cent. The discrepancy between the theoretical 3.7 per cent and the observed 2 per cent is typical and is not well understood. It means that cross-overs are not absolutely independent, but this does not affect the significance of the theory. The phenomenon is known as interference. Crosses of *Drosophila* flies differing in as many as nine characters were made, and the results—which incidentally have recently been analyzed for interference effects with the aid of a large computer—were entirely compatible with the theory of a linear order of genes between which occasional cross-overs occur.

No case of three genes having equal recombination between all three pairs was found. Such a finding would represent a triangular or circular linkage group.[2] Likewise, no

[2] In the next chapter it will be shown that circular maps appear to be the rule in viruses and bacteria.

evidence of a branched or **Y**-shaped linkage group has been found.

One could imagine genes as lying on a surface which might crack, with a portion then joining with a portion cracked off from the other parent's surface; or genes might be visualized as having fixed positions in a solid. But the fact is that linkage values only make sense if the genes lie in a one-dimensional unbranched array. This is a very precise and important finding; it says a lot. The idea of breakage and reunion of linkage groups, called crossing-over, is made use of in arriving at this theory, but the precise mechanism of crossing-over can be left vague without damaging the theory. The essential feature of crossing-over that can be inferred is that a break must occur at exactly the same place, between the same two genes, on the paternal and the maternal linkage groups. If this were not so, the two linkage groups, after a crossing-over, would be of unequal length; one would have more genes than the other, and this imbalance would be lethal—perhaps not immediately, but certainly after several generations, when imbalance would pile up.

A representation of a linkage group in which the genes are arranged in order, with known distances between them, is a genetic map. No elaborate apparatus is required to make genetic maps. About five hundred genes in *Drosophila*, each associated with a distinct character, can be assigned their places on one of the four linkage groups, using no more equipment than a hand lens to distinguish characters and a few hundred milk bottles with bananas or other food to breed the flies. The qualities required to propose and establish the theory are, first, a stroke of genius, a kind of intuitive construction of the idea; then, the courage of conviction to sustain a great deal of work with many disappointments. Most disappointments would arise from the choice of unsatisfactory characters, for as we shall see in Chapter VII, many characters are complex and are not controlled directly by a single gene.

In the next chapter a different approach will be described, one which used very different techniques but which fits well with the genetic theory that has just been described.

V *Chromosomes: Two Pursuits Reach Common Ground*

Cytology is concerned with what one can see in a cell by looking through a microscope. Before its relations with genetics were realized it was a purely descriptive science. Previous chapters have shown how the geneticist usually starts with a hypothesis in mind and sets up an experimental cross to test this hypothesis or to get suggestions for a new idea; the work itself may be dull, but after a week of counting hundreds or thousands of *Drosophila* flies, he is rewarded with meaningful results. In contrast, the cytologist, until recently, spent his time looking at cells, and especially at the nuclei inside cells, very carefully. The most powerful microscopes and the most refined methods of preparing and staining slides were essential. It was the work of discovery; no one really expected to see anything in particular, but curiosity, with a certain aesthetic pleasure, drove the cytologist to long hours of work. With proper technical care he regularly saw objects such as those in Plates 1 and 2. These pictures show what can be seen in cells which are in the process of division.

The threadlike objects which are the feature we are interested in are the chromosomes. They were given this name because they stain deeply. In living cells they cannot be seen unless one uses one of the recent developments in microscopy, phase contrast. Otherwise, the cells must be killed with suitable poisons that coagulate all the proteins, just as boiling an egg coagulates the white and keeps things in place; then they must be dipped in a special ink or stain that colors the chromosomes in a distinctive way.

The number of chromosomes is always the same in the same species, eight in *Drosophila melanogaster*, twenty in corn, seven in *Neurospora*, forty-six in man, forty-eight in the chimpanzee. Not only are the numbers constant, but many chromosomes can be recognized by their length and other characteristics; every cell has the same complement of recognizable chromosomes. This uniformity is due to the fact that they divide precisely, by a process called mitosis. When a cell is about to divide, each chromosome splits down its axis to form two identical chromosomes, one of which goes to each daughter cell. At a special part of the life cycle, represented by division of the zygote in species like *Chlamydomonas*, but occurring at the formation of germ cells in higher forms (see Fig. 10), there is a different kind of division, called meiosis. The reason for this difference in higher forms is described at the beginning of the next chapter. Whenever it occurs, the process of meiosis is similar: all the chromosomes pair up longitudinally, one of each pair being derived from one parent and one from the other parent. Each chromosome then splits into two. Groups of four similar strands, called tetrads, are thus produced. The mother cell then divides into four cells, and one strand or chromosome from each tetrad goes to a cell of the quad (Figs. 4 and 5, and Plate 2).

Close inspection reveals another feature of meiosis, known as chiasma, which has proved to be important in genetics.

There are regions in the tetrad where two of the strands appear to cross, and as the chromosomes are pulled apart these regions become more apparent because the chromosomes are temporarily held together there (Plate 2); these regions are the chiasmata. In order to understand how a chiasma is formed, we must explain that when the chromosomes divide they do so throughout their length except for a special point on the chromosome called the centromere, drawn as a clear circle in Figures 4 and 5.

In Figure 5 a single chromosome is shown in detail, with one chiasma. There are usually three or four chiasmata in a reasonably long chromosome. The details seen under the microscope are not easily interpreted; the only feature that is seen clearly is that certain parts of the chromosome stick tightly together as though tied in a knot. The knot or knots then slip along the chromosome, as the strands are pulled apart at the position of their centromeres, until they fall off the end and the four resulting daughter chromosomes are free, each going to a separate cell at the next cell division. We will return to the details of chiasmata a little later.

This process occurs in all chromosomes of the cell and could be shown for all three of the pairs of chromosomes in Figure 4 in a more elaborate diagram. It is of interest that there actually are organisms with only one pair of chromosomes; one such is a nematode worm, parasitic in the horse, *Parascaris equorum* var. *univalens;* we must add that the chromosome of *Parascaris* fragments into smaller pieces as the zygote develops into the embryo, a very peculiar and obscure behavior.

Let us recapitulate; the proportions of different kinds of offspring in various crosses led geneticists to propose units of heredity, genes, which are arranged in linear unbranched arrays called linkage groups. Linkage groups divide precisely at a nonsexual division, as when *Chlamydomonas* divides vegetatively, but in the zygote the linkage groups from both parents

FIGURE 4

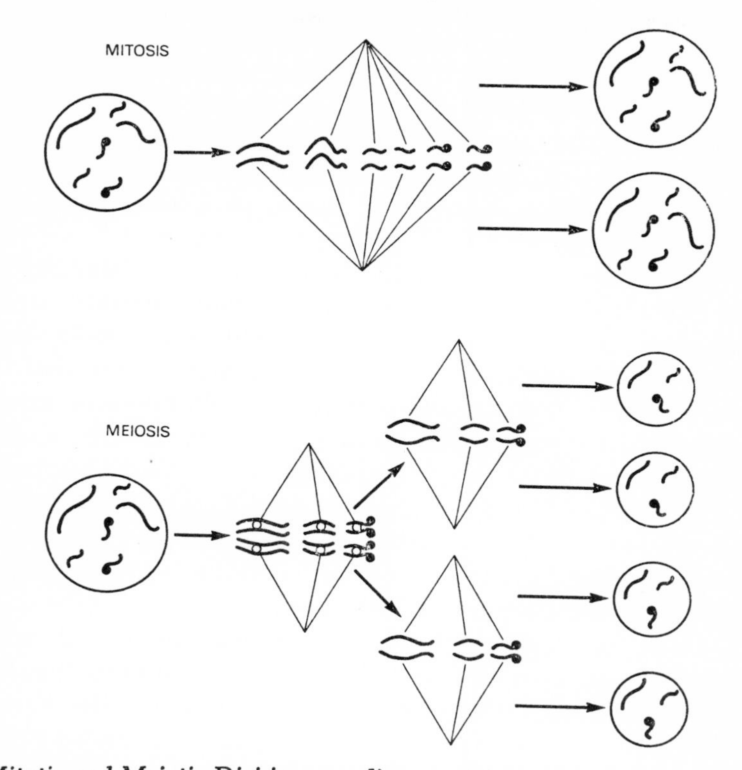

Mitotic and Meiotic Divisions are diagramed for a hypothetical organism with three distinguishable pairs of chromosomes—one long, one short, and one short with a knob on the end. Circles around the chromosomes represent the nuclear membrane which disappears during nuclear division. (Compare with photographs, Plates 1 and 2.)

intermingle and, in *Chlamydomonas,* divide, and are distributed, one linkage group to each cell with an occasional crossover between them. The correspondence between these hypothetical linkage groups and the visible chromosomes is obvious. Another fact that fits the idea is that the number of linkage

FIGURE 5

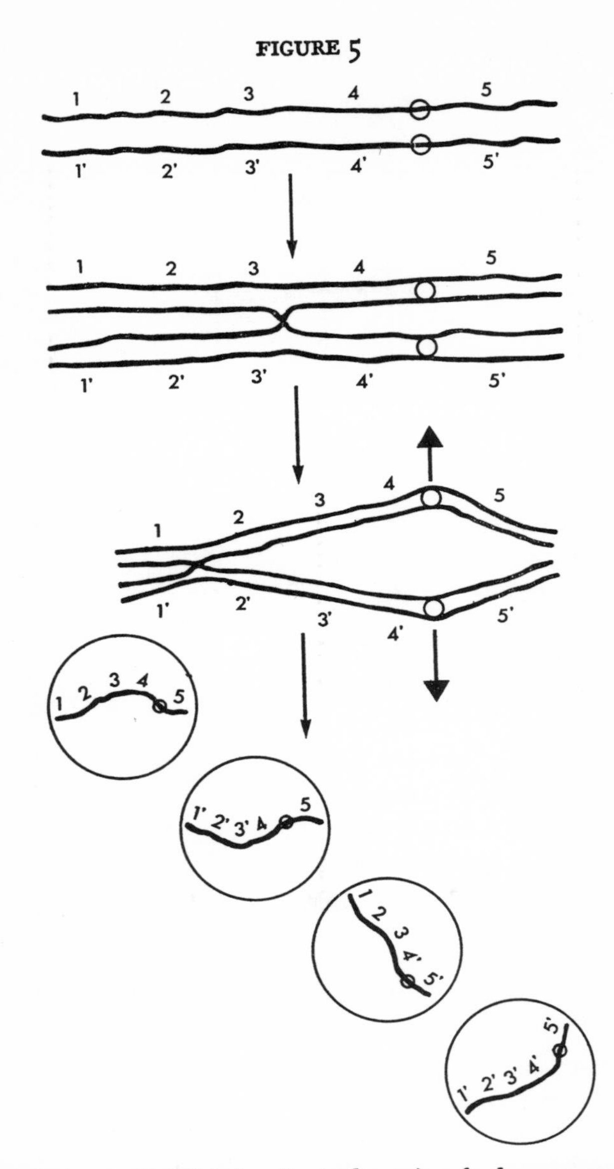

Single-Chromosome Meiosis. A single pair of chromosomes going through meiosis is shown in more detail than in Figure 4. Regions of the chromosome are numbered 1–5 for the paternal chromosome, 1′–5′ for the maternal. The second sketch shows a chiasma formed between region 3 and 4; it is shown next when it has slipped along past region 2, and will finally slip off the end. The four cells of the resulting quad are shown diagonally; two of them are recombinant for this particular chromosome between region 1–2–3 and region 4–5.

groups is the same as, or in diploid organisms half, the number of chromosomes.

Chiasmata, as we shall see, can be interpreted as points of crossing-over. The correspondence is obvious now, but it was not at all obvious in 1903. In that year two biologists published the idea: an American, Walter S. Sutton, and a German, Theodor Boveri. This is another case where an idea came to several men simultaneously. I do not know whether Sutton had been in communication with Boveri about that time, but Sutton was influenced by the great cytologist E. B. Wilson who was at Columbia University, New York. Wilson had previously been to Germany, where he had visited Boveri.

New ideas like the law of gravitation or the atomic theory take time to become familiar; complexities are forgotten and only essential features are remembered and taught. So it is with genetics and cytology; when the essentials of linkage theory are described without unnecessary complications it does not need much ingenuity to see that the chromosomes are material counterparts of linkage groups. Genetic theory requires that there be such objects, and the cytologist happily sees them; each approach confirms the other. Mendel's work was known to Sutton, but the theory of linkage had not been worked out. Neither had the minute details of chiasmata in meiotic divisions been established. In addition, breeding experiments up to that time had been performed with diploid organisms, which, as we shall see in Chapter VI, are not so easy to analyze as haploid organisms like *Chlamydomonas*. Although Sutton's idea must have caused raised eyebrows among the more conservative at the time, it was rapidly accepted as new facts came to light. Not long afterward two ingenious but somewhat complex experiments were carried out, one with corn and the other with *Drosophila,* which showed that when a genetic cross-over is indicated by the types of progeny, there is also visible exchange of chromosomes. In these two cases chromosome exchanges could be detected under the microscope because particular chromosomes had distinctive features, knobs and gaps, which could be recognized. It can also be roughly shown, in favorable cases, that the number of chiasmata between two points on the chromosome corresponds to the number of cross-overs between genes known to lie at these points.

A little later we will describe how genes can be ascribed to regions of the visible chromosome, but first the relation between chiasmata and recombination must be considered in more detail. In Chapter IV cross-overs were represented, for the sake of simplicity, as occurring between two strands. The other two strands of the tetrad were omitted. From these diagrams it might be supposed that if chiasmata represent crossing-over, the percentage of chiasmata should equal the percentage of recombinant progeny. The truth is that the percentage of recombinations between two genes is equal to half that of the chiasmata in the region. The reason for this is that in a chiasma only two of the four strands of the tetrad cross over, leaving the other two strands intact. Thus, wherever there is a chiasma two of the four cells of the quad will have recombinant genes and the other two cells will have parental combinations. If between the ends of a chromosome there is one chiasma at every meiotic division, there will be 100 per cent chiasma and 50 per cent recombinant progeny. If there is an average of 30 chiasma in 100 meiotic divisions, there will be an average of 15 recombinants in 100 progeny (*i.e.* 60 in 400). All the zygotes in which there is a chiasma between two given genes will produce quads in which fifty per cent, two out four, are recombinant for those genes (Fig. 5).

The proper interpretation of chiasmata was first given by the Belgian cytologist F. A. Janssens in 1909, and it is worth digressing to tell how he was led to it. The exact structure of meiotic chromosomes is not easy to see. Only under ideal conditions, and perhaps using a little imagination, can one say that one has seen only two out of four strands at a chiasma cross. Before 1909 the details of chiasmata were in dispute, and the train of thought which led Janssens, in that year, to his conclusions is curious. It contradicts a statement made earlier that cytology was purely descriptive. Janssens started from the well-established observation that meiotic division always results in four cells. This led him to the thought that an all-powerful and wise Creator would not have provided this unless the four cells were different. He then set to work to construct a theoretical model which would result in four cells all different from one another. His conclusion was that if only two strands out of four crossed, then all four resulting strands could contain different chromosomes (Fig. 5). But if both paternal chromosomes crossed with both maternal chromosomes or if paternal and maternal chromosomes crossed before they divided, then two cells of the quad would be similar and have one recombinant type and the other two would also be similar and have the other recombinant type. Janssens' line of reasoning is curious, but it led him to an important idea. The purist may ridicule a biologist who invokes the Deity, and for him we can say the same thing in the more cumbersome but rational statement that in the course of evolution only efficient processes survive and that the production of four cells is efficient only if there is survival value in all four cells being different.

The foregoing is convincing evidence for the correspondence between linkage groups and chromosomes. In 1933 a correspondence between parts of the chromosome and the genes was suggested in a brief paper by T. S. Painter. It must be put down to good luck that the particular organism, *Drosophila*, chosen by leading geneticists of the time has giant-size salivary chromosomes. The salivary glands of the larvae of *Drosophila* are quite easily removed and stained on a microscope slide. Not only are the chromosomes in the cells of salivary glands about a hundred times as large as normal chromosomes, but they are marked by numerous cross bands which are distinct and can be recognized (Plate 3). The way in which certain bands were shown to correspond to certain genes depends upon the fact that chromosomes sometimes break and rejoin. This chromosomal rearrangement is a process distinct from crossing-over. It does not take place between the same genes on corresponding paternal and maternal chromosomes, but between different chromosomes or between two different regions of the same chromosome. Chromosomes I and II may break and rejoin the wrong way around so that we have two new chromosomes each consisting of part of the old chromosome I and part of the old chromosome II (translocation); or there may be two breaks in the same chromosome and the portion between the breaks may join up the wrong way around; it will be inverted. Or again, a very small piece of a chromosome may be lost or added. These chromosomal rearrangements, deletions, or duplications are rare, but when they occur they are stable (Table 5).

A rearrangement of the bands on salivary chromosomes is made relatively easy to detect by a further lucky circum-

TABLE 5

Old Chromosome I *A B C D E F*		Old Chromosome II *G H I*
Translocations *A B C H I*	and	*G H D E F*
Inversion *A B E D C F*		
Deletion *A B E F*		
Duplication *A B C D E F*		

stance, but to explain this the matter of diploidy, which is the theme of the next chapter, will have to be anticipated. Briefly, there are two sets of chromosomes in salivary-gland cells, as there are in a zygote. Each chromosome pairs with its opposite number as it does during meiosis. The pairing is strictly specific, gene to gene as far as can be seen. Now in so-called heterozygotes, where one chromosome of a pair is changed by an inversion or deletion or duplication or translocation, the two chromosomes cannot pair normally but assume characteristic patterns, the simplest and most useful being the case of a deletion heterozygote. The characteristic patterns are shown in Figure 6 (see also Plate 3).

When breeding tests are made and linkage groups are mapped, the rearrangements show up. If there has been an inversion, then the genes in that region will be inverted on the genetic map. Instead of getting the order of genes *a-b-c-d-e-f* we might get *a-b-e-d-c-f*. If a part of one chromosome has been translocated to another, then the new linkage groups will be different: instead of linkage group I, *a-b-c-d-e*, and linkage group II, *g-h-i-j*, we might get linkage groups *a-b-i-j* and *g-h-c-d-e*. When the salivary chromosomes of flies with such genetic rearrangements are examined, it is found that the order of bands is changed in a corresponding way. In a stock of flies which is known genetically to have an inversion between certain genes, the salivary chromosomes are found to be inverted between certain bands. The bands are far more numerous than the genes that have been studied because only a small fraction of the total number of genes have been identified. Chromosomal rearrangements have only been found for a small number of regions, but by this method many genes have been identified with bands. The distances between genes on the genetic map, as measured by recombination percentages, correspond pretty well to the actual distances between the corresponding bands as measured through the microscope.

FIGURE 6

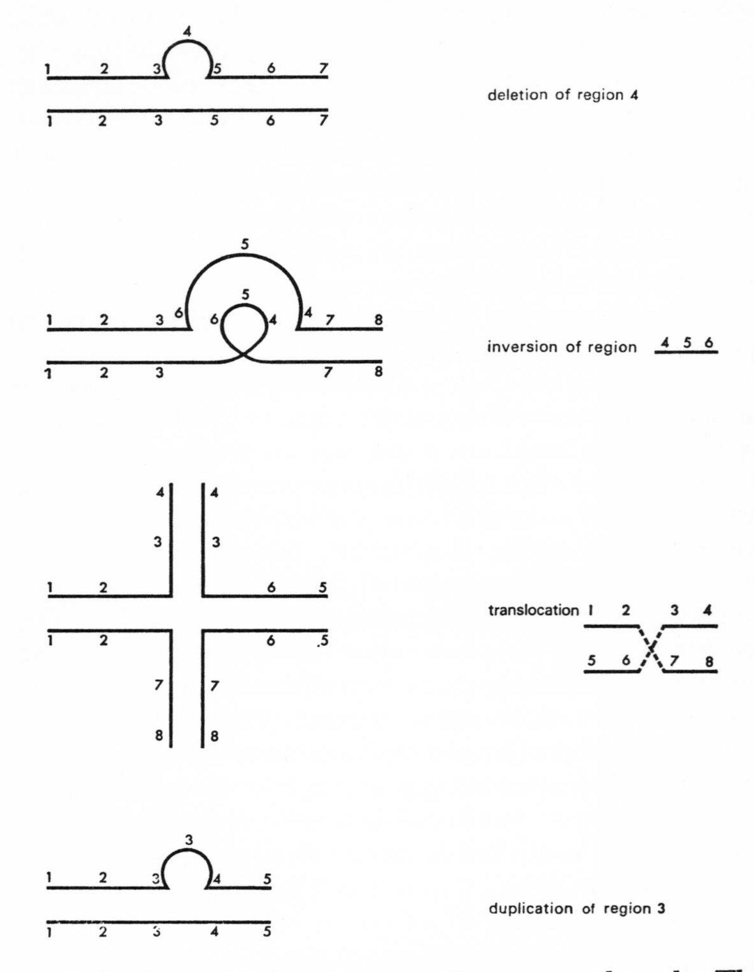

It is often said that the exception proves the rule. This usually means that something abnormal is found but that in some ways it follows the rule developed for the normal. An excellent example in *Drosophila* is the character bar eye, where the eyes are reduced in size and are oval or slit-shaped. Bar eye behaves like a normal Mendelian character in breeding tests but when the region of the salivary chromosome corresponding to the gene for eye shape is examined, a certain band is found to be double. Now this is unexpected; each bar, or possibly the space between bars, is believed to represent a gene, but no one hopes to detect visually the difference between two different forms, alleles, of a gene. The bar-eye band on the salivary chromosome should look just like the wild-type eye band. The fact is, however, that one bar represents the wild-type eye and two bars, implying two similar genes, represents bar eye. When two bar-eyed flies are crossed, a peculiar thing happens: a few flies among the progeny are of the wild type and a few are what are called "double bar," having a very great reduction in the size of the eye. When the salivary chromosomes of double-bar flies are examined it is found that they have three identical bands in place of two. The explanation for this is as follows: theory demands that at meiosis the maternal and paternal chromosomes pair very precisely, each paternal gene opposite its maternal kind. In bar-eyed flies there are two similar genes alongside each other and a small error in pairing might be expected. This would lead occasionally to a small error in crossing-over, which would account for the production of a triple- and a single-gene chromosome. Imaginary genes *w*, *x*, *y*, and *z* have been included in the diagram (Fig. 7) to clarify the process. Notice that the *b*'s on the top line on the left do not lie directly above the *b*'s on the bottom line.

FIGURE 7

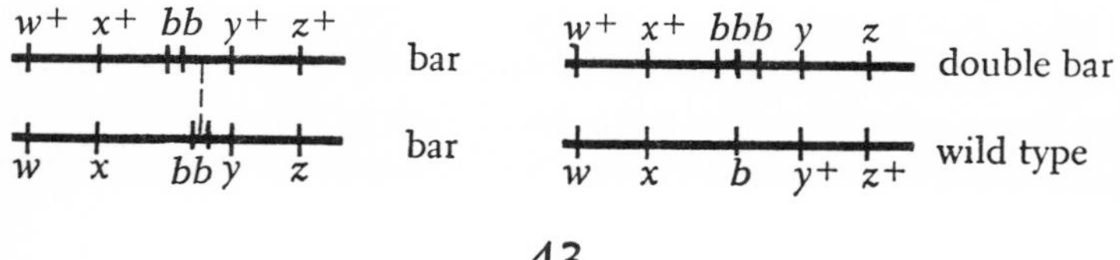

The case of bar-eye presents two exceptions to the rule: first, the odd appearance of new types in crosses, and second, the fact that an allele of a gene appears to be a duplication. The two oddities together make sense, if one has the ingenuity to see the sense. The whole theory of chromosomes and genes is strengthened and a new fact is learned, namely, that two similar genes in tandem can determine a character different from that determined by a single gene or by three genes in a row.

In the last ten years a new approach to the study of linkage groups has become available through the use of microorganisms. In particular, the intestinal bacterium *Escherichia coli* has shown striking similarities and also differences from higher forms. A sexual process in bacteria was established in 1947 by Joshua Lederberg, a student of Edward Tatum's in the Botany Department of Yale University. Lederberg and Tatum both received the Nobel Prize a few years later. This was an important discovery, and it opened up a whole new field of genetics which has been extensively cultivated in numerous laboratories. A good question is why it was not discovered earlier, and the answer is that biologists were looking for the wrong thing, using the wrong techniques. Sex, until the time of this discovery, had meant sexual organs and a visible sexual process. The fungi, especially the lower fungi, had revealed most intricate male and female sexual organs, and it was hoped that some mating process could be found in bacteria if only one looked hard enough. Some workers described figures of two or more bacteria clumped together in various ways which were interpreted as a sexual process, but others disagreed and there was no way of settling the argument; the figures that were seen were not definite enough to be generally accepted and so it remained a matter of opinion. The approach of Lederberg and Tatum was quite different. They were not primarily interested in seeing a sexual process;

they set out to demonstrate genetic recombination, which they considered to be the essence of sex. It turned out that with most *E. coli* strains a sexual mating is very rare. Only about 1 in 100,000 bacteria mate, and the chances of seeing this process without knowing exactly what one is looking for are exceedingly poor.

Two new techniques which were used at the time indicate the proper approach: the culture of strains having special chemical requirements, and the selection of rare types by growth on a medium on which only the required type would grow. By treatment with X-rays or other agents which will be described in Chapter VIII, mutant strains of *E. coli* were obtained which could not grow unless the vitamin biotin was added to the medium. Other strains were obtained which required the amino acid leucine. Several million cells of the strain requiring biotin but not leucine, $b\ l^+$, were mixed with several million cells of a strain requiring leucine but not biotin, $b^+\ l$. After mixing, the cells were spread on plates of agar which contained the usual nutrients but no biotin or leucine. Any bacterium which grew on this medium and formed a colony visible to the naked eye would have to be different from either parental strain. It would have to be a recombinant $b\ l^+, x\ b^+\ l \rightarrow b^+\ l^+$. There might be other recombinants, of the form $b\ l$, but these would not be detected since they could not survive on the nutrients provided. A few colonies were, in fact, seen, and further tests showed conclusively that they did represent recombinants. Strains of *E. coli* were found later which gave a much more abundant harvest of recombinants; they mated much more frequently. With these high-frequency strains, and using some three dozen distinct characters, the genetics of *E. coli* has been developed. Linkage was found between various characters, and genes could be arranged in a linear unbranched sequence as in other organisms. Some new features not found in higher organisms were also revealed. A complication is that only parts of the linkage group take part in any particular mating, and allowance has to be made for this fact. The final picture that emerges is curious, but it is simple and the essentials are well established.

There is one single linkage group and only one chromosome in *E. coli*. This chromosome has a peculiarity which must shock a *Drosophila* or corn geneticist: the chromosome is circular except during mating. Bacteria mate in pairs; the outer cell walls are broken down at the point of contact (Plate 4) and the chromosome from one of the cells slips into the other cell. The donor can be justly called male and the recipient cell, female. Mixtures that produce a high yield of recombinants depend upon the male cells, which are called Hfr (for "high frequency of recombination"). Besides Hfr and female cells (F^-), there is a third sexual state, designated F^+, which can be thought of as potentially male. The difference between F^+ and F^- cells is that the former have what is called a sex factor in the cell. This sex factor is probably a short length of chromosome bearing the particular genes that make a cell male. The sex factor is thought by many to be a circle, like the chromosome of F^- and F^+ cells. F^+ cells become Mfr (male) cells at a certain low rate, perhaps one in a thousand; in this process the sex factor instead of lying free in the cytoplasm becomes a part of the main chromosome of the cell. If the sex factor is really circular, this could take place by a crossover between the two circles, giving rise to one large circle, a

FIGURE 8

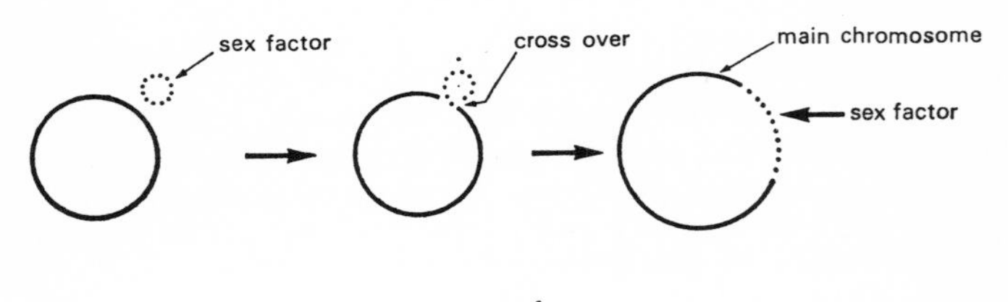

portion of which would be the sex factor (Fig. 8).

Upon mating, the large ring breaks somewhere in the region of the sex factor, and the chromosome slips into the female cell in the form of a rod (Fig. 9). The early experiments

FIGURE 9

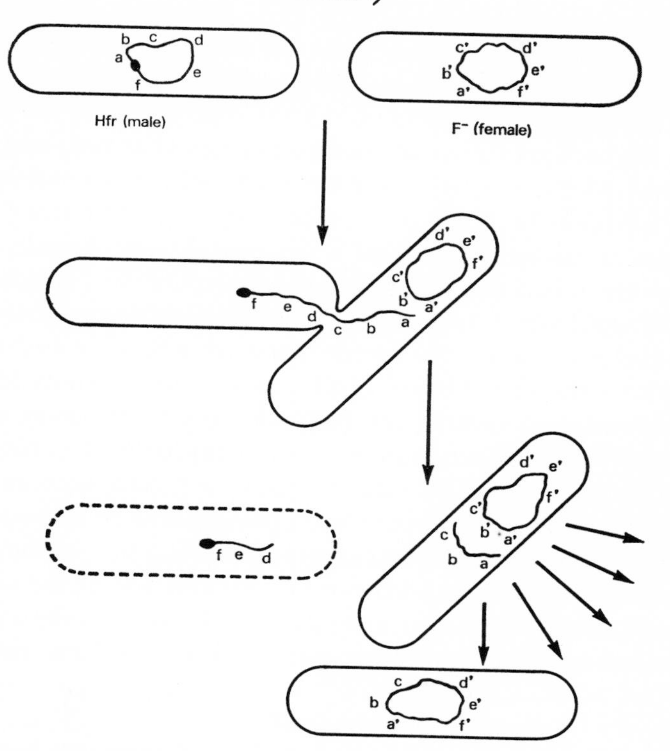

A *Cross in the Bacterium* E. coli. The parents are shown on the top line. Just below, they are in the process of mating; regions a, b, and c of the male chromosome have penetrated the female, and the cells are presumed to break apart at this stage. The female cell divides to produce progeny of different genotypes. The particular progeny shown at the bottom right has regions b and c from the male parent and factors a′, d′, e′, and f′ from the female parent.

The diagram is unrealistic because each *E. coli* cell actually has two or three nuclei. This complication affects the result only by making the pure recombinants appear after several more cell divisions. The diagram is also misleading in that it shows the chromosome as a short, thick rod whereas in reality it is very long and thin (see Plate 5). The sex, or F, factor is shown as an oval knob on the chromosome, whereas it is probably a length of chromosome quite similar in structure to the main bacterial chromosome and about 2 per cent of the length of the main chromosome.

It is likely that the breakage and travel of the male chromosome is related to its duplication, so that the ring shown in the top male cell would be present in the mated male cell, the rod chromosome being a duplicate of it.

Notice that some parts of the chromosome are lost. In this case regions a, b′, and c′ are lost. The female cell can divide to produce a variety of types of progeny.

yielded a low proportion of recombinant cells because the male cells used were mostly F^+; mating could not be consummated until the change from F^+ to Hfr occurred, and as was mentioned, this is a rare event. Later experiments were performed with pure cultures of Hfr cells, which give a yield of recombinants about a thousand times greater. The chromosome of *E. coli* is very long, thin, and tangled, and is difficult to study even under an electron microscope. Plates 5 and 11 show the best that can be achieved with modern techniques; they can be compared with the pictures (Plates 1, 2) of chromosomes in higher organisms.

Nothing like a salivary-gland chromosome exists in *E. coli,* but an ingenious experiment can nevertheless be performed which shows that the linkage group is a real physical structure. It takes twenty minutes for the chromosome of a male *E. coli* to slip into the female bacterium. During this time the pairs of mating bacteria can be put into a blendor, something like the one used in the kitchen to chop up carrots or make malted milk, and the bacteria can be broken apart before the whole chromosome has entered. Bacteria can be separated in this way at any time from one to twenty minutes after they have been brought together, and their characters can then be examined. When this is done the results fit very well with theory. If the linkage group of the male strain used is composed of the genes *a, b, c, d, e, f,* then after one minute only the character *a* will be found in the progency of the female. After two or three minutes the characters *a* and *b* will be found, after four minutes, *a, b,* and *c,* and so on for all the characters (Fig. 9).

This must not be taken to mean that after four minutes *a, b,* and *c* from the male will always be found in the progeny. It means that after four minutes these three characters may be found and that more distal characters will not be found. It is natural to suppose that once a bit of male chromosome has got into a female, there is a process similar to crossing-over by which some or all the male genes become incorporated in the female chromosome. In Figure 9 it is supposed that *b* and *c* got incorporated but *a* did not. Pieces of chromosomes not incorporated must be eliminated in one way or another or broken down by special enzymes.

We said above that a complication of *E. coli* genetics is the fact that only part of the linkage group takes part in recombination. This is because even when the parents are not broken apart with a blendor, the male chromosome is still apt to break during copulation and only rarely does the whole chromosome enter the female cell.

The circular chromosome of a potential male can be broken at several points, or perhaps at any point, depending on where the sex factor gets incorporated in the ring; and this makes it possible to obtain a number of different rod-shaped male chromosomes. If the chromosome in Figure 9 were broken between *d* and *e,* the chromosome *e-f-a-b-c-d* would be formed; if broken between *b* and *c,* then a chromosome *c-d-e-f-a-b* would result. The order of genes is always the same, although the starting point can be different. In an F^+ culture used for a mating experiment Hfr bacteria would be formed, but they would be different from each other in having chromosome rods that started and ended at different points. It is not difficult to imagine the confusion that this caused in the early work with *E. coli.* It was not until pure Hfr strains were obtained in which all the individual bacteria had the same rod-shaped chromosome and a high frequency of mating that an interpretation became relatively easy.

When recombination in bacteria was first discovered it was natural to assume, or at least to work on the assumption, that the process was similar to that known in higher organisms. This would presume that two bacteria, perhaps any two in a population not necessarily differentiated into male and female, would mate, form a zygote, undergo a kind of meiosis and give rise to recombinant cells. Careful and laborious genetic analysis of crosses showed that this model would not fit the facts. First came the demonstration that there were male and female cells and that recombinants only came from the female. Then it was realized that complete zygotes were rarely formed and usually only a part of the male chromosome participated in the recombinant event. Finally, the genetic map appeared to be circular.

These features represented rather wild departures from orthodox genetics, which had been based on higher organisms. In order to make them credible it was helpful to obtain evidence of a different or more direct sort. We have already mentioned how evidence for a linear array of genes along a material chromosome was obtained by the use of a blendor. More recently, direct evidence for a circular chromosome has been obtained. This is especially interesting since the genetic evidence is indirect. A circular chromosome model fits the genetic facts, but as with all models, consonance with the facts does not prove that a model is correct or even useful. In this particular case, another model may be constructed in which all bacteria have rod-shaped chromosomes which are sections of a hypothetical circle, but the circle need not actually exist as a physical entity. The model will require the addition of certain other features to make it fit the facts, but this can easily be accomplished.

The direct evidence for a circular chromosome was obtained by photography. Not ordinary photomicroscopy or even electron microscopy—The best electron photographs of bacterial chromosomes (Plate 5) do not allow one to be sure whether or not the strand is a ring. The technique used was to grow the bacteria in a radioactive form of a substance that is used to synthesize chromosomes. The bacteria were then broken so that the chromosomes could get out; the chromosomes were then floated on the surface of a liquid where, being somewhat rigid, they untangled and lay in a more or less circular shape. They were then laid on a photographic film for two months, and the film developed and studied under a microscope. The radioactive atoms caused dots to appear on the film which were large enough to be seen under a high-power light microscope. The line of dots then showed the shape of the chromosome, which is circular (Plate 11).

This technique, known as autoradiography, is also used to study the way in which these chromosomes duplicate.

Although *E. coli* is exceptional in having a circular chromosome, it still conforms to the rule that genes are arranged in a linear unbranched array and, in fact, the circle becomes a rod before mating time. Later chapters will describe how the chromosomes of bacteria and also viruses are fundamentally similar in their chemical nature to those of higher organisms.

As with other organisms, we see that the linear array of genes in *E. coli* can be deduced from breeding experiments and demonstrated by quite different techniques.

In the foregoing chapters we have considered a gene

simply as a unit controlling a particular character. An individual in *Chlamydomonas* with a gene v^+ has little volutin, one with v, a great deal of volutin. In the next chapter we will examine the relationship between genes and characters in more complex cases.

VI *One to Spare: The Complication of Diploidy*

Two brown-eyed parents can have a blue-eyed child, and sometimes a peculiarity will be visited onto the third or fourth generation. Atavism, in which a character skips a generation or two, must have been familiar to the ancients but it does not seem, at first sight, to follow Mendelian theory as outlined in Chapter III. As a matter of fact, in *Chlamydomonas* atavism does not occur. The reason that it occurs in higher organisms, including man, is that they are diploid.

Let us think again (Fig. 2) of the zygote *Chlamydomonas* and note that it has two sets of chromosomes and genes, one paternal and one maternal. The zygote divides by meiosis, producing four cells each having one set. Imagine now that it divided instead by mitosis, in which the original chromosomes are duplicated; in that case two cells would result, each having two sets of chromosomes. If these two divided again by mitosis we would have a total of four cells, each with two sets, and so on to 8, 16, 32, 64, . . . cells, each having two sets of chromosomes. This is what happens in higher organisms, where all the cells have two sets of chromosomes except the germ cells. The germ cells, or gametes, have only one set of chromosomes because the special meiotic division occurs just before the formation of eggs and sperm. The essential features of the life cycles of *Chlamydomonas* and of man are shown in Figure 10. These represent two extreme types; there are many

FIGURE 10

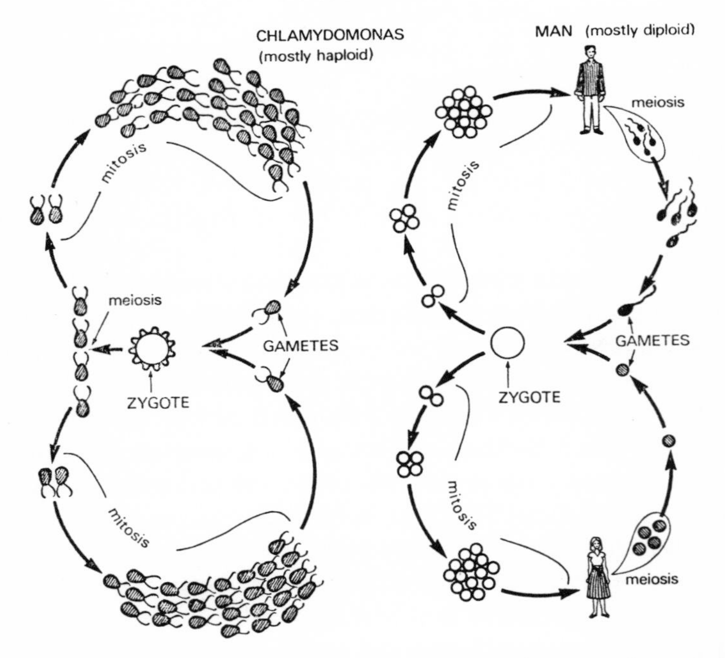

Life Cycles of Chlamydomonas *and Man.* The diagram of man's life cycle is inaccurate in that the sperm actually fertilizes the egg inside the body of the female and the embryo develops there. A true meiotic division occurs in the female, but only one of the four cells survives to become an egg cell. It is a general rule that the zygote has two sets of chromosomes (2n) and each of the gametes only one set (n). The number of chromosomes in the adult *Chlamydomonas* is n; in the cells of adult man, 2n.

varieties of life cycles throughout the plant and animal kingdoms—in particular, the mosses and ferns are partly haploid and partly diploid—but the details of various life cycles are not pertinent to our main theme. The essential point is that in man, most animals, and the higher plants the cells of the body are diploid and the sperm and eggs are haploid, whereas in *Chlamydomonas* all cells are haploid except for the zygote, which is diploid.

We have already seen that the characters studied in *Chlamydomonas* are apparent in the vegetative cells, which are haploid, not in the zygote; in man and higher organisms characters are, on the contrary, exhibited by the diploid part of the life cycle. When we cross a paralyzed *Chlamydomonas*, p, with a wild type, p^+, the zygote, being diploid, has both gene p and gene p^+; it does not have flagella, but if it did would they be paralyzed or not? The same question arises in man when a man with blue eyes fertilizes a woman with brown eyes. His haploid sperm will have the gene *b* for blue, and her eggs will have the gene *B* for brown. The zygote and the child, which are diploid, will have both gene *b* and gene *B*. The fact is that the color of the child's eyes will be brown. This effect has been given the name *dominance*. A gene for a particular character may have several alternative states; each of these is known as an allele. The gene for brown eyes, or let us say the brown allele for the eye-color gene, is dominant over the blue allele of the same gene. Contrariwise, blue is recessive to brown. By convention, dominant genes are denoted by capital letters and recessives by small letters.

We said that an individual with the eye-color alleles *B* and *b* will have brown eyes. An individual with two brown alleles, *BB*, will also have brown eyes, and an individual with *bb* will have blue eyes, as we would expect. This means that when one looks at an individual with blue eyes one knows that he must have the alleles *bb*, but when one looks at an individual with brown eyes one cannot tell whether his alleles are *Bb* or *BB*. In order to avoid confusion, two terms are in common use: an individual's phenotype denotes what he looks like (brown or blue eyes for instance) and his genotype indicates what alleles he has (*BB*, *Bb*, or *bb*).

The essentials of the Mendelian laws as applied to diploid organisms can be shown by following a cross through to the grandchildren. Take a girl with pure blue eyes from a stock that has had nothing but blue eyes as far back as memory goes, such as may be found in parts of Sweden, perhaps. Mate her to a pure brown-eyed boy of some dark Mediterranean race. All of their children will, or should according to theory, have brown eyes. These children will constitute the first filial generation, abbreviated conventionally F_1. Now breed these F_1 children among themselves and in each family three-quarters of the children will be brown-eyed and one-quarter blue-eyed. These will be the second filial generation or F_2. Among humans, where families usually consist of three or four children instead of three or four hundred, the composition of a single family will not indicate much, but if the members of the F_2 generation in many families are considered together, the totals will approach three-quarters brown-eyed and one-quarter blue-eyed.

How these ratios result from the segregation of genes can be easily shown. The original blue- and brown-eyed parents have respectively two alleles for blue eyes, *bb*, and two for brown eyes, *BB* (Fig. 11). At meiosis all the gametes of the first will be *B* and those of the second, *b*. All the children will have the genotype *Bb*, and brown eyes. These F_1 children will each produce two kinds of sperm or two kinds of egg: half of their gametes will be *B* and half will be *b*. If a brother and sister are mated, it will be a matter of chance what type of sperm fertilizes what kind of egg. Sometimes a *B* sperm will fertilize a *B* egg; sometimes a *B* sperm and a *b* egg will com-

FIGURE 11

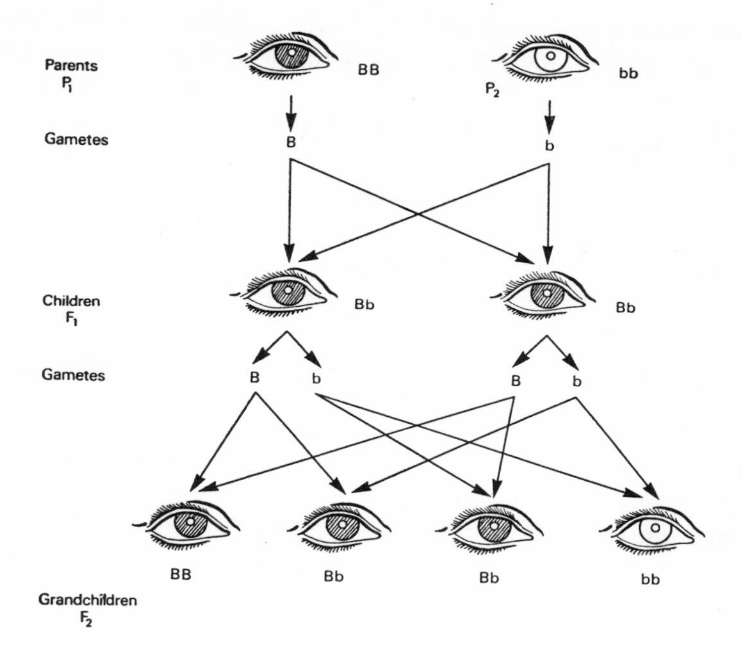

Brown-Eyed–Blue-Eyed Cross. A cross between a pure (homozygous) brown-eyed person (P_1) and a blue-eyed person (P_2) is shown. Each of these parents will produce only one kind of gamete as regards eye color, and all children (F_1) will be heterozygous brown-eyed. The F_1 will produce two kinds of gamete (egg or sperm) and the random combination of eggs and sperm will give the ratio of three brown-eyed offspring to one blue-eyed.

The random combination of gametes $(\frac{1}{2} B + \frac{1}{2} b)^2$ can be written in the form of a table:

		Sperm	
		$\frac{1}{2} B$	$\frac{1}{2} b$
Eggs	$\frac{1}{2} B$	$\frac{1}{4} BB$	$\frac{1}{4} Bb$
	$\frac{1}{2} b$	$\frac{1}{4} Bb$	$\frac{1}{4} bb$

bine, or a *b* sperm and a *B* egg, or a *b* sperm and a *b* egg. These four combinations will be equally likely, and so if the numbers considered are large enough, the four types of grandchildren—*BB*, *Bb*, *bB*, and *bb*—will be equally frequent. But remember that both persons with the alleles *BB* and those with *Bb* have brown eyes and only those with *bb* have blue eyes, so of the four genotypes—*BB*, *Bb*, *bB*, and *bb*—the first three (*bB* is equivalent to *Bb*) will have brown eyes and the last will have blue, giving the previously mentioned ratio of three-quarters to one-quarter.

A student of genetics examines many ratios other than this simple 3 to 1 ratio of the F_2. If two characters are involved which assort independently, the F_2 will consist of four phenotypes in the ratio 9:3:3:1, and most textbooks of genetics go through the steps leading to this result—it can be obtained by expanding the binomial $(3/4 + 1/4)^2$. Two linked genes give more complicated results, but no new principle is involved and the arithmetical details need not be elaborated here.

Dominance means that individuals are not always genetically what they appear to be; some alleles, the recessive ones, are sometimes hidden and can then only be detected by breeding. A brown-eyed individual may have the genotype *Bb* or *BB*. To discover which, we may cross him with an individual with blue eyes (invariably genotype *bb*); then if he is *Bb*, half of the progeny will be blue-eyed, but if he is *BB*, all will be browneyed. In genetic symbolism, *Bb* x *bb* → ½ *Bb* (brown) : ½ *bb* (blue), but *BB* x *bb* → *Bb* (brown). A recessive allele may be carried for many generations without ever showing; then if it reaches a child with another of the same recessive allele, it will show up. This is the explanation of atavism.

Let us now turn our attention to a most striking difference between individuals, the difference in sex, repeating what was outlined in Chapter I. The alternatives male and female are peculiar in that even in a purebred stock families are not all of one kind, but consist of approximately equal numbers of boys and girls; the difference between the sexes is peculiar genetically in that it is not controlled by two alleles of a gene, but by whole chromosomes, the *X* and *Y* chromosomes. Females in most higher animals, except birds, have two *X* chromosomes, but males have only one *X* chromosome plus a less important *Y* chromosome. Thus males produce two kinds of sperm, *X* and *Y*, and females produce only one kind of egg, having an *X* chromosome. An *X*-carrying sperm will produce a female child and a *Y*-carrying sperm will produce a male. Modern methods of analysis, centrifugation or electrophoresis, have been successful in some cases in separating the two kinds of sperm. When this becomes practical with man, the sex ratio in humans will be taken out of the realm of chance and added to that ever-increasing class of events controlled by the wisdom or folly of our intent.

Males are haploid as regards the *X* chromosome and females diploid. Since a male only mates with a female and vice versa, the progeny, when large enough numbers are considered, are always one-half *XX* and one-half *XY*, or one-half male (symbolized ♂) and one-half female (symbolized ♀).

The odd thing about sex determination is that the *X* chromosome has a full complement of genes, most of which control characters that have nothing to do with sex at all. These *X*-chromosome genes are known as sex-linked and are inherited, as might be expected, in a peculiar way. If they are genes for a rare recessive trait such as hemophilia, the bleeder disease, actual manifestations of the trait are rare in men and practically never found in women. This is because a daughter would have to inherit the recessive allele from both parents; if it is a rare trait the small chance of this occurring will compound the rarity. But a man with a recessive allele in his *X* chromosome has in his *Y* chromosome no corresponding allele which might be dominant. Sex-linked traits are inherited by

FIGURE 12

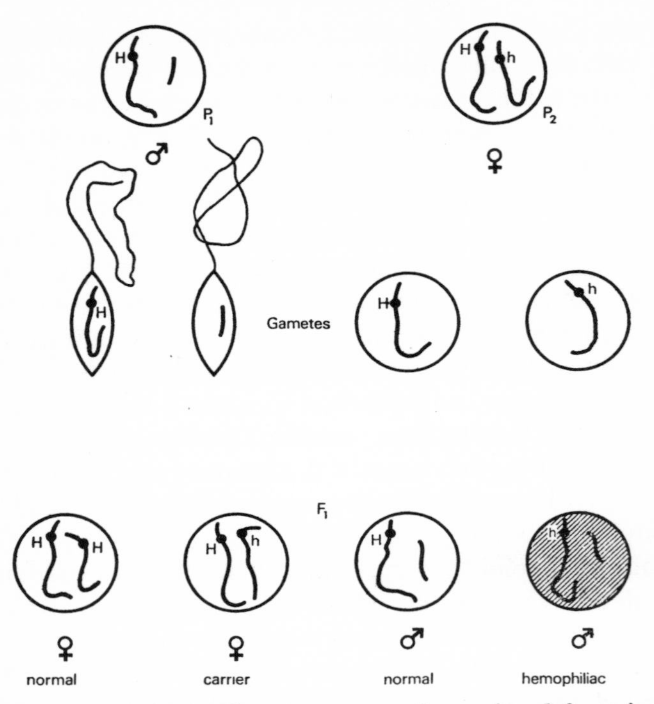

Hemophilic Cross. A cross between a normal man (top left ♂) and a heterozygous woman (top right ♀) is shown. Only the X and Y chromosomes are included, and the gene for hemophilia, either normal (*H*) or hemophilia (*h*). In the second line the sperm and eggs are shown, and in the last line, the four types of offspring. These are all equally probable. Half the boys and none of the girls will be hemophilic; half the girls will be carriers.

The combinations of sperm and eggs are:

		Eggs		
		X^H	X^h	
Sperm	X^H	X^HX^H	X^HX^h	girls
	Y	X^HY	X^hY	boys
		normal	hemophiliac or carrier	

sons from their mothers, if their mothers are carriers. Afflicted males pass the gene to their daughters, who become carriers. In Figure 12 it is presumed that the mother is a carrier of hemophilia (*h*) and it can be seen how half of her sons will have the trait.

Human genetics is obliged to make use of different techniques from those used with other organisms. With *Drosophila* one can mate two flies having a specially constructed, complicated ancestry and analyze several thousand progeny within a couple of weeks. Nothing of this kind can be done with humans even by the most ardent and ruthless geneticist. Even a brother-and-sister mating such as that presumed in Figure 11 is not accepted outside ancient Irish, Egyptian, and Inca royal families. On the other hand, the frequency of a trait can be accurately measured in humans and many family trees can be examined. We keep good statistics on human populations. In the past and in the less developed countries, personal ancestry was and is probably better known than today in America. A notable case is that of royal family trees.

J. B. S. Haldane has examined hemophilia in the royal families of Europe with some interesting results (Fig. 13). He notes that records of hemophilia are biased in two different directions: among royal families, people afflicted tried to hide the fact, and among the less high-born, normal men sometimes claimed the affliction in order to avoid military service. Other aspects of hemophilia and of Queen Victoria's family tree will be mentioned later in connection with mutation and eugenics. Hemophilia is a serious diease because if something like a bad cut or a tooth extraction occurs, the blood fails to clot and the person concerned may bleed to death. In Denmark 13 men in every 100,000 have the disease.

The family tree (Fig. 13) fits well with the theory that hemophilia is a sex-linked recessive trait. About half the sons of a presumed carrier mother show the trait.

FIGURE 13

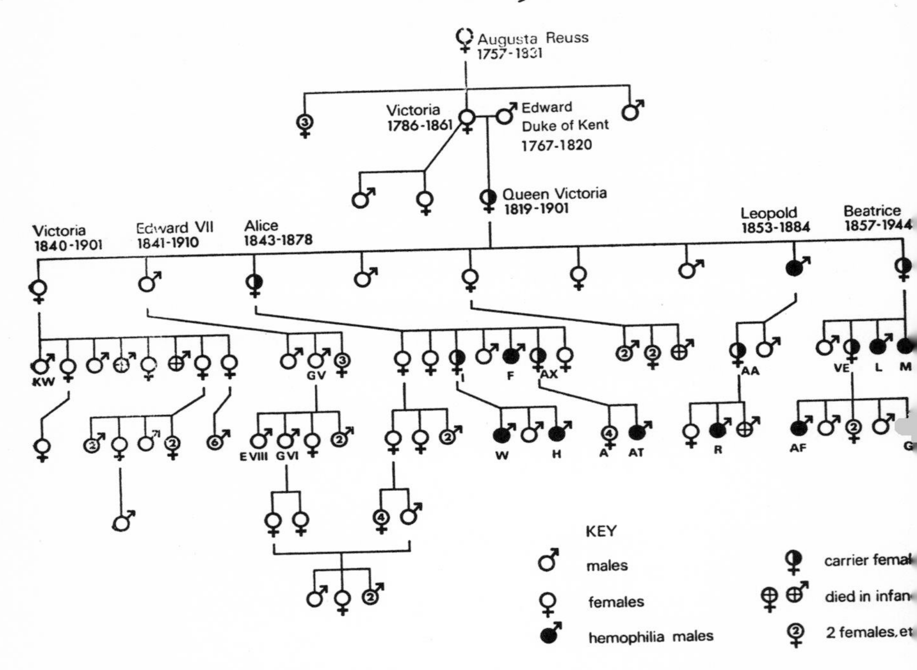

Hemophilia in Royal Families. A family tree shows hemophilia in the royal families of Europe. All the affected persons may have gotten the hemophilia gene from a mutation in Queen Victoria's father, Edward, Duke of Kent, since there is no history of the disease in Queen Victoria's ancestors. It will be seen that about half the sons of a carrier mother are affected and half the daughters are carriers. About half the daughters of an affected father are carriers, but none of his sons are affected. Females marked as carriers are presumed to be so because of their progeny. Spouses have been omitted except for Queen Victoria's parents, and are assumed to have been neither affected nor carriers. For reasons of space and clarity only a few of the persons are identified. The key to initials is as follows:

A = Alice of Athlone
AA = Anastasia, 1901–1918
AF = Alfonso, 1907–1939
AT = Alexis, Tsarevitch, 1904–1918
AX = Alexandra, 1872–1918
G VI = George VI, 1895–1952
H = Heinrich, 1900–1904
I = Irene, 1866–1953
KW = William II, Kaiser of Germany, 1859–1941
L = Leopold, 1884–1922

E VIII = Edward VIII, 1894–
F = Frederick William, 1870–1873
G = Gonzalo, 1914–1934
G V = George V, 1865–1936
M = Maurice, 1891–1914
R = Rupert, 1907–1928
VE = Victoria Eugenia, 1887–
W = Waldemar, 1889–1945

(Based on J. B. S. Haldane, *New Paths in Genetics*, Harper & Brothers, New York and London)

Another human character which illustrates some important principles is the blood group, of importance in blood transfusion. It is commonly known that blood cannot be transfused with impunity from one person to another. Certain rules have to be followed to insure safe transfusion. People can be classified in four blood groups, A, B, AB, or O; the safe transfusions are shown in Table 6.

TABLE 6

Donor	A	B	AB	O
A	✓	+	✓	+
B	+	✓	✓	+
AB	+	+	✓	+
O	✓	✓	✓	✓

A check mark indicates that transfusion is safe; a plus sign indicates that the donor's red-blood corpuscles will clump in the recipient's serum and may cause death. The clumping is due to an antigenic reaction; the red-blood corpuscles contain antigens which react with antibodies in certain serums. A person of blood group O, a universal donor, has corpuscles with no antigens. An A person has A antigens, a B person B antigens, and an AB person both A and B antigens.

No person has antibodies in his serum which can clump his own red-corpuscle antigens. Thus AB people have neither A nor B antibodies and are universal acceptors, but they can give blood only to their own group. So much for the physiology of blood groups, a subject being studied in detail in many laboratories. Other blood groups have been discovered, and progress is being made on the important problem of how antibodies are produced, but let us pursue the genetic aspect. Through the study of numerous families and of the frequency of blood groups in various communities, it has been established that a single gene determines the blood group. This gene has three alleles, I^O, I^A, and I^B, and each allele produces the antigen in red corpuscles indicated by the superscript. The allele I^O is recessive to I^A and I^B, but there is no dominance between I^A and I^B, thus the genotypes of the four blood groups are as shown in Table 7.

TABLE 7

Phenotype	*Genotype*
A	I^AI^A or I^AI^O
B	I^BI^B or I^BI^O
AB	I^AI^B
O	I^OI^O

Types O and AB are the only ones that must be of one unique genotype. In addition, group O has two similar alleles; it is homozygous for I^O. Individuals that are homozygous produce only one kind of gamete and therefore breed true when mated with similar individuals. In other words, two O-group parents can produce only O-group children. Two AB individuals, on the other hand, can have A, B, or AB children because each parent produces I^A and I^B gametes. The blood groups of children from all ten combinations of parents can easily be worked out (Table 8).

The blood-group gene is different from genes that we have discussed so far in having three more or less equivalent alleles, none of which can be called the normal or wild-type allele. Between the alleles I^A and I^B there is no dominance: one does not mask the other—both express themselves, and in consequence an I^AI^B person has both A and B antigens.

TABLE 8

Parents' Groups	*Children*
A and A	A or O
A and B	A or B or O or AB
A and AB	A or B or AB
A and O	A or O
B and B	B or O
B and AB	A or B or AB
B and O	B or O
AB and AB	A or B or AB
AB and O	A or B
O and O	O

Things could have been arranged differently. In fact for a time there was a widely held theory that two genes were concerned, each of them having a dominant and a recessive allele. Then genotypes of the four blood groups according to this theory would be as shown in Table 9.

TABLE 9

A	AAbb or Aabb
B	aaBB or aaBb
AB	AABB or AaBB or AaBb or AABb
O	aabb

If the kinds of children that various parents can have according to this scheme are calculated, the results are not so very different from the accepted one-gene theory. Some of the differences lie in the proportions of different kinds of children expected from various crosses; other differences are more absolute. For instance, according to the accepted theory if both parents are AB, none of the children can be O because none of the sperm gametes or the egg gametes contains the allele I^o. According to the second theory, however, the AB parents might be *AaBb* and *AaBb* and a sperm *ab* might fertilize an egg *ab*, giving rise to an *aabb* child, who would be of blood group O. Actually it was not easy to distinguish between the two theories because in certain rare families such exceptions do occur, but these are now believed to be due to mistaken paternity or to other phenomena, such as mutation. The inheritance of blood groups is commonly recognized in courts of law, but it is not often realized that the generally accepted one-gene theory is not established incontestably; genetic theory would not be terribly upset if it were proved wrong.

These two theories of blood-group inheritance offer examples of how Mendelian theory works. The best way to become familiar with and understand the mechanics of the theory is to work out examples and problems, and it is instructive to work out the progeny of various crosses according to the two-gene hypothesis and compare them with the offspring predicted under the accepted one-gene theory.

We have seen that in diploid organisms one allele of a gene is generally dominant over another, but that sometimes, as in the blood-group antigens, both may express themselves. It must now be said that many other alleles show partial or incomplete dominance. An example is a gene *R*, producing crimson flowers in snapdragons. *RR* plants have crimson flowers, *rr* plants white, and *Rr* plants have flowers of an intermediate pink color. Incomplete dominance gives us a clue to the understanding of complete dominance. If a gene functions by making some substance which in turn gives rise to the character, then the wild-type allele will be expected to produce the maximum amount of this substance and an allele, say the white-flower color allele, will fail to produce this substance. A heterozygote having one fully functional allele and one nonfunctional allele will be expected to produce half the amount of substance and an intermediate character, pink flower color. In cases of dominance like hemophilia, it must be assumed that half the amount of the substance is as good as the whole amount. The idea can be illustrated by an analogy. Imagine two glasses and some not very deep red ink. Pour into the first glass two jiggers of ink and into the other, one jigger of ink and one jigger of water. The ink in the first glass will appear red and the ink in the second, a shade of pink; this is incomplete dominance. We must imagine that red ink is the product of one allele and water of the other.

Now take the same glasses but use a very deep black India ink and perform the same operation. This time the ink in the two glasses may appear to the eye to be equally black. This is complete dominance. If the two apparently black inks were analyzed by more refined techniques, they could probably be distinguished as being of different intensities of black, but to the naked eye they appear similar. The same is actually true of dominance. In many cases of apparently complete dominance, the heterozygote can be distinguished from the normal or pure homozygote by more refined techniques. In the case of hemophilia, a heterozygous female ($X^H X^h$) has blood which can be shown to clot a little more slowly than that of a homozygous ($X^H X^H$) female, but the difference is small and needs careful measurement. The same is true of many hereditary diseases of man, and the detection of heterozygotes can be of importance in marriage counseling.

VII *Particles Produce People: A Network of Interactions*

The breeding experiments which led to the concept of the gene, and the theory of linkage which led to the construction of genetic maps, have been described in previous chapters. The theory is impressive and intellectually appealing. A feature of this work which may trouble the thoughtful reader is that the characters dealt with are rather trivial and mostly rare; paralyzed flagella, inability to grow without para-aminobenzoic acid, red flowers, hemophilia, albinism. What of the more obvious characters—height, size, intelligence, athletic prowess, two arms, wide shoulders, in fact all the differences between a man and a mouse—do these characters obey Mendel's laws? The answer is yes, they are believed to do so, but these characters are much more difficult to analyze and theory must therefore be based on specially chosen characters.

The reasons why some of the more obvious and interesting characters cannot be easily analyzed can be put into three categories. Two of these we will merely mention, without elaborating upon them. The first is that we cannot cross a man with a mouse and for that reason differences as great as those between two such disparate organisms cannot be analyzed by breeding experiments. All evidence points to the conclusion, however, that the difference between the fertilized egg of a mouse and that of a man lies in the sets of genes within the nuclei of those cells. The second category of difficulties includes environmental factors. A character such as height, and perhaps intelligence, is influenced greatly by the environment as well as by genes. The height of a plant is affected to a very great extent by the amount of water, sunlight, wind, fertilizer, and the like that is available. Similarly, man is affected by the amount of food, vitamins, and the like available to him, especially in childhood. The changing of features by what is now termed cosmetic surgery must be classed as an effect of the environment. If a geneticist had lived during the age of Attila and had examined the heredity of the character "flat nose" among ancient Huns, he would have been disappointed, for this was controlled by the environment. In the words of Darwin, "As with the skull, so with the nose; the ancient Huns during the age of Attila were accustomed to flatten the noses of their infants with bandages. . . ." The difference between size of feet in upper- and lower-class prerevolutionary Chinese women was similarly due to bandaging.

In general, all characters are affected by both genes and environment—by nature and by nurture. The genticist can avoid confusion by trying to keep the environment as constant as possible. Small organisms like *Chlamydomonas*, fungi, and bacteria can be grown on a specified medium in incubators with constant temperature, but some characters, like size in larger animals, are so sensitive to changes in the environment that it is difficult to eliminate this factor. Identical twins have exactly the same genes because they arise from two cells produced by mitotic division of the zygote (*i.e.* they are monozygotic), but they show some differences even when they are brought up under similar conditions.

The effect of environment merges into that of pure chance. Some differences between identical twins may be due to environment in the same sense that the determination of whether a tossed penny falls heads or tails is due, if you like, to the environment.

A curious recent discovery about sex chromosomes deserves passing mention here. In the last chapter we said that males have one X chromosome and females have two. If one believes that a man is every inch as good as a woman, the question arises as to why women have this extra, useless chromosome. It turns out that in reality they do not have two X chromosomes—at least, not two functional X chromosomes in every cell of the body. What happens is that one or other of the X chromosomes in each female cell loses its function and becomes a small mass of chromosomal material which can be seen in a stained cell. This allows one to distinguish any cell of the body, say, in a scraping from the mouth, as being from a male or female. When a female is heterozygous for sex-linked genes, she may be one or the other type or, more frequently, a mosaic of the two, since during development of the embryo some tissues may lose the function of one X chromosome and some, the other. Human females have been found who show a mosaic of different kinds of sweat glands for this reason. A consequence of this discovery is that identical twin girls may not be as identical as twin boys.

The third category of difficulties is genetic and is fundamental; it has to do with how genes affect characters. In higher animals a great deal goes on between the fertilization of the egg and the development of the mature adult. Each gene plays a particular role in this process, but the consequences of each small action are difficult to trace. Many characters are known which are greatly changed, sometimes in a similar way, by several different genes. On the other hand, many genes are known which affect more than one character. Where two or three genes affect the same character, each gene can be studied by obtaining two parents which differ in only one of the genes concerned. In some cases, like height and size, there may be a large number of genes affecting the character about equally; for these, different methods have to be used, which will be described in Chapter XIX.

In general, all or almost all genes probably affect, to some extent, all characters, but certain genes affect certain characters predominantly, and the effect of other genes can usually be ignored. Some geneticists use the terms *polygenes* and *minor* genes for the many genes which have slight effects on a character, and *major genes* for the ones which have a predominant effect and can be studied singly. The distinction is arbitrary, and the same gene may act as a major gene for one character but as a minor gene for another. Some examples of various effects of genes which have been studied in higher and lower organisms will be described below, but first let us present the general picture by an analogy.

It should be understood that the process by which a set of genes, in man or in *Chlamydomonas*, produces the finished adult product is very hazy to geneticists and therefore the analogy represents a particular view of the writer; but it is an orthodox view and will not be violently disputed by competent critics. Consider the erection of a large building and let it represent an organism. Let the men who do the various tasks be genes; I suppose many thousands or hundreds of thousands will be involved. One of the first tasks will be to dig foundations. Let us suppose that the machines for this are available; they are used for other buildings and are taken ready-made, like vitamins. The steel for girders will have to be mined by miners, smelted in blast furnaces by smelters. The steel will have to be rolled or cast into appropriate shapes by specialized workers, then transported to the particular part of the building by carriers; window glass will have to be manufactured, woodwork formed, concrete mixed and poured. Workers will rivet the girders together, attach the floors and walls, and finally plaster the inner surfaces and paint the inside and outside with paint prepared with appropriate chemicals. The environment will not affect the fundamental structure much, it is true, but soft ground may make it slope like the tower of Pisa in spite of the intentions of the workers.

Now let us consider how differences in the workmen will be related to differences in the building. If the men digging foundations or the men making steel are grossly incompetent, the building obviously will be stillborn. In biology such "incompetent" alleles of important genes are known as lethals; the organism dies before adulthood, often early in the embryonic stage. However, if the maker of glass turns out a glass that is too brittle, or too thin, or colored, then the building will be more or less all right except for the windows. If the woodwork holding the windows is faulty, this may cause broken windows. Two types of faulty workmen may thus produce the same change in character—broken windows. Faulty woodworkers may also produce faulty floors and so two characters, broken windows and crooked floors, may both be due to the same cause. In general, a fault that occurs early in construction—in the foundations, the skeleton of steel girders, the manufacture of cement—will preclude a habitable structure; biologically it will correspond to a lethal allele. A fault in later processes—in the plumbing or electrical systems, or the color of a particular room—will detract less from the usefulness of the building; it will correspond in a living organism to a gene amenable to study.

The analogy must not be pushed too far. Living organisms, with a few exceptions among the lower groups, are constructed on a cellular basis, and each cell contains all genes, or at least all chromosomes. We will not be sidetracked by the interesting but unexplained fact that in the midge *Sciara*, in some of the *Cecidomyiidae*, and in a nematode worm certain chromosomes are systematically eliminated from certain cells of the body. Another weakness of the analogy is that in diploid living organisms there are only two genes of each kind in each cell. The analogy would be a little better in this respect if we imagined our workmen to be not the genes themselves, but the basic chemical substances that genes produce. These, as we shall see in a later chapter, are enzymes.

Our actual knowledge of how genes interact in higher organisms is scant, but a few examples will be described. Much more is known of the properties of genes in microorganisms because they are more amenable to study at present. This subject will be taken up later, and the reader can then contemplate the clues it offers for an understanding of vertebrate development. The information that we have on what genes do in vertebrates comes largely from research concerning three subjects: mice, chickens, and the hair of mammals. Work on all three was started over twenty years ago and is still being pursued by some of the original investigators. The varied effects of several genes in the mouse have been studied by Hans Grüneberg in England, among others, and we will limit description of this work to Figure 14, where eight genes have been chosen from a much larger number to show how they all affect two or more of the six characters listed. This picture is probably typical of the network of effects which relate genes to characters in higher organisms.

A mammal is different from *E. coli* or *Chlamydomonas* because it has a protracted embryonic period. The four cells that pop out of a *Chlamydomonas* zygote are adults; they exhibit all the adult characteristics. A human fertilized egg, on the other hand, does not look like a human adult at all; it looks more like an amoeba. It takes the form of a man only after ten or fifteen years and perhaps forty-three generations of cell division, sufficient to produce 2^{43} cells, equal to about 10^{13}—ten billion (British), or ten trillion (American). Even after fifteen years the organism's full potentiality may not be developed; to tell what sort of a brain the developing man really has one may have to wait until he is twenty-one or so.

FIGURE 14

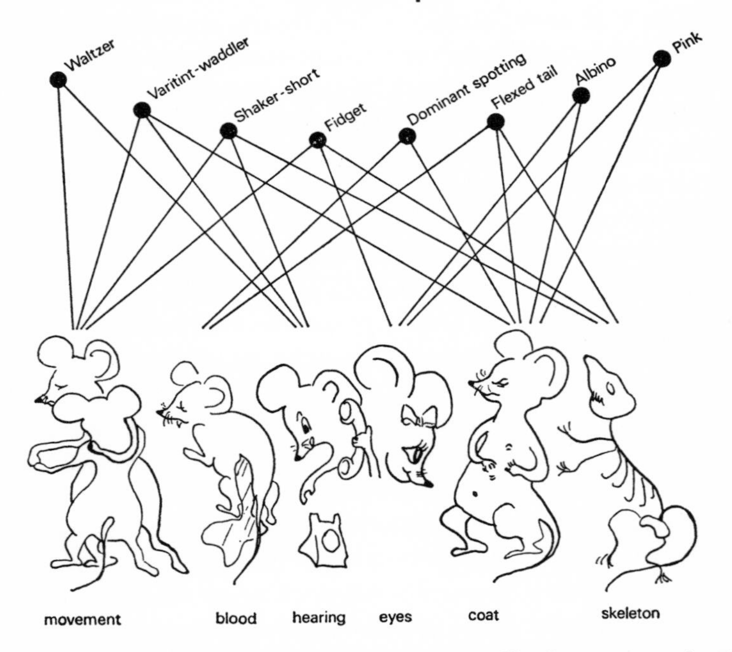

The Multiple Effects of Genes. Geneticists usually choose to work with single genes that have single effects, but one must be aware of the fact that most genes affect many characters and most characters are affected by many genes. The network of action of eight genes on six characters in mice is shown in the diagram.

A character of the adult is therefore the final result of a long developmental process, and a gene may act at any time during this process. An example which throws some light on the time during development that genes act is to be found in chickens.

A gene named "creeper," the effects of which can be distinguished in a chick embryo by the time it is forty-eight hours old, has been extensively studied by Walter Landauer, of the University of Connecticut, and others. The gene is dominant and lethal when homozygous. Homozygous chickens die after about seventy-two hours. The damage appears to be a general retardation of growth, but the retardation is not proportional —long bones are retarded more than short bones. Other parts of the body are also affected, notably by microphthalmia (in which the eyes are abnormally small, a defect reputedly congenital in man) and the absence of a fibrous layer of tissue around the eyeball. A question which can be studied is whether this disturbance is due to some hormone or substance formed in one part or parts of the body which spreads throughout all parts, or whether all cells or tissues are primarily affected. The answer seems to be that both processes can be seen to occur, depending on what organ of the body one observes. The way in which the problem was attacked was to transplant organs of one chick embryo into another. The legs of a chicken arise from small buds in the embryo. If these buds are removed from a sixty-seven-hour-old embryo which has the creeper defect and transplanted to a normal embryo, the legs that grow from them are abnormal, are creeper. If the same kind of experiment is done with eye rudiments, the results are different; the eyes that grow from the rudiments are normal (Fig. 15). The reciprocal experiment has been performed; eye rudiments from a normal embryo were transplanted to a creeper embryo and abnormal eyes grew.

The reason that certain bones are longer than others is that they grow at a faster rate, not that they go on growing longer or start earlier. The different rates of growth are established early in the development of the embryo and the creeper gene must affect these rates. The various effects of the creeper

FIGURE 15

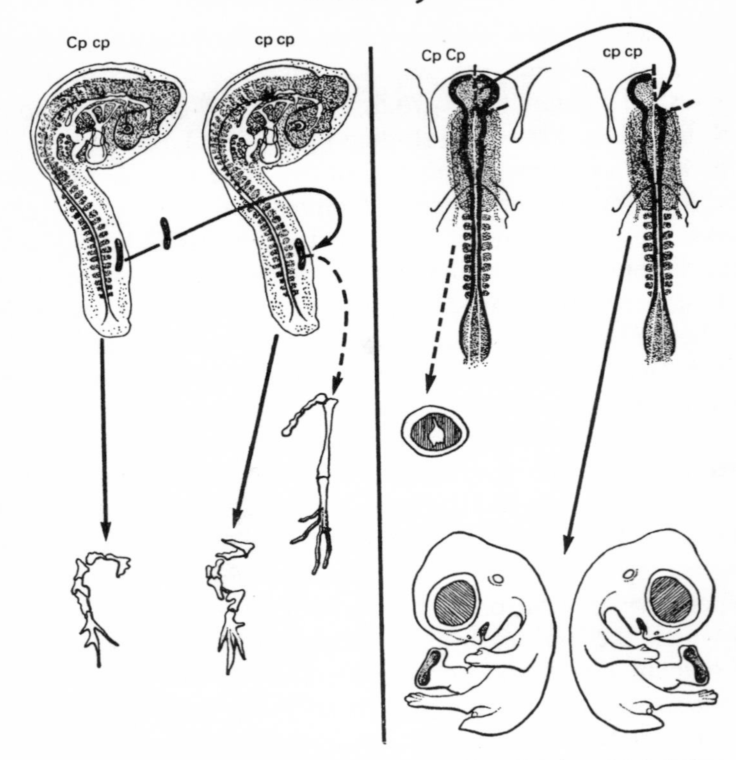

Transplantation of Limb Bud (left) and Eye Region (right) from a Creeper Embryo into a Normal Embryo. The first experiment was performed by Viktor Hamburger, and the second by Kenneth Gayer and Viktor Hamburger. Limb buds were taken from heterozygous creeper embryos (*Cpcp*) about sixty-seven hours old and implanted into normal embryos (*cpcp*) of the same age. (The normal allele is *cp;* the dominant creeper allele is *Cp.*) It will be seen that the implanted bud grew into a leg that resembled a creeper's leg (drawn under creeper embryo) not a normal leg (to the right, indicated by dotted arrow).

Eye transplants were made between thirty-five-hour embryos. The donor was a homozygous creeper because heterozygous creepers have normal eyes. Only the right-eye region was transplanted, so that the resulting eye could be compared with the normal left eye. In this case the transplant grew into a normal eye and did not have the defects of the creeper eye (to the left, indicated by dotted arrow). Both sides of the experimental chick are shown; the transplanted right eye is shown in the right-hand diagram.

This means that the limb defect, but not the eye defect, is due to a defect in the cells of the limb bud and cannot be corrected by the surrounding environment of a normal embryo. It is of interest to know how soon this defect of the limb buds occurs in the developing embryo. Dorothea Rudnick has succeeded in performing a more complicated transplantation experiment in which she has demonstrated that it occurs at 24–32 hours.

gene on various parts of the body are constant and specific, but this is more a function of the way in which a chicken develops than of the creeper gene itself. The creeper gene probably upsets some process at a particular stage of development, resulting in all the specific characters found in the creeper. Evidence for this is that one can inject a variety of substances, such as boric acid or insulin, into the yolk sac of a normal chicken's egg and produce all the characters of a creeper. These substances could damage the same developmental process that the creeper gene affects, a process which must occur at a certain stage of development and be especially sensitive.

The gene controlling the character creeper acts early in development. An example of a gene that acts late is the gene for Huntington's chorea, a dominant defect in man which is characterized by disordered and involuntary movements and progressive mental deterioration. The average age of onset of this defect is about thirty-five, but in many individuals it does not become apparent until the age of fifty or later. The gene most probably came to Boston from England in 1630 with the Puritan leader John Winthrop. It probably caused many of its victims to be burned at the stake as witches, but not before they were old enough to transmit the gene to their children.

The following example concerns a gene which can be considered to act so late in development that it affects the next generation. This interesting investigation was carried out many years ago on snails. These animals have not attracted much genetic research apart from this particular work because of their slow habits of reproduction. They are hermaphroditic, and generally perform the unusual feat among animals of fertilizing themselves. Sometimes a snail will receive sperm from a suitor; in this case the outside sperm seems to have a competitive advantage over the snail's own sperm, which is fortunate for the experimenter. The character studied is the direction in which the shell coils. There are only two possible directions: to the right, dextral, and to the left, sinistral. Most snails are dextral, but in a pond were found four individuals which were sinistral and these sinistral snails were crossed with dextrals. Now the peculiar thing about the gene that controls the direction of coiling is that it acts not early in development, not in adulthood, not even in old age, but in the next generation! A mother snail with an allele for dextral produces baby snails with shells coiling to the right no matter what their own genes may be. The character is inherited in a perfectly Mendelian way, controlled by a single gene with the dextral allele, *D*, dominant over sinistral *d*, but the genotype of each generation controls the phenotype of the next generation. A cross between a snail from a pure-breeding and therefore homozygous dextral line and one from a homozygous sinistral line is diagramed in Figure 16.

One cannot help feeling a pang of sympathy for the British biologist A. E. Bayton and his co-workers, who published their first paper on snails after three years of hard work but failed to perceive the point of their own story. The true explanation was suggested to them by an American *Drosophila* geneticist, A. H. Sturtevant, in a paper published the same year. In Bayton's subsequent paper he writes, ". . . Sturtevant was right in his inspired guess (for with the data at his disposal it certainly reached that degree) that the essential facts could best be explained by dextral dominance and delayed inheritance."

FIGURE 16

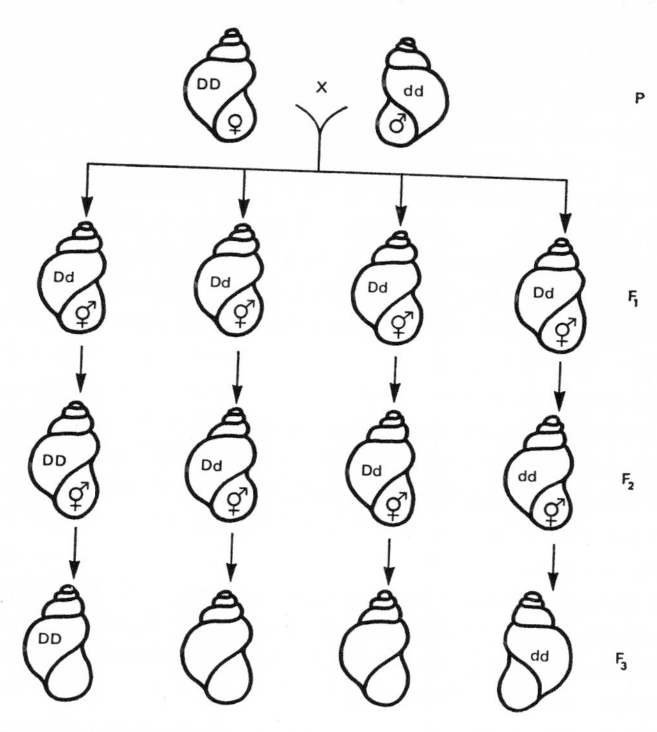

Inheritance of Shell Coiling. The two parents (P) are from pure-breeding lines of dextral and sinistral snails. Four representative lines of F_1 progeny are shown, with the F_2 and F_3 obtained by selfing. Genotypes are shown by letters in the shells. The middle two snails in the bottom line may be *DD, Dd,* or *dd.* It will be seen that each snail shell coils in a direction determined by the genes of its mother and that dextral (*D*) is dominant over sinistral (*d*). In a reciprocal cross in which the sinistral parent (*dd*) is a female, all the F_1 will have sinistral shells, but the diagram will be otherwise identical.

Examination of developing snails has shown that the direction of coiling depends on the way in which the second division of the zygote occurs, the division resulting in the four-cell stage. It is probable that all the characters of the very early embryo, up to what is called the gastrula stage, are maternal, *i.e.* are determined by the genes of the mother, not of the embryo itself. This would apply to mammals as well as snails.

Maternal inheritance must be distinguished from what has been called cytoplasmic inheritance. The latter is better called nonchromosomal inheritance; a great deal could be written describing the various phenomena that fit into this category. No attractive theory has yet been forthcoming to cover these phenomena, and apart from some work in the genetics of small microbial organisms, to be described in later chapters, description of the phenomena will be omitted. Nonchromosomal inheritance concerns hereditary units, usually in the cytoplasm, such as the green particles in plants called chloroplasts; or it may concern some nonparticulate factor in the cytoplasm. Such hereditary units can be shown by breeding tests not to be in any linkage group, and in fact, they usually do not obey Mendelian laws. Since the egg contains more cytoplasm than the sperm, they are usually inherited maternally, but it will be appreciated that this phenomenon is quite distinct from the maternal inheritance of snail coiling, which is basically Mendelian.

Some cases of nonchromosomal inheritance behave very much like an infection, a virus infection which alters but does not kill the host. In other instances a particle subject to nonchromosomal inheritance seems to be a structure of the cell, a chloroplast or mitochondrion, which is capable of self-division and which when damaged produces damaged progeny. When lost it cannot be created *de novo* in the cell. Still other cases of nonchromosomal inheritance suggest that we have to think in different terms, to think of a process rather than a particle. This does not mean that we must return to the idea of a blending type of inheritance, for as will be explained in connection with repressors, there may be only two or a few stable states of a process. A cell may be in one state or another, but it cannot remain in an intermediate state for long. Which state it gets into may depend not on the genes, but on past history, for once something puts it into a certain state it cannot easily change. Since these metabolic processes occur in the cytoplasm, the gamete that contributes most of the cytoplasm in a cross will dominate the state of the zygote and progeny. Some pretty mathematical calculations can and have been made about steady states, but no one really knows what part they play, if any, in inheritance.

Nonchromosomal inheritance may prove to be important in development and heredity, but at the present time much more is known about characters controlled by Mendelian genes. Perhaps one of the most studied characters in mammals is the color and texture of the coat; some general findings will be described as an example of a type of interaction between genes. In mice, guinea pigs, rabbits, and many other mammals there is a gene determining the presence or the absence of pigment (albinism). In general, and in man, the albino allele, *c*, is recessive to alleles for color. If the animal is of genotype *cc*, it is albino. If it is *Cc* or *CC* it is colored, but the particular color, black or brown or red, and the particular distribution of color, solid or spotted, is due to other genes. In mice, for instance, there is a color gene with two alleles: black (*B*) dominant over brown (*b*). Two other alleles control distribution of color: solid (*S*) dominant over spotted (*s*). All mice with alleles *cc* are white. All mice having *Cc* or *CC* are colored; mice with *CCBB* are black; those with *CCbb* are brown. Add *SS* or *Ss* to either genotype and the mice are solid-colored; add *ss* and they are spotted. The five kinds of mice which are determined by these three genes are shown in Table 10.

These three genes are not the only ones known that affect the color of mice; six or more genes, producing over thirty

TABLE 10

C–	B–	S–	. . . Black
C–	*bb*	S–	. . . Brown
C–	B–	*ss*	. . . Spotted Black
C–	*bb*	*ss*	. . . Spotted Brown
cc	—	—	. . . All White

A dash replaces an allele when it does not matter which allele is present.

recognizable phenotypes, have been well studied in mice and other mammals. In general, the way in which color is controlled is similar in mice, rabbits, mink, guinea pigs, horses, cattle, and other animals that have been studied; the details, however, are different for each animal. Most have an albino allele which is recessive but overrides all other genes affecting color. Other widespread genes control the distribution of pigment either in space (as in piebalds), or in time (as in agoutis, in whom each hair root produces a succession of different pigments).

In many instances there are more than two alleles of a color gene. A good example of this is the *C* gene in rabbits. Along with the *C* allele, giving color, and the *c*, producing white, there are two more: c^{ch} for chinchilla and c^{h} for Himalayan. Chinchilla rabbits are more or less the same color all over, like the full-colored rabbits; but they are silvery gray instead of brown or black; Himalayan rabbits, on the contrary, are white except for the extremities, the tail, ears, tips of legs, and nose, which are black. The dominance relationship between these four alleles is as follows: *C* is dominant over the other three, c^{ch} is dominant over c^{h} and *c*, c^{h} is dominant over *c*. The phenotypes produced by the ten possible combinations of these alleles are shown in Table 11.

Himalayan rabbits are of interest in another connection. We have already mentioned the fact that the environment

TABLE 11

Full Color	*Chincilla* (Silvery Gray)	*Himalayan* (Black Extremities)	*Albino*
$C\,C$	$c^{ch}\,c^{ch}$	$c^{h}\,c^{h}$	$c\,c$
$C\,c^{ch}$	$c^{ch}\,c^{h}$	$c^{h}\,c$	
$C\,c^{h}$	$c^{ch}\,c$		
$C\,c$			

can often make the same change in an organism that known genes make. The substitution of the albino allele *c* for the color allele *C*, with the appropriate other color genes, can make the difference between white hairs and black. Temperature does the same thing in Himalayan rabbits; at cold temperatures the hair is black and at warm temperatures the hair is white. The extremities are normally the coldest part of an animal and are thus black. This effect of temperature was discovered at the time of the First World War by experimenters who pulled out white hairs from a part of the body and then cooled that part down to below 11°C.; the new hairs that grew in were black. Whatever the processes that make black and white hair, the allele *C* must control a process leading to black, the allele *c*, that producing white, and the allele c^{h}, an unstable process sensitive to temperature such that at low temperatures the black pigment is formed, but at higher temperatures the process does not work and no black pigment is synthesized. In more recent work many of the chemical changes leading to black pigment have been studied, and several enzymes which cause these changes are known. It is most likely that one or more of these enzymes are destroyed or made inactive at higher temperatures in Himalayans.

Temperature is a very obvious environmental factor, but the condition of the blood and many other internal factors can be considered part of the "environment," and it is often useful to speak of them as the "internal environment" even though they may be themselves controlled by genes. In the case of the Himalayan rabbit the temperature of the extremities can be altered by altering the blood supply, and in fact, it has been shown that cutting certain sympathetic nerves or hyperthyroidism will change the color of the hair.

The difference between male and female is determined by genes, but these act by controlling the development of certain organs which in turn produce certain hormones or mixtures of hormones which cause the growth of the sexual characters. Injection of the right hormones, or even accidents during development, can result in a change in sexual characteristics. The difference between a male and a female certainly represents an important difference in internal environment, and it might be expected that some genes would have different effects in the two sexes. The most striking of these are the "sex-limited" genes, genes which have no effect at all in one sex. There are many genes which control the amount and quality of milk in cattle, but they obviously show their phenotype only in cows, never in bulls—unless perhaps the bulls have been castrated and treated with female sex hormones. Sex-limited characters are sometimes confused with sex-linked characters, but reference back to the discussion of the latter in Chapter VI will make it clear that they are quite distinct phenomena. Sometimes sex makes a difference in the dominance of an allele. This has been claimed for baldness in humans. There is a gene *B* such that homozygotes *BB*, whether men or women, are bald; the homozygotes with the alternative *bb* are nonbald irrespective of sex; the heterozygotes, *Bb*, are bald if men but nonbald if women. The allele *B* is dominant over *b* in man, but *b* is dominant over *B* in women. This implies that more men are bald than women.

Whatever substance is responsible for causing hair to grow or not to grow, one can easily imagine a situation in which no substance (*bb*), or a double dose of the substance (*BB*), would make a difference regardless of the environment. In the heterozygote, with only one dose of the substances, the environment —male or female—might tip the scale between hair and no hair.

The environment affects the expression of a gene in many ways. Cows with the same alleles for high milk production will not all produce exactly the same amount of milk; their production will depend on what they eat and drink, the exercise they get, and more subtle factors that cannot be analyzed. There is a gene in humans, studied in Norway, which causes an abnormally short index finger. The allele for the short finger is dominant over that for a normal finger. There are, however, two degrees of shortness and these were both found in persons with the same allele for shortness; the difference between the two degrees was not genetic but environmental in origin, or perhaps was due to a very complex interaction of many other genes concerned primarily with other characters. In other cases there is an all-or-none effect: the environment makes the difference between having the character and not having it at all. Polydactyly, where extra fingers or toes are produced, is such a case. Sewall Wright, who worked for many years at the University of Chicago, has studied inbred lines of guinea pigs which, as far as he could establish, had the same genes for polydactyly; yet in litters from these pigs only a certain proportion, say 40 per cent, were polydactylous. Different lines of inbred pigs showed different proportions of polydactyly in their litters, but for any particular line the percentage was constant. This must be thought of as being due to an environmental threshold for the appearance of the character. If the various environmental factors fell above the threshold then the animal was polydactylous; if they did not, then the animal was perfectly normal. These must be very subtle environmental factors, verging on pure chance, as with the toss of a penny. Different genotypes in the different inbred lines would have different thresholds. This recalls the case of black hair in the Himalayan rabbits, where the environmental factor was simply temperature and the threshold about 11° C.

If the environmental factor varies among individuals in such a way that in 90 per cent of the animals it reaches a certain degree or threshold, in 80 per cent of individuals a higher degree, in 70 per cent a still higher and in a small proportion, say 10 per cent, a very high level, genes which express themselves at the various thresholds will produce the character in 90 per cent, 80 per cent, . . . , 10 per cent of individuals having the gene. The same reasoning can be applied to different environments affecting different parts of each individual. If 90 per cent of the skin area of a rabbit is, in general, above 10°C., 70 per cent is above 11°C., 50 per cent above 12°C., and so on, then different Himalayan alleles having thresholds at 10°C., 11°C., and 12°C. will produce rabbits that are 90 per cent, 70 per cent, and 50 per cent white, respectively. Alleles which only show up in a percentage of individuals are, as may be imagined, difficult to study. The classical Mendelian ratios are badly disturbed.

Sometimes two genes affecting a character interact to produce a new character. The Wyandotte breed of chickens has a flat comb with one posterior point, called "rose." Leghorns have a large comb with several points, called "single." When rose-combed chickens are bred with single-combed, the members of the first generation, F_1, are all rose-combed and the F_2 are three-quarters rose and one-quarter single, suggesting that the character is controlled by a single gene, the rose allele (*R*) being dominant over the single allele (*r*). Brahma chickens have a different kind of comb, called "pea." When pea-combed chickens are bred to single-combed, the F_1 are pea and the F_2 are three-quarters pea and one-quarter single; thus pea is dominant over single. The question arises of whether we are dealing with a single gene with three alleles, one for rose, one for pea, and one for single, or whether two genes are involved. A cross of rose with pea should give a clue; if there is a single gene this cross will tell us whether the rose allele is dominant over the pea allele or vice versa. It so happens that the cross of rose and pea gives a completely different comb, called "walnut," and these F_1 walnuts when crossed between themselves give an F_2 with a 9:3:3:1 ratio of walnut: pea: rose: and single, a typical two-gene segregation (Fig. 17). If only one gene were involved and walnut were a heterozygote containing only the alleles for rose and pea, then a cross between two walnuts could not possibly give any single combs.

In the cases of interaction of genes described above, and in many similar instances which could be mentioned, the details of how the genes interact to produce the character are little known. We will turn now to some of the current work done with microorganisms, which has rapidly assumed a dominant role in genetic research. The interactions between genes that are studied in these systems are basic to a wide variety of organisms and can be pursued in detail. The characters that are most easily studied in these investigations are chemical requirements, like the need for para-aminobenzoic acid described earlier in *Chlamydomonas*. The way in which this work is done is characteristic; whereas the genetics of mammals and chickens is, by the very nature of the animals, a slow, leisurely pursuit, the work we will describe is done with fast-growing molds, yeasts, or other microorganisms, and it is pursued energetically—"feverishly" would not be too strong a word. The coordination of rapid discoveries in many laboratories requires periodic international symposia, one or two a year, for geneticists working in the same field. Private newsletters are circulated for people working on the same organism —*Neurospora*, yeast, or bacteria. Geneticists can also participate every five years in a grand international congress of genetics, the eleventh of which was held in 1963 in Holland and

FIGURE 17

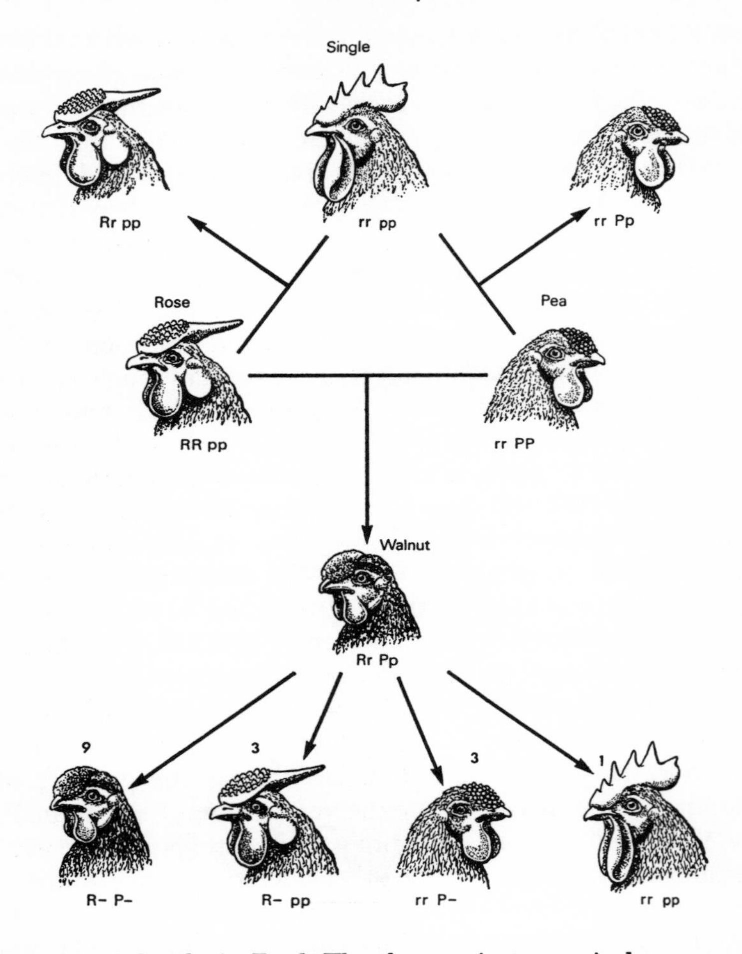

Genetics of Combs in Fowl. The three main types, single, rose, and pea, are illustrated in a triangle. Rose crossed with single gives rose; pea crossed with single gives pea. Rose crossed with pea gives a new type, walnut. If the F_1 walnut are bred among themselves all four types, shown below, are obtained, in the ratio 9:3:3:1. Genotypes are given below each illustration. Combs are somewhat different in each sex: the pea comb as drawn resembles Batesons photograph of a female. Pure-breeding walnut combs, *RRPP*, exist in a breed known as "Malay."

was attended by over a thousand delegates from all over the world. International congresses of biochemistry held recently in Moscow, New York, and Tokyo have included more and more genetics.

Large international congresses and numerous smaller international meetings are a fairly recent feature of scientific work. They undoubtedly play a social role in the life of contemporary scientists. The scientific communication they promote is remarkable in traversing space rather than time. A scientist today is often better acquainted with the work of a colleague on the other side of the world than with that done in his own university. On the other hand, he is often ignorant of work done ten or twenty years ago.

In our grandfathers' day, communication was largely by letter and knowledge of past work was more remarkable than that of contemporary work in other lands. This is well-illustrated by the fact that Charles Darwin, in the middle of the last century in England, was ignorant of the contemporary work of Gregor Mendel in Austria, but was well aware of the work of Peter Simon Pallas (1777) showing that "the Asiatic antelope Saiga appears to be the most inordinate polygamist in the world."

The biochemical genetics which we will describe was initiated by George W. Beadle and Edward L. Tatum in the early 1940's in California with strains of the mold *Neurospora*. By treating *Neurospora* spores with radiation and other agents, they developed a number of mutant strains which were called arginineless (arg) because they would not grow unless an amino acid, say arginine, was added to the medium. When crossed with the wild type they segregated 1:1, showing that they were each due to a single gene. The fact that *Neurospora* is a haploid organism facilitated the genetic analysis. A lazy or unimaginative geneticist might have dropped the subject at this point and gone on to other work. Beadle and Tatum asked the further questions of whether all these mutant strains were exactly alike and whether arginine was the only substance which would allow growth. The experiment to answer the second question was obvious: try some other substances. There are very many chemicals available and a choice had to be made of the most likely candidates. Arginine is made, in the wild-type *Neurospora*, from a whole complex of processes changing one chemical into another, and in 1932 the chemist Hans Adolf Krebs discovered that liver extracts could change ornithine (orn) into citrulline (cit) and that citrulline was changed into arginine; consequently, these two substances were likely candidates. All of the mutant (arg) strains, together with a wild-type strain as a control, were inoculated into four kinds of media: minimal medium with added arginine, with added citrulline, with added ornithine, and without any addition. The results may appear complex at first, but make very good sense upon reflection. Only the wild type grew on the medium without addition, which was to be expected. Among the mutant strains some grew on each of the other media and some particular strains grew on two or three other media. Upon analysis it was found that all the strains that grew on ornithine also grew on the other two media, all strains that grew on citrulline grew also on arginine but not necessarily on ornithine, and some remaining strains grew only on arginine. This places the three substances in an order—ornithine,

TABLE 12

	Min	*Orn*	*Cit*	*Arg*
Mutant Strain 1)	–	growth	growth	growth
" " 2)	–	–	growth	growth
" " 3)	–	–	–	growth

A dash signifies that there is no growth.

citrulline, arginine—and if all strains having exactly the same growth pattern are considered similar we are left with three types, whose growth is shown in Table 12.

The chemical formulae for the three substances are shown in Figure 18.

FIGURE 18

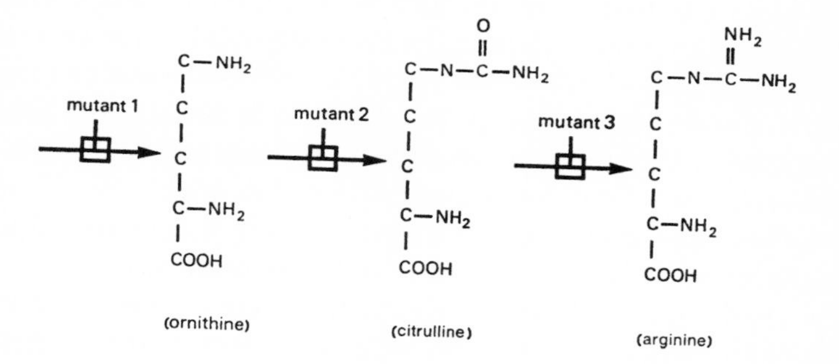

Hydrogen atoms attached to carbon atoms have been omitted for simplicity. It will be seen that the three formulae are very similar, and moreover citrulline is more like arginine than is ornithine, which also suggests the sequence shown in the diagram.

Chemical changes of this kind can often be performed with simple chemical reagents, using strong acids or alkalis and high or low temperatures. In living organisms reactions take place at mild and constant temperatures by the mediation of complex substances called enzymes, which are proteins and therefore have a high molecular weight. Knowing these facts, Beadle and Tatum proposed a simple but pregnant hypothesis. They proposed that most, if not all, genes cause their effect through enzymes and that each gene controls the production of one enzyme.

In our example three enzymes would be concerned,

namely X $\xrightarrow{\text{enzyme 1}}$ ornithine $\xrightarrow{\text{enzyme 2}}$ citrulline $\xrightarrow{\text{enzyme 3}}$ arginine. The gene of strain 1 has a faulty allele of some gene whose wild-type allele is responsible for enzyme 1; therefore neither ornithine nor citrulline nor arginine is made from the minimal medium, but enzymes 2 and 3 are all right in this strain so that if either ornithine or citrulline or, of course, arginine is available, everything is all right and *Neurospora* will grow. In strain 2, which has a faulty allele of a different gene, ornithine can be made all right but the further change to citrulline is blocked because enzyme 2 is faulty. It is therefore useless to add more ornithine from outside; growth will only occur if either citrulline or arginine is added. Strain 3 is the most fastidious; only arginine will allow growth of this strain because the block is just in front of arginine.

Although Beadle and Tatum's work with *Neurospora* was the spark which lit a fire of activity in the genetics of chemical reactions, they were not really the first to discover such genes. Before the First World War, the English physician A. E. Garrod had already described a case of genetic control of a chemical reaction in humans. Garrod studied a trait called alkaptonuria, in which affected people are distinguished by their production of black urine. The trait is not serious, though victims may feel distressed or humiliated by their particular symptoms. It was found that black urine is due to the abnormal secretion of homogenistic acid in the urine. In normal people there is an enzyme which converts homogenistic acid into something else which in another two steps produces fumaric acid and acetoacetic acid; these in turn go on to other substances used in normal metabolism. People with alkaptonuria lack an enzyme which can act on homogenistic acid; this substance, therefore, accumulates in the blood, and when it reaches too high a concentration it is released into the urine by the kidneys. This is a little different from the previous example because here the lack of acetoacetic acid or fumaric acid as nutrients is not important—they can be obtained from other chemical reactions; what is important is the piling up of the chemical in front of the block. The actual enzyme concerned is now well known and was shown in 1958 to be absent from the liver of alkaptonurics. Another related and more serious disease, phenylketonuria, has since been studied and shown to be inherited, like alkaptonuria, as a single gene. Phenylketonurics lack the enzyme which converts phenylalanine to tyrosine (Fig. 19), and the former substance accumulates in the

FIGURE 19A

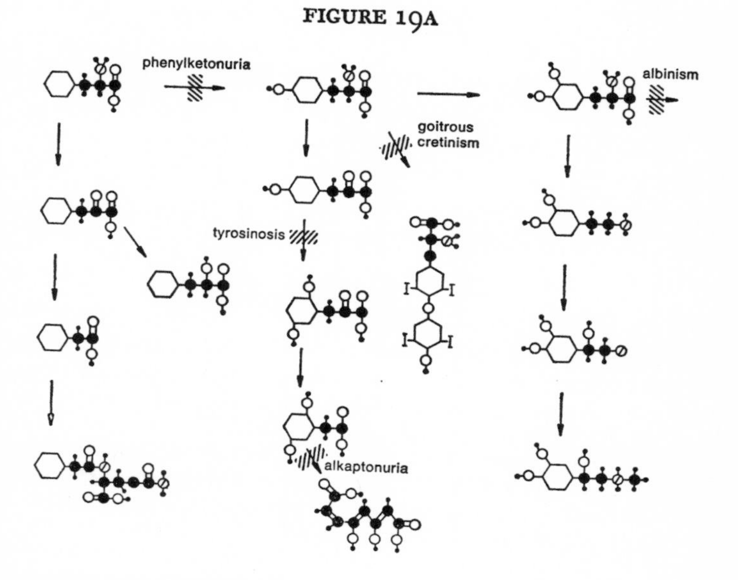

blood, resulting in dire effects on the brain, and causing deep-bluish urine and light-colored hair. These two examples of enzyme blocks due to known genes must suffice. In a bacterium or in *Chlamydomonas* there must be over five hundred enzymes to carry out the basic chemical reactions necessary

FIGURE 19B

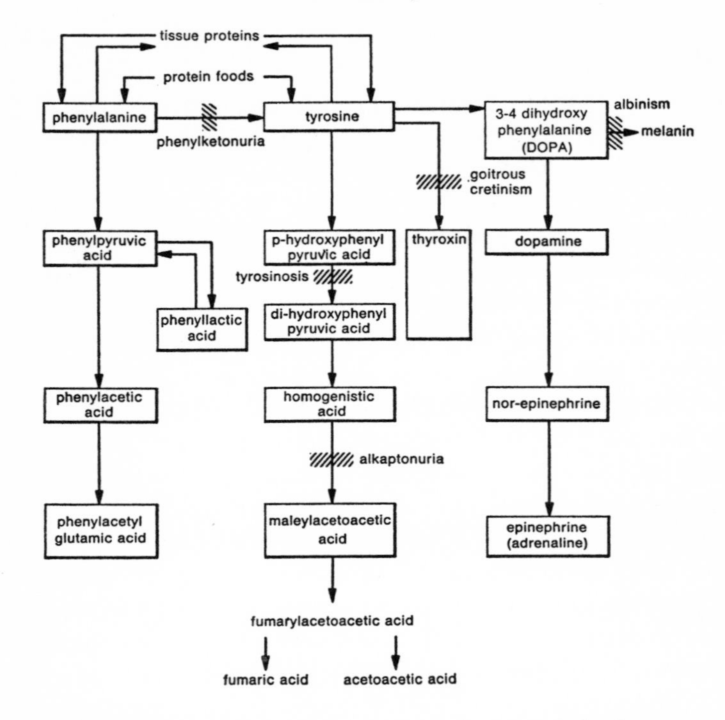

Some Inborn Errors of Metabolism in Man: a few of the known metabolic steps concerned with the metabolism of the amino acids phenylalanine and tyrosine. Formulae of the chemicals, and positions of the enzymatic blocks which produce the indicated diseases, are shown in Figure 19a. The names of the chemicals are given separately in the boxes in Figure 19b, which also includes some substances, like melanin, which are complexes whose metabolism and structure are not known in detail. Most of the steps shown are catalyzed by a single enzyme which has been studied in detail; some of the steps have not yet been thoroughly studied and will, most probably, be broken down into several smaller changes, each catalyzed by a separate enzyme. Symbols for atoms are: ● = carbon, ○ = oxygen, ⊘ = nitrogen, • = hydrogen, ⬡ = a benzene ring (there are hydrogen atoms at each angle which have been omitted for simplicity), I = iodine.

to all independent life on earth. Higher organisms would require more enzymes for special chemical reactions in the various tissues. Many of these enzymes and many more of the reactions they perform are now known. They represent a vast complex of chemical reactions, with many branches and cycles.

It is generally believed that the whole of development, from egg to adult, is due to the action of the right enzymes at the right time and place in the right amounts. Furthermore, all enzymes are believed to be the direct product of genes, and it is by determining where and in what quantity enzymes are produced that genes in a mouse egg make it develop into a mouse and those in a woman's fertilized egg cause it to grow into a man. This is the general working belief, but there is plenty of room for new ideas. There may be other roles for genes besides controlling enzymes. The "right" time, place, and quantity conceals a vast unknown territory. We will describe later some new ideas about the turning on and off of the production of an enzyme by a gene, but there remain profound mysteries as to whether and how a set of some hundreds or thousands of enzymes can lead to the development of a man.

We have described, in this part, what can be called classical genetics. Knowledge of the general concept of genes, how they are transmitted, and what sort of things they do provides a solid framework on which further ideas can be hung.

With this theory as a starting point, two directions have been followed. Some geneticists have been interested in the smaller scale; they have discovered the molecular structure of genes and something of how they produce proteins. Others have been interested in the larger scale, in the laws governing populations, how they reach equilibrium, and how they change. These two areas will be taken up in the next two sections, along with a few incidental topics concerning our own species.

Part Two ♀/♂

VIII *Mutation: Fundamental Accidents*

The units of heredity called genes are characteristically stable. We have already drawn attention to the fact that a recessive allele can pass through innumerable generations of heterozygous individuals, where it does not show, and yet emerge, atavistically, with unaltered phenotype in a homozygous individual. Stable, but not absolutely stable: genes do sometimes change from one allele to another. The process by which they change is called mutation—to be precise, gene or point mutation; the new allele and the new strain are called mutant.

In about one person out of 50,000 a normal allele of the hemophilia gene changes into the hemophilia allele. There is good reason to believe that the hemophilia allele present in the royal families of Europe (Fig. 13) originated in Queen Victoria's father, for the trait is not known in any of her ancestors; in Haldane's words, "The gene must have originated by mutation, and the most probable place and time where the mutation may have occurred was in the nucleus of a cell in one of the testicles of Edward, Duke of Kent, in the year 1818. The event in question could not have been observed with the most powerful microscopes. It initially affected a single gene, that is to say a particle much less than 1/1000 mm. in diameter. But it had an appreciable effect on world history."

We have, as yet, said nothing of the nature of the gene. Some of the properties of this minute biological organ should nevertheless have become familiar. They are remarkable properties for a particle no bigger than a large molecule. The first thing a gene must do is produce some substance—we have suggested that it is an enzyme—which controls chemical reactions, the metabolism of the cell. We must envisage genes in this way controlling development and the final shape of the adult. This means that genes must contain a great deal of specific information, a complex blueprint so to speak, in a small space, to be handed on to the next generation through egg or sperm.

Second, a gene must duplicate itself exactly at every cell division, including the special meiotic division. Third, when it does mutate to a different allele, it must thereafter duplicate the new allele. The hemophilia allele that Queen Victoria had must have multiplied into thousands of hemophilia alleles in her body and her eggs and in turn into innumerable other hemophilia alleles in her descendants. If it should mutate back again into the normal allele, then it would thereafter duplicate the normal allele.

One in 50,000 is rather a high rate for spontaneous point mutations. Most genes in man, *Drosophila*, corn, and *E. coli* mutate at the rate of only one in a million or less. The process of mutation is obviously an interesting one, and already in 1922 H. J. Muller suggested that a study of conditions under which mutations occurred might lead to an understanding of the nature of the gene. Five years later Muller had completed extensive work showing that X-rays increase the rate of mutation significantly. The trick in this work was to show that it was really X-rays that produced the genetic changes. This entailed getting enough mutants to estimate the rate of production; doing this is not so easy in a diploid organism, for a recessive mutation—and most of the ones obtained are recessive—will not show up unless the same genes on both homologous chromosomes are mutated. He obtained the mutants by irradiating male flies, crossing them to specially marked female flies, and looking for sex-linked mutants in the grandsons, where recessives would show up. As we know, males are, in effect, haploid for all genes on the X chromosome. Most of the changes produced were lethal—the flies died before becoming mature—but out of some eight hundred flies irradiated, three mutations were produced which were of the sort used in genetic studies. In subsequent work it was found that there was nothing specific about X-rays: they produced the same kind of mutations as those arising spontaneously. Mutation appears to be a random process and X-rays only increase, by about one hundredfold, the probability of its happening. Ultraviolet light also increases the mutation rate in a similar way, but cannot be used so easily on *Drosophila* because it does not penetrate the tissues. An important fact about the production of mutations by radiation is that it does not matter how the dose is given; that is to say, it does not matter whether one irradiates at a high intensity for a short time or a low intensity for a long time—the effect will be the same. This is like the action of light radiation on photographic film. One can expose at f/8 for 1/400 of a second or at the lower intensity f/16 for the longer 1/100 of a second and the picture will be the same. This rule must be qualified somewhat. As a result of intensive work with mammals it has been found that at very low intensities there does seem to be some kind of healing process; exposure to very low intensities for a very long time gives fewer mutations than expected, but the rule is nevertheless generally true.

Genetics is, by and large, a pure rather than an applied science, although it is heavily supported by grants for cancer and agricultural research. During the Second World War many geneticists put aside their pure or fundamental pursuits and contributed their efforts to more urgent applied problems. One of these was Charlotte Auerbach, in Edinburgh, Scotland, who studied the effects of mustard gas with a view to discovering efficient antidotes. Few biologists can tell what she found about how to combat mustard-gas attacks, but her name is associated, together with that of her co-worker J. M. Robson, with the discovery that mustard gas is a potent mutagen, like X-rays. The publication of her paper was unfortunately delayed, perhaps because of an erroneous fear that this knowledge would impair the morale of the British nation.[1] Its publication opened up a whole new field of research into chemical mutagens. Many other chemicals have been found to cause mutations, including hydrogen peroxide, formaldehyde, various phenols, epoxides, acriflavine, the caffeine present in tea or coffee, and other more subtle chemicals which will be described in Chapter X. With very sensitive techniques, Aaron Novick and Leo Szilard, two Chicago atomic physicists who turned to genetics after the Second World War, were able to show that some chemicals—adenosine is one of them—are antimutagenic: they reduce the mutagenic effect of mutagens, caffeine, in particular, and also reduce to some extent the spontaneous rate.

At one time many geneticists believed that the production of mutations by radiation would prove to be the key by which mysteries of the gene would be unlocked. Estimates of the size of genes by calculations according to a "target theory" were made. The effects of oxygen and other factors were studied in detail. Emphasis has now shifted away from these studies because it was gradually realized that the effects of radiation are indirect. In other words, radiation produces chemicals in the cell which in turn act on the genes, directly or through

[1] A notion, I believe, due to the Indian geneticist and aphorist J. B. S. Haldane, who died in 1964.

other chemicals. One of the clearest experiments that demonstrated the role of chemicals in producing mutants was accidental. A certain laboratory was studying mutation of the microbe *Staphylococcus* to penicillin resistance. The *Staphylococcus* was grown in broth, irradiated with ultraviolet light, and then spread out onto a series of Petri dishes filled with medium containing penicillin and solidified with agar. Only mutant staphylococcal cells would grow to produce visible colonies. The mutation rate could be measured by the number of colonies appearing. The story goes that a technician charged with doing the manipulations was forgetful and irradiated the broth without having inoculated it with the microbes. In a naïve attempt to cover up the mistake, he inoculated the broth after irradiation and continued the experiment. The surprising result was that although the *Staphylococcus* itself had not been irradiated, the number of mutants was nevertheless greater than in the control. The rays must have produced substances in the medium—peroxides, free radicals, or others—that were mutagenic.

Recent interest in the mutagenic effects of radiation has concentrated on attempts to estimate the amount of damage to humans caused by man-made radiation from atomic and H-bombs, medical X-rays, atomic power plants, television screens, and radioactive paint on wristwatches. The calculations are approximate and complicated because we do not know much about mutation rates in man and also because the results can be presented in many different ways, according to the effect that the writer wishes to make upon the public. Two statements can be made without fear of serious contradiction. First, there is no clear threshold of radiation for mutation.[2] The smallest increase in radiation produces some increase in the mutation rate. Second, most mutations, whether sponta-

[2] The word "clear" has been inserted so as not to contradict what was said earlier in this chapter about healing processes.

neous or induced by radiation, are recessive and are harmful. Thus it can be argued that all radiation is bad, but one must bear in mind that some mutations can be beneficial, and as we shall see in the last section, are necessary for evolution. Radiation produces other harmful physiological effects on man, and for these there may be a threshold, a level at which the radiation need not harm us because its effects can be cured by repair processes. For this kind of damage it is possible to state a maximum dose which is tolerable. For genetic damage, on the other hand, where there is no threshold, it is extremely difficult for legislators to prescribe a maximum level of radiation beyond which we should not trespass. Some idea of magnitudes can be given briefly. The units of radiation are themselves rather complicated. The older measure of radiation is the Roentgen unit, which was defined by physicists as the amount of radiation which would produce ions carrying one electrostatic unit of electricity in one cubic centimeter of air. The measure now adopted to calculate biological effects of radiation is the REM (roentgen equivalent man), which represents radiation that would cause an absorption of 100 ergs per gram of living tissue, corrected for the type of radiation —gamma, X-ray, and the like. Apart from man-made radiation, the earth has always been subject to a certain background radiation, amounting to some 3 REM in thirty years, which is taken as the average reproductive period of an individual. This natural background radiation accounts for part of, but by no means all, the spontaneous mutation rate. The important question is, How much have we increased our mutation rate by man-made radiation? The measure of this is usually taken as the amount of radiation which would double our spontaneous rate. This is often taken as about 30 REM, but it is a difficult value to estimate and in special cases may be as high as 100 REM or as low as 10 REM. It is about four times as great when the radiation is given over very long periods at a very low intensity because of the fact, mentioned above, that under these conditions there is some protective or healing process. Compared to this doubling rate the average medical radiation that individuals in sophisticated societies receive is 1 or 2 REM in thirty years. This is mainly due to X-rays used for diagnostic purposes, and estimates from several European countries of diagnostic X-ray doses agree more or less. Estimates from Leiden, Holland, and from Cairo and Alexandria, in the United Arab Republic, are about ten times lower. (The amount of radiation received varies with the type of equipment used and the way it is used.) A person standing a little less than a mile away from a one-kiloton nuclear bomb exploded in the air would receive the doubling dose of some 30 to 50 REM in a day or so.

Starting in the year 1945 great nations polluted the atmosphere with radioactive particles by bomb testing. The most intensive period occurred between 1954 and 1958 and in 1961. The increase in radiation due to testing will last a long time; only after 20,000 years will we have had 90 per cent of it. By the year 2000 we will have had about half of it. The estimated dose that we and our descendants will eventually get due to testing between 1954 and 1961 is about .1 REM to the gonads and .4 to the bone marrow and cells lining bone surfaces. Each person will receive in his gonads during the years 1954–2000 half of this, or .05 REM.

The radiation we now receive from medical sources is greater than that from bombs, but we must remember that medical radiation can be diminished or stopped entirely by the will of the individual or the state. Radiation from bomb testing will be with us for many years to come; furthermore, international legislators of the powers concerned cannot convince us that the present rate of pollution will not be increased. When the effects of radiation are stated in terms of the actual numbers of individuals who will have mental defects, congenital malformations, neuromuscular defects, hematological and endocrine defects, defects of vision or hearing, cutaneous and skeletal defects, or defects in the gastrointestinal and genito-urinary tracts, then a more somber picture is presented. About 4 to 5 per cent of all live births in the United States have such defects and about half of these are known to be genetic. This means that of the 100,000,000 children who will be born to the presently alive population of the United States, over 2,000,000 will have these defects. If we receive a doubling dose of radiation, we will eventually add another 2,000,000 to this figure. The question of estimating the number and effect of harmful mutations will be mentioned again in connection with evolution and eugenics.

Mutation is a fundamental biological phenomenon, and our understanding of it has presented us with novel and important ethical problems. The geneticist is professionally involved in the first stage of our thinking about these problems. But on technical matters he must use judgment in presenting the facts. It may be true that radiation due to bomb testing is ten or a hundred times less than background radiation, but it is also true that the bomb testing may affect over 80,000 people throughout the world. The two statements have a different impact and the geneticist, without deviating from true calculations, can influence his audience by the way in which he presents the data.

The awful importance of decisions about mutagens lies in the widespread effects of radioactive fallout in time and space. Policy cannot restrict itself to what is best for a certain nation for a given generation. Decisions made now will affect people all over the world a thousand generations hence.

IX *Combinations: The Cryptography of Life*

Study of the mutagenic effects of radiation gave some indication of the size of genes but little of their nature. Progress in discovering the chemical nature of the gene has required other techniques. Many of them are pure biochemistry: extracting chemicals from cells and subjecting them to analysis by the modern machinery of the chemist, ingenious ways of using very high speed centrifuges called ultracentrifuges, the use of long columns of starch or charged resins to separate very similar molecules, and the production of organic chemicals labeled with radioactive or heavy atoms are some of the much-used newer techniques. The organisms used are, in the main, bacteria and viruses which are even more microbial than *Neurospora.*

It required quite an effort of the imagination and of rational faith, or perhaps of faith in rationalism, to think of the gene as a chemical. The properties of the gene presented in the 1940's an insoluble complexity in terms of known chemical and physical phenomena, much as the functioning of that larger organ the brain appears to us today. Two substances with very large molecules were known to be implicated. These substances were isolated by Frederick Miescher in 1869. He found that a fairly large number of pure nuclei, free from the rest of the cell substance, could be prepared by treating pus, obtained from hospital dressings, with dilute hydrochloric acid, pepsin, and ether. The nuclei sank to the bottom of the solution and yielded a substance which was very acid, rich in phosphorus. Miescher called this nuclein; it is now known as nucleic acid. It was a rather unexpected finding, and such was the distaste for excitement at the time that he was advised to delay publication until 1871. When Miescher moved to Basle he left the malodorous source of nuclein used previously and worked with salmon sperm, which could be obtained from the soft roe of salmon. A sperm cell is almost all nucleus and must contain the genetic contribution of one parent. Miescher found that salmon sperm contained nuclein and also a nitrogen-rich basic substance which we know now to consist of basic proteins.

Protein and nucleic acid are joined together as necleoprotein. Both of these chemicals are made up of smaller units joined together in a linear array. The units of protein are amino acids, of which about twenty different kinds are found in most proteins. The units of nucleic acid are nucleotides, of which there are four different kinds in a nucleic acid chain. The only part of a nucleotide that varies is the nitrogen base; the other components—sugar and phosphate—are identical in all four nucleotides. The complete chemical structure of a small part of a nucleic acid chain containing a representative of each of the four bases is shown in Figure 20. It is difficult to give a figure for the length of the chains of nucleic acid because they break up into different lengths during extraction. We will have more to say about this later, but for the present imagine a chain of molecular weight of at least 100,000,000, which can be written 10^8. The average molecular weight of a nucleotide

FIGURE 20

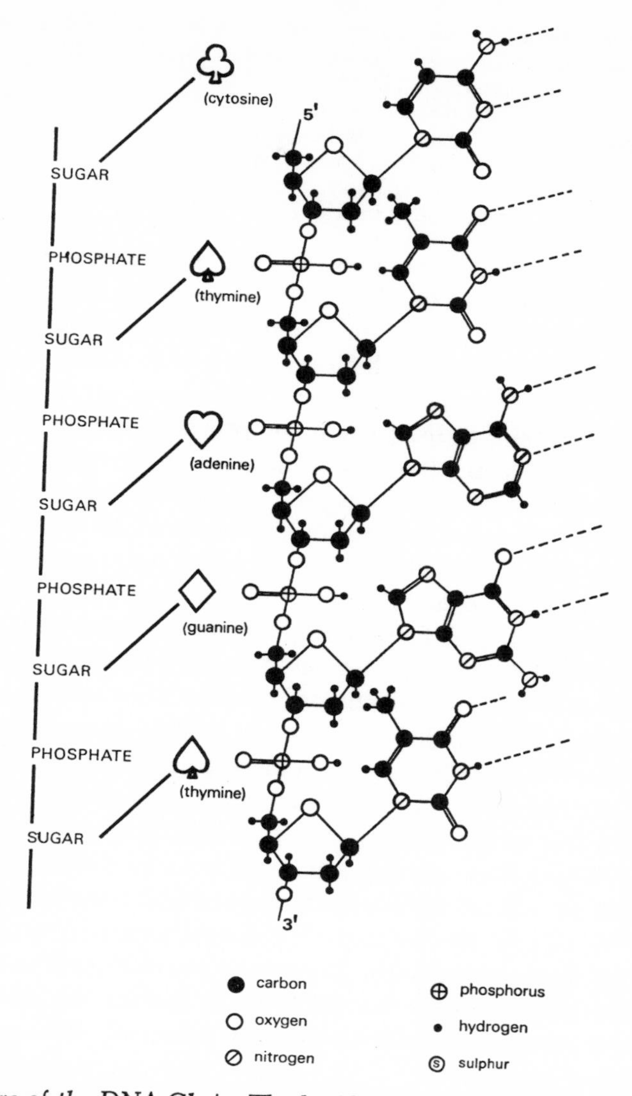

Structure of the DNA Chain. The backbone of the chain is formed by joining phosphates to sugars. It will be noticed that the two ends of a chain can be recognized because the phosphate attaches to a different atom of the sugar at each end. The free bond at the top of the diagram is known as 5′ and that at the bottom as 3′. The DNA of chromosomes consists of two such chains; the second chain would lie to the right, and its complementary bases would be held by hydrogen bonds, represented in the diagram by dotted lines. The position of these bonds is such that only complementary bases would fit, ♡ to ♠ and ◇ to ♣. The double chain is then coiled into a helix (see Plate 6).

is about 300, so there would be over 300,000, or 3×10^5, nucleotides, and since, as we shall see later, the distance between bases is 3.4 Angstrom units, the length would be about 1,000,000, 10^6, Angstrom units, which is a tenth of a millimeter.

Regarding proteins the situation is different. The long chain of a protein, at least when the protein is an enzyme, is folded up into a more or less spherical tangle which has a definite size and molecular weight, ranging from about 10,000 to 500,000. If the average molecular weight of an amino acid is taken as 125, then a chain of molecular weight 100,000 will have 800 amino acids. The way in which amino acids are joined together to form a protein is shown in Figure 21.

Of these two macromolecules, opinion at first favored the proteins for the role of bearers of heredity. They are the more complex molecules and therefore seem capable of more variety than the monotonous nucleic acids. Moreover, proteins are known to constitute the enzymes, so it was thought some special forms of protein might constitute a special kind of enzyme which was autocatalytic, was able to direct its own synthesis as well as fulfill its other chemical functions. This would be one of the important qualities expected in genes.

The first guess proved, however, to be wrong. The essential structure of genes is known to lie in the nucleic acid, not the proteins, and we will describe the lines of evidence that led to this conviction.

In 1944, O. T. Avery, C. M. MacLeod, and Maclyn McCarty, working at the Rockefeller Institute for Medical Re-

FIGURE 21

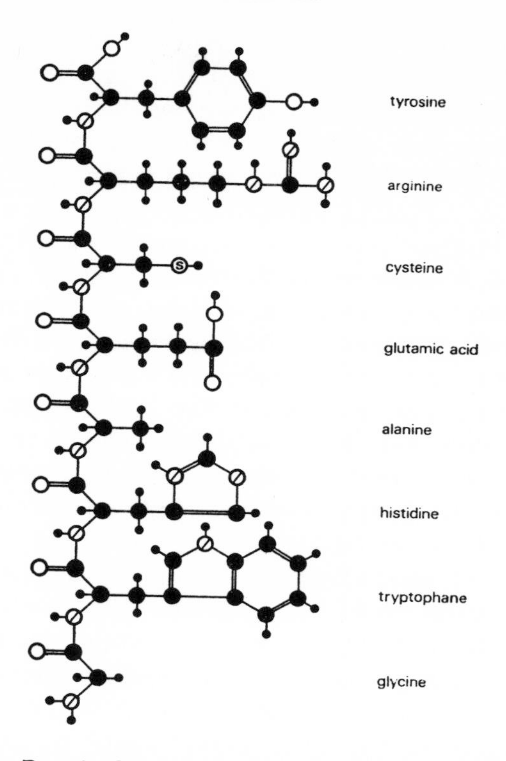

Structure of a Protein Chain: a short section containing eight representative amino acids. One end of a protein chain always has an acidic group (COOH, top end in diagram); the other has a basic group (NH_2, bottom end). Additional amino acids are joined by an interaction of their basic group with the acidic group of the chain; water (H_2O) is eliminated and a new acidic end is left. It must be realized that all free amino acids have at least one basic and one acidic group. Some amino acids, *e.g.* glutamic acid, have two acidic groups; others, *e.g.* arginine, have two basic groups. Cysteine is unique in having a sulfur atom. This is important because two cysteines on different protein chains or on different parts of the same chain can join together in a strong bond to form another amino acid, cystine. Symbols are the same as in Figure 20. See Plate 8 for the folded appearance of a protein chain.

search, published a paper on the phenomenon of transformation which opened up the possibility of studying genetic material chemically. The phenomenon had, as in so many other instances, been discovered many years before, but it had not been followed up; the time, measured in terms of the development of scientific ideas, had not been ripe. In 1928 Griffith in England reported experiments in which mice were inoculated subcutaneously with a well-known strain of pneumococci. The same mice were subsequently injected with a different strain, but this time the bacteria were killed prior to injection. The result was that the first strain was changed into the second strain by the action of the dead cells of the second injection. Avery and his associates used the same bacteria as Griffith, but performed the experiment in test-tubes. The difference between the strains used lies in the nature of the outer layer of bacteria, which is called a capsule and is a polysaccharide, like starch and cellulose. Capsules may be present or absent, but when present are characteristic for a given strain. After more work they found that it was not necessary to use the whole dead bacterium to effect a transformation, but that a chemical extract from one strain, poured into tubes containing living cells of the other strain, would transform them. Once transformed, the cells would reproduce the new type when they divided. Details of the process are shown in Figure 22. Not all of the bacteria, to be sure, would be transformed, but the transformed proportion would be significant and well above the spontaneous mutation rate for this character. As soon as they were able to work with extracts the next step was to fractionate the extract into a protein fraction, a nucleic fraction, a fatty fraction, a polysaccharide fraction, and so on. This work showed conclusively that it was pure nucleic acid, with little or no contaminating protein or other substance, that caused the transformation.

Transformation has since been accomplished in other

FIGURE 22

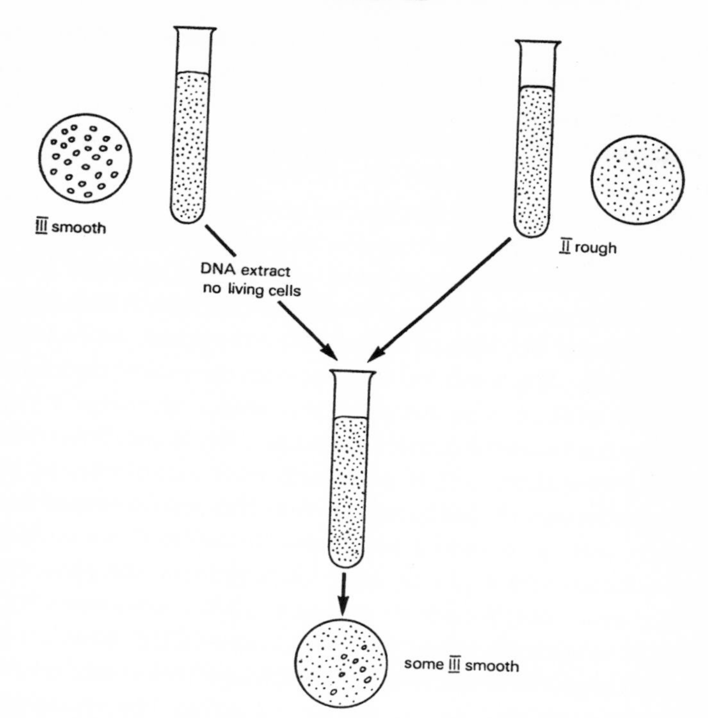

Transformation. The two test-tubes at the top of the diagram represent liquid cultures of a smooth strain of type III pneumococcus and a rough strain of type II pneumococcus. Beside each is a Petri dish, illustrating the fact that the colonies of rough and smooth pneumococci can be distinguished on solid media. An extract of the bacteria of type III smooth is then added to the living bacteria of type II rough (middle test-tube, below). When these are put on solid medium (bottom Petri dish) most of the colonies, as would be expected, are rough; a few, however, are smooth. They have been transformed by the chemical DNA. When these few colonies are isolated, grown in larger quantity, and tested immunologically, they are found to be of type III. These smooth pneumococci have a polysaccharide capsule around each cell and are more virulent than rough pneumococci. Other characters and other bacteria can be transformed in a similar way.

bacteria and with characters such as resistance to drugs and the ability to ferment certain sugars. Unfortunately, organisms in which transformation is possible are not the most suitable for study by other genetic techniques; nevertheless a lot has been learned.

One interpretation that had to be eliminated was that the nucleic acid was merely acting as a chemical mutagen, increasing the mutation rate of all genes at random, so that if one looked for a particular mutant character one would be likely to find it. This did not seem a reasonable interpretation from the outset because the kind of transformed character or mutant that one found corresponded to the strain of bacteria from which the nucleic acid came. It was specific; it could be called a directed mutation, but transformation is a better name and has been adopted. A confirmation that this was different from mutation was discovered later. It was found that occasionally a nucleic acid extract can be made to transform two characters together and this occurs at a much higher frequency than would be expected from the frequencies with which each separate character is transformed. Not any two genes tend to be transformed simultaneously in the same bacterium, but only certain pairs, pairs that are presumably closely linked. It is logical to infer that such pairs of characters are controlled by two closely linked genes and that the bit of nucleic acid which causes both to transform contains both genes. The details of how a piece of chromosome can enter a cell and impose itself on the hereditary makeup of the cell are not understood, but we can still draw the conclusion that the substance that causes the transformation is a normal carrier of hereditary properties, at least in bacteria.

Another line of evidence that is persuasive in identifying nucleic acid as the material of inheritance comes from the viruses, known as bacteriophage, which parasitize bacteria. Viruses are the smallest living creatures and are on the borderline between life and nonlife. Their claim to life is that they reproduce their kind, but they do so only as parasites on other, more respectable, forms of life, and bacteriophage in particular have received a great deal of genetic attention. Before getting to the point about nucleic acid, we must make note of some other interesting properties of phage. Phage units infect bacterial cells, multiply some hundredfold inside the bacteria, kill them, and escape, and their progeny infect some hundred new bacterial cells. The whole cycle may take about half an hour. When a phage unit kills a bacterium it "lyses" it; that is, it breaks it up so that it is no longer recognizable. When phage is introduced into a test-tube full of a bacterial culture, the whole culture clears and becomes transparent as a result of lysis of the bacteria. On a Petri dish covered with growing bacteria, each phage unit will produce a clear area, visible to the naked eye, called a plaque.

Two kinds of character are commonly studied in phage: the size and shape of plaque formed, and the particular strains of bacteria which can be attacked by a particular phage. Bacteria can be infected with two different phage units simultaneously, and when this is done, a number of phage progeny can be recovered which show a combination of the characters of the parental phages. In this way phage crosses can be made and linkage demonstrated between phage genes. Linkage maps can be made for phage, but the calculations are complicated because in any cross there are several rounds of mating during the seven or eight rounds of duplication of phage units. In fact, mating can be triparental; if a bacterium is infected with three different phage units, then progeny may appear exhibiting characters from all three parents. When a phage unit gets into a bacterium it appears to block the activity of the bacterium's own genes, or at least most of them, and to divert the machinery of the bacterium to making the substance of more phage, under the control of the phage's genes. Phages are the ultimate parasites; they not only break down the substance of the host and use the released molecules as food to build their own substance, but they subvert the bacteria's chemical machinery into channels detrimental to the bacteria's own interests.

Some phages, known as temperate phages, are less subversive. They enter the bacterial cell but do not kill and lyse it. They multiply in step with the bacterium in a state known as lysogeny. Their only demand on the bacterial host is that their genetic material be allowed to lodge there. Lysogenic bacteria appear quite normal, but they can be detected by the circumstance that every now and then their latent phage, prophage, will exhibit intemperate behavior, kill and lyse the bacterial cell, and be ready to infect other bacteria. Slight exposure to ultraviolet light will induce an enormous increase in this reversion to the natural parasitic state.

Bacteriophage can be obtained in quantity by filtering off the bacteria in an infected culture, and they can be analyzed chemically. They consist of protein and nucleic acid almost exclusively. Ingenious experiments have been performed to determine which of these two chemicals is the hereditary substance. A glance at Figures 20 and 21 will show that nucleic acid contains the element phosphorus, but no sulfur, whereas proteins contain some sulfur, but no phosphorus. Both phosphorus and sulfur can be obtained in radioactive form and this was the basis of experiments performed in 1951 by A. D. Hershey and Martha Chase, working in the Carnegie Institution of Washington at Cold Spring Harbor on Long Island, New York. Bacteriophage were grown on bacteria in media containing radioactive phosphorus and radioactive sulfur respectively. In time, all molecules containing sulfur or phosphorus in both bacteria and phage would be radioactive and thus labeled.

Two lots of phage were obtained in this way, one in which

the phosphorous of the nucleic acids was labeled and the other in which the sulfur in the protein was labeled. Bacteria were infected with each separately and then put into a blendor to shake off any material of the phage which was merely sticking to the walls of the bacteria. The bacteria were then analyzed to see what part of the phage had penetrated. It was found that whereas 85 per cent of the labeled phosphorus was inside the bacteria, less than 25 per cent of the sulfur was recovered, indicating that most, if not all, of the nucleic acid of the phage penetrates, but most or all of the protein merely sticks to the outer wall. Furthermore, it has been found that when the experiment is allowed to go further and the radioactivity of the phage progeny is measured, then 30 per cent of the labeled nucleic acid is recovered in the phage progeny, whereas less than 1 per cent of the protein is found in the phage progeny (Fig. 23). Loss of some of the radioactive atoms in experiments of this kind is inevitable and does not invalidate the conclusion that nucleic acid is the substance that carries the hereditary properties of phage.

At the time these results were obtained the electron microscope was becoming generally available. With this instrument, and with data obtained from electron-diffraction pictures and some other sources, a rather complete and detailed picture of the structure of viruses has been obtained. A typical phage which infects the common colon bacillus turns out to be simple chemically but remarkably effective biologically. The nucleic acid thread is coiled four layers deep, with twelve or thirteen turns to each layer. One end, subject to being pulled, lies in the center like the end of a ball of string. There is a single molecule of nucleic acid of molecular weight about 10^8, which represents a length of about $\frac{34}{300 \times 2} \times 10^8$ Å $= 6 \times 10^5$ Å or roughly 6/100 of a millimeter since 3.4 is the distance between

FIGURE 23

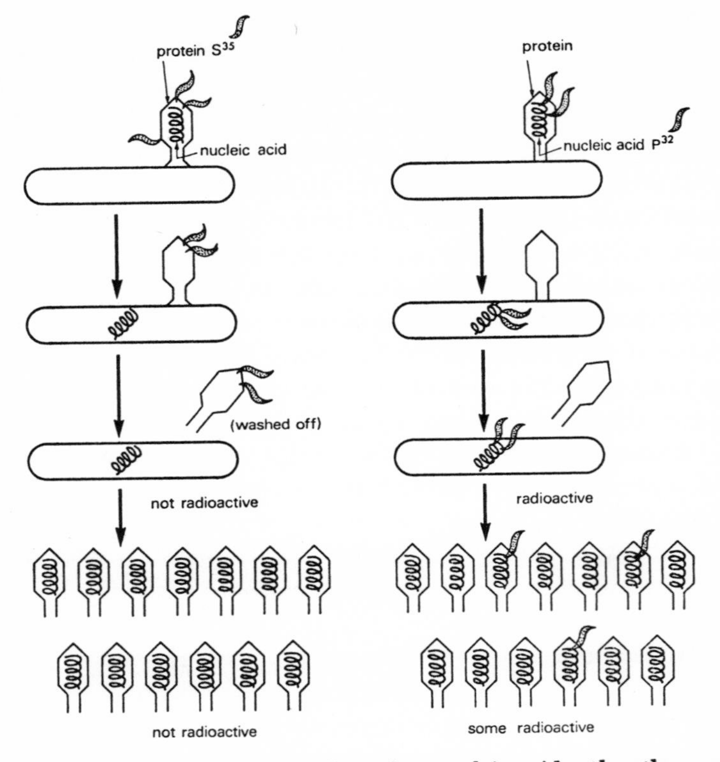

Phage DNA. An experiment to show that nucleic acid rather than protein is the hereditary material of phage is shown. On the left-hand side of the protein is given a radioactive label, and on the right-hand side, the nucleic acid. After washing, the bacteria on the right are radioactive, but not those on the left. The progeny phage on the left contain no radioactivity, but some of those on the right do. The number of phage progency for each bacterium is actually about a hundred, much more than indicated in the diagram. More than one progeny phage will be radioactive because the DNA is broken up into pieces by recombination during multiplication in the bacterium and an original single unit of DNA ends up in two or three or more progeny. This experiment is proof that DNA and not protein is transmitted to progeny and is a very strong indication, but perhaps not conclusive proof, that DNA contains all genetic information. Brief contact of the protein could, with a stretch of the imagination, be sufficient to pass on information to the bacterium as to what kind of progeny phage to manufacture.

nucleotides and 300 is the average molecular weight of a nucleotide. The figure 2 appears in the bottom part of the fraction because, as we shall see, nucleic acid molecules actually consist of two chains of nucleotides lying side by side. The head of the phage is made of protein and is about 7×10^{-5} or 7/100,000 of a millimeter in diameter. Coiling the genetic thread inside its protein case is like coiling 60 meters of string into a ball 7 centimeters in diameter. Phage particles have a hollow tail—"nose" might be a better word—with which they attach themselves to a bacterium and through which the nucleic acid passes into the bacterial cell. The protein case and tail remain on the wall of the bacterium, and these can be sheared off in a blendor.

Other experiments indicating the roles of nucleic acid and protein were performed at Berkeley with the tobacco-mosaic virus, which causes a mottling of the leaves and various other diseased conditions on tobacco plants. The virus consists of a rod with protein on the outside and a coil of nucleic acid inside. The nucleic acid is slightly different from the kind described above and is known as RNA; the nucleic acid found in the chromosomes and the phage previously mentioned is known as DNA. Protein and nucleic acid parts can be rather easily separated and put together again. The protein part cannot infect plants but the nucleic acid part can, albeit only about a hundredth as efficiently as the complete virus. This shows again that the nucleic acid is the genetic material. An even more refined experiment was made by putting the nucleic acid of one strain of virus into the protein of another strain. Infectivity was increased, and the disease produced corresponded to that of the virus from which the nucleic acid came, not of the virus from which the protein came (Fig. 24). The protein constituent thus appears to protect the virus and aid infection, but does not contribute genetically.

Although the best evidence that nucleic acid constitutes the hereditary material comes from bacteria and viruses, there

FIGURE 24

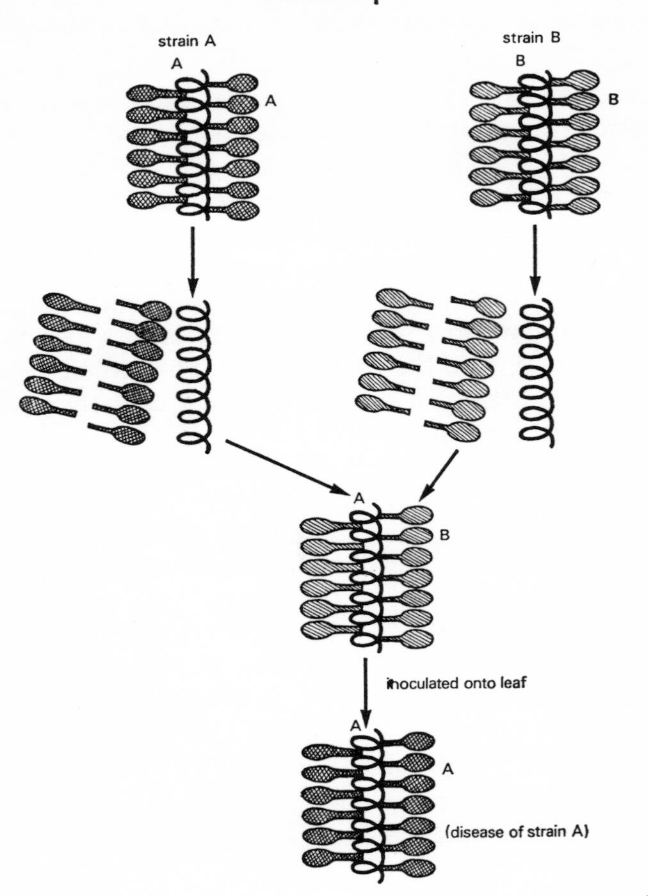

Heredity in a Virus. Tobacco-mosaic virus multiplies in the leaves of tobacco plants. Several strains are known, each producing characteristic symptoms on the leaf. The virus unit consists of nucleic acid and protein. The nucleic acid is a long chain of RNA twisted into a spiral. The protein consists of a large number of identical subunits which are found in between the coils of nucleic acid, one subunit to every three nucleic acid bases. They are tightly packed and thus form an outer protein spiral surrounding the inner nucleic acid spiral.

Two strains, A and B, are represented in the diagram. The virus is represented in cross section, the nucleic acid appearing as a spiral and the protein appearing as units (shaded) on each side of it.

The protein and nucleic acid of tobacco-mosaic virus can be separated without damage to either part. This separation is represented in the second row. In the third row nucleic acid from strain A is mixed with protein units from strain B. Some live virus is obtained, which can infect tobacco leaves and multiply.

The progeny are in every way identical to strain A. This is further evidence that nucleic acid and not protein is the hereditary substance.

is little doubt that the essential genetic material in chromosomes of higher animals and plants is also nucleic acid. One approach that has supported this theory is measurement of the amount of nucleic acid found in each nucleus. This is found to be remarkably constant for a given species. Furthermore, in the somatic cells of higher organisms the amount of nucleic acid per nucleus is twice the amount in each sperm. This is exactly what we would expect, because in diploid organisms there are twice as many chromosomes and genes in body cells as there are in germ cells.

As the knowledge that genes were made of nucleic acid rather than protein was assimilated, a change in attitudes toward the basic problem of gene structure took place. About this time, in the early 1950's, electronic computers, information theory, and the new word "cybernetics" were receiving considerable publicity and attention. This may well have contributed to new thoughts among geneticists. Instead of thinking of genes as complex minute organs consisting of some kind of enzyme which could catalyze its own synthesis, they regarded them as carriers of information. When one thinks of the gene as a carrier of information one imagines not a complex machine, but a code—and an efficient code means a great deal of information is packed into a small space. Consider the building of a house. The information required to build a particular kind of house can be drawn on blueprints. The information could also be put into words or, better still, into

Morse code, which uses only two symbols—the dot and the dash. In a similar way, the information concerning a man could conceivably be put into some kind of code made up of a small number of symbols. The code would have to be read before the information meant anything, but this is another problem.

We have seen that there are four subunits in nucleic acid; these can be taken as four symbols of a code, say ♡ ◇ ♣ ♠, to represent respectively adenine, guanine, cytosine, and thymine. If we take only pairs of two symbols, we can write 4^2, or 16, different messages with these four different units (Fig. 25).

FIGURE 25

♡ ♡	◇ ♡	♣ ♡	♠ ♡
♡ ◇	◇ ◇	♣ ◇	♠ ◇
♡ ♣	◇ ♣	♣ ♣	♠ ♣
♡ ♠	◇ ♠	♣ ♠	♠ ♠

But there are over 300,000 nucleotides in a phage unit, more in a bacterium, and many more in the chromosomes of higher organisms. The number of different messages that can be written with 100,000 symbols of four different kinds is $4^{100,000}$ which is about $10^{60,433}$, a very large number indeed. However one looks at this number, it is ample to account for all the different kinds of virus that exist or ever have existed, or for all the characters of a virus that one can imagine anyone listing. If one considers all living organisms instead of one virus, this conclusion would still hold. The number of atoms in the universe as far as the most powerful telescope can penetrate has been estimated to be less than 10^{75}. The human population of the world is about 3×10^9. Man has existed for about 10^6 years or 5×10^4 generations. If we grossly overestimate and say that the population of the earth has always been as large as it is now, we find that $3 \times 5 \times 10^9 \times 10^4$, or over 10^{14} humans have lived on earth—a very small number compared to the number of different messages that could be contained in phage nucleic acid.

When one thinks in these terms, nucleic acid becomes an ideal chemical to pass a great deal of information from one generation to the next in a small packet such as sperm.

Storing information is only one of the things a gene must do. Another essential property is duplication. It happens that the structure of nucleic acid is very suitable for the function of duplication. Biologists have always—or at least since the seventeenth century—been particularly pleased when structure could be related to function, but the work described in the next chapter brings this trend to its ultimate conclusion: the relation of molecular structure to basic biological function. The ideas are very recent but have already been widely accepted and are unlikely to constitute a profound error.

It will be seen that in duplicating the original molecule of DNA is not destroyed, but rather a new molecule is modeled on it. This means that the DNA is extraordinarily stable not only during the life of a cell, but also during cell division throughout the developing organism and from one generation to the next. The reader may ponder the fact that there may be a certain chemical molecule in his body that is the very same molecule that existed in a distant ancestor. It could have been passed on to him intact. This occurrence is possible and curious but, as a few simple calculations will show, rather infrequent.

X *How to Make a Copy: The Template Mechanism*

The Watson-Crick model of nucleic acid is a landmark in genetics comparable to the theory of the gene, the theory of crossing-over and genetic maps, the discovery of salivary-gland chromosomes, and the advent of microbial genetics. Like all of these, it opened up new prospects and enticed men to greater efforts.

The work was done, or perhaps we should say the idea was hatched, in Cambridge, England. The first paper on the subject by James D. Watson and Francis Crick, in 1953, is a short one, opening, "We wish to suggest a structure for the salt of deoxyribose nucleic acid (DNA). This structure has novel features which are of considerable biological interest." They then mention earlier biochemists, Linus Pauling and B. B. Corey, who had suggested a spiral structure, which is a feature of the Watson-Crick model.

The idea probably occurred to Pauling and Corey because they had already shown that protein chains sometimes assume a spiral form. Toward the end of Watson and Crick's paper comes the point in which we are here interested; they write, "It has not escaped our notice that the specific pairing we have postulated immediately suggests a possible copying mechanism for the genetic material." This was elaborated upon in subsequent papers.

The copying mechanism that was proposed is a familiar one, a negative template making a positive copy. A rubber stamp is a negative template which stamps out a positive on paper; a photographic negative prints out a positive on paper; the master-negative film of a motion picture is run through a machine which prints a positive film for use in cinema theaters. In these analogies a master negative prints out one or more positives. What we need for genetic material is a way for a unit to reproduce itself. In the Watson-Crick model this is accomplished by having two complementary strands of nucleic acid in each molecule, one of which can be thought of as a positive and the other, negative. If we represent the two strands as P and N, then when the molecule duplicates, the P strand will stamp out an N strand and the N strand will stamp out a P strand. The total result is two units identical to the one that existed before (Fig. 26).

FIGURE 26

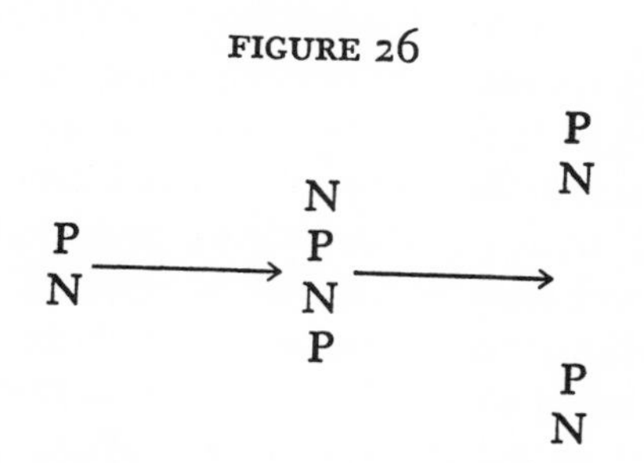

We have seen that nucleic acid consists of a long chain of four different nucleotides. To have a positive and a negative template we would have to have two long chains. In these chains each nucleotide would have to stamp out a specific one of the four when the chain duplicated. This is quite feasible chemically. First of all, two of the nucleotides, adenine (♡) and guanine (◇), are larger than the other two, cytosine (♣) and thymine (♠). Two large nucleotides cannot pair together because they would each stick out too far from the backbone and would force the backbone chains apart. Similarly, two small nucleotides cannot pair because they would not meet. So size alone restricts us to four kinds of pairs, ♡ ♣, ♤ ♦, ◇ ♣, and ◇ ♥. In addition, the spacing of the various atoms on the four bases makes it easiest to form hydrogen bonds between ♡ and ♠ and between ◇ and ♣. Thus, each base has one other base with which it prefers to pair. A small piece of nucleic acid from a chromosome might be imagined as represented in the top part of Figure 27. The curved lines on the outside would represent the strong chemical bonds between sugars and phosphates and the interior dots the weaker hydrogen bonds between specific pairs of bases.

When this double chain replicates, the two single chains separate and each base attracts its opposite type from a pool of nucleotides which is presumably available. This process is shown in the middle and lower parts of Figure 27. Hydrogen bonds are very suitable for holding complementary nucleotides together; they are weak enough singly to be easily broken, yet two or three of them are firm. Presumably each of the four kinds of nucleotide in the pool is tried randomly until the right one gets there; it then forms two or three hydrogen bonds which will only very rarely be broken. It will be seen that the double-stranded unit represented at the top has become two identical units, shown at the bottom of Figure 27.

This is the idea that Watson and Crick referred to at the end of their paper. It is a pregnant idea and would be worth pursuing even if false. The world being as it is, good ideas are usually correct. But to be accepted, even by their authors, there had to be supporting evidence.

FIGURE 27

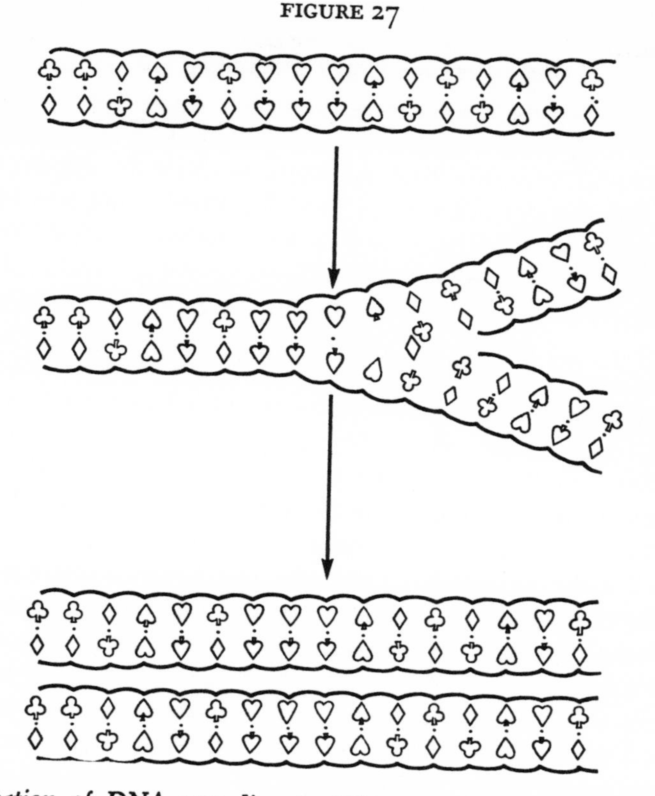

Replication of DNA according to Watson and Crick. The double strand at the top of the diagram replicates to form the two identical double strands at the bottom. In the middle, the right-hand end has already replicated; the two strands separate, and each unpaired base then attracts a complementary base. Finally, the phosphate-sugar bonds join up the chain of bases. Nucleic acid bases are represented by playing-card symbols, phosphate-sugar chains by curved outer lines, specific hydrogen bonds between bases by dots. Compare with Figure 20.

The evidence for a kind of structure that we have outlined is impressive. By X-ray diffraction and other methods it can be shown that indeed there are most probably two strands of nucleic acid. They are not straight, as diagramed in Figure 27, but take the form of a spiral, or helix, as shown in Plate 6; however, this difference is just a detail. It introduces a difficulty in that there must be a good deal of unwinding during duplication, but this is not an unsuperable difficulty.

As regards the pairing of specific nucleotides, biochemists have not yet succeeded in finding the exact order of nucleotides in any long stretch of double-stranded DNA, but it is relatively easy to find out how much of each nucleotide there is in a molecule of nucleic acid. If the model is correct, one would expect the ratio $\frac{\heartsuit + \clubsuit}{\diamondsuit + \spadesuit}$ to be always equal to 1, since the amount of $\heartsuit = \spadesuit$ and $\diamondsuit = \clubsuit$. This has been found to obtain. The ratio $\frac{\heartsuit + \spadesuit}{\diamondsuit + \clubsuit}$, on the other hand, can vary for each kind of nucleic acid, and in fact, does vary from 0.51 to 1.86 in different bacteria. The latter ratio should be constant for a particular species or strain, and if all the cells of the body have the same genes, it should be the same in different tissues of an organism. This also has been roughly confirmed.

In 1957 Arthur Kornberg, at the Rockefeller Institute in New York, succeeded in synthesizing nucleic acid *in vitro*, and his requirements for doing this fit well with what one would expect for a Watson-Crick model. All four nucleotides were required, as well as some previously made nucleic acid, to act as the first template or primer. If any nucleotide were absent, synthesis would not occur. In addition, the synthesis proceeded better at a high temperature because then the double helix of nucleic acid separated into single strands. This also is to be expected. A special enzyme was required, and some magnesium.

The duplication of a natural process in the test tube is very pleasing, but we must add that recent experiments have complicated the picture. The trouble seems to be that the enzyme Kornberg isolated and used is not the one nature uses in the intact cell. This became apparent when the newly synthesized test-tube DNA was examined with the help of an electron microscope. It was found to be a complex of branched filaments quite unlike natural DNA. This does not injure fundamental aspects of the theory, but it does mean that we have not yet found the enzyme that allows the DNA template mechanism to work in the living cell, producing unbranched DNA. It is probably a very difficult enzyme to find. Theoretically, just one molecule of this enzyme per chromosome would be required. The enzyme Kornberg did extract may repair blemishes in nucleic acid in the living cell.

There remain, to be sure, details which present difficulties, but none of them are great enough to challenge the theory. The uncoiling of a very long double spiral is one difficulty that we have already mentioned. *E. coli* duplicates in about twenty minutes, and its chromosome does not appear to duplicate any faster. Since there are about 10^7 base pairs in the chromosome of *E. coli,* and since there are ten base pairs to every complete turn of the spiral as proposed by the Watson-Crick structure, the molecule must untwist at the rate of about 10^6 turns in twenty minutes, or 50,000 turns a minute. This, at first sight, seems pretty fast. There is also a difficulty about the hydrogen bonds, which are supposed to hold specific base pairs together. The two nucleic acid chains can be separated by heat, which is what one would expect where hydrogen bonds are concerned, but the rate at which they separate is not quite right, according to some calculations, for a great many independent hydrogen bonds.

One double spiral is the simplest model for a chromosome, but there are some experiments which suggest to a few workers that there are actually two double strands. If this is the case, each double strand would open up only temporarily during duplication and would close up again immediately afterward. Two new strands would be stamped out while it was open, and these two new strands would join together. Understanding of the way in which a tremendous length of nucleic acid is coiled or folded to form the large chromosomes seen in metaphase (Plates 1 and 2) has not yet been achieved. But these are all details, and it can be said that, in general, the Watson-Crick model has stood up well to close examination. Whatever modifications may be developed, the main idea is too good not to be true.

The theory that nucleic acid chains make an exact copy of themselves by the fit of each nucleotide in the chain to its complement explains the action of a new type of chemical mutagen. We have said that mutation—whether spontaneous or induced—is random. Now we must qualify this statement because the chemical mutagens to be described are not random and they are believed to act directly on the nucleic acid. These mutagens are known as base analogs because they are nucleotide bases which are similar enough to one of the four natural nucleotides to get assembled on the template, but they are different enough to cause errors in the duplication. Five-bromo-uracil (5-BrU), one of the most-used base analogs, is very similar to thymine. If the synthesis of thymine in the cell is stopped, either by a genetic mutation or by a chemical inhibitor, and if plenty of 5-BrU is added to the medium, then 5-BrU, instead of the absent thymine (♠), will be attracted to adenine (♡) during duplication. This may not have much effect on the organisms immediately because 5-BrU in a gene may not alter the gene's action, but at some later duplication 5-BrU may attract guanine instead of the adenine which thymine would have attracted. When this happens (Fig. 28), the code has been changed at that point from adenine-thymine to guanine-cytosine and this change will be permanent—it will be a mutation. This does not mean, however, that we can mutate any gene at will with base analogs; all genes presum-

FIGURE 28

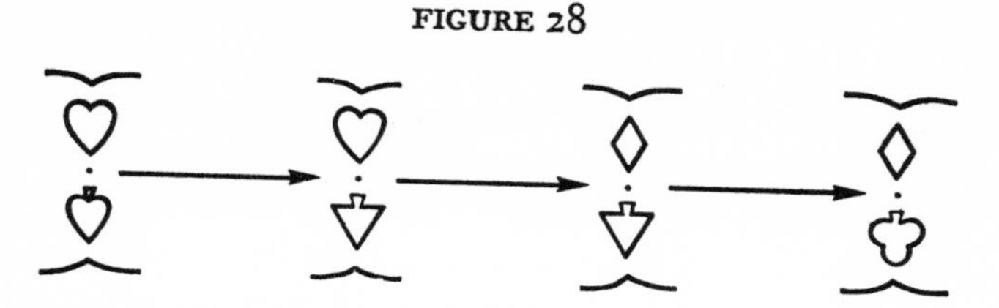

Production of Mutations by Base Analogs. An adenine-thymine pair (left-hand pair) is changed to a guanine-cytosine pair (right-hand pair). The base analog used is 5-bromo-uracil, represented by a triangular symbol. This can replace thymine and form an adenine–5-BrU pair, and it can also, at some subsequent replication, pair with guanine (third pair from the right). Finally, with further replication guanine pairs with its correct complement, cytosine, and a stable mutation is completed.

ably have a large number of adenine-thymine pairs, and we cannot control which will be affected.

The template method of synthesis adds a new idea to biochemistry. We can now say that there are two ways in which chemical reactions are catalyzed in living cells: by enzymes, and in the case of the macromolecules, nucleic acid, and protein, by templates. It may be objected that an enzyme probably works by a template mechanism in the sense that the substrate molecules fit into a part or site of the enzyme, but the distinction between the two methods of catalysis is clear. Synthesis by templates always requires the presence of special polymerizing enzymes in addition to the template. Template syntheses are irreversible, whereas enzymatic reactions are reversible to some extent. In the template mechanism for enzyme action, enzymes never have more than three sites for substrate molecules to fit onto, and usually only one or two, whereas the templates synthesizing macromolecules assemble at least several hundred small molecules in line.

In the next chapter we will consider how the Watson-Crick model for nucleic acid and synthesis by template can go some way toward explaining how genes control the phenotype.

XI *Translation: The Gene Code to Enzymes*

There are two qualities of an object that we can be curious about: its shape and its composition. The shape of living organisms, both the outside and the inside, can and has been described in great detail. Similarly, the chemical composition of most tissues is well known. More interesting to a geneticist are the problems of how organisms become a certain shape and how their chemical substances are produced. Little is known about the first of these, but we have learned a great deal about the second. This chapter will describe the way in which genes control the production of chemical substances. The subject brings the field of genetics close to that of biochemistry, and we will be dealing with questions which belong to both of these branches of science.

The first biochemical reactions to be studied were those producing beer. In 1837 the German naturalist Theodor Schwann showed pretty conclusively that the process of fermentation was due to a living organism, the fungus yeast. The last paragraph of his paper is worth quoting. "The connection between alcoholic fermentation and the development of the sugar fungus should not be misunderstood. It is highly probable that the development of the fungus causes the fermentation. Because a nitrogen-containing substance is also necessary for the fermentation, it appears that nitrogen is necessary for the life of this plant, as it is probable that every fungus contains nitrogen. The alcoholic fermentation must be considered to be that decomposition which occurs when the sugar fungus utilizes sugar and nitrogen-containing substances for its growth, in the process of which the elements of these substances which do not go into the plant are preferentially converted into alcohol. Most of the observations on the alcoholic fermentation fit quite nicely with this explanation." The idea that living organisms should be thought of as chemical factories was new at the time, and Schwann's conclusion that sugar was fermented by a living organism was denied by many, including the foremost German chemist at that time, Justus von Liebig. It was not until Louis Pasteur's extensive work on various fermentations became known some twenty years later that the idea was accepted among scientists. When it did become accepted, it was taken rather too seriously. Alcoholic fermentation was taken to be a process that was essentially vital and not the kind of chemical reaction that could take place outside a living cell. In 1897 Eduard Buchner showed that a juice could be extracted from yeast which would ferment sugar in a test-tube and produce alcohol. He also indicated that the active agent was a protein. A few enzymes were known at the time; the difficulty in accepting Buchner's discovery lay in the fact that alcoholic fermentation is not a simple one-step reaction, but requires several complex changes involving a whole interconnected series of enzymes. It is now generally taken for granted that nearly all the chemical reactions in living cells are catalyzed by specific enzymes.

Before the Watson-Crick model of replication was proposed, most biochemists probably guessed that proteins were also synthesized by enzymes; that is to say, they believed that enzymes themselves were made by specific enzymes. Pursuing this line of thought, one comes up against an ultimate class of enzymes which must be directly determined by genes. But at a time when genes could be thought of as proteins, the genes themselves were believed to act in a way similar to ordinary enzymes. The revolutionary idea of synthesis by a template mechanism required some flexibility of mind to accept. But when the concept of the duplication of nucleic acid by a template mechanism became familiar, it was natural to pursue this line of thought and consider the synthesis of proteins by a template mechanism.

As a matter of fact, a kind of template mechanism for the synthesis of nucleic acid and protein had been proposed by Cyril Hinshelwood and P. C. Caldwell in England in 1950. They likened this new type of synthesis to crystal growth, where "an ordered structure catalyzes its own formation." They proposed that nucleic acid guided the way in which the amino acids in proteins were laid down and vice versa. As we shall see, the first proposal is correct, but not the second. Proteins do not act as a template for nucleic acid synthesis.

A fundamental point to establish experimentally is whether the nucleotides along the nucleic acid chain are colinear with the amino acids along the protein chain. This means that if certain points along the nucleic acid chain are known to be in the order A-B-C-D and are known to correspond to amino acids a, b, c, and d, then these amino acids should lie in the order a-b-c-d in the peptide chain. Evidence for this was found in 1964, after the main features of protein synthesis had already been established, or at least accepted. The evidence for co-linearity has come from two independent sources. Charles Yanofsky,[1] whom we shall have occasion to

[1] The few names of scientists that are mentioned throughout the text have been chosen somewhat arbitrarily. When one person is named as having

refer to later, found that the order of a number of mutations, all affecting the enzyme tryptophane synthetase, corresponded on the genetic linkage map to the position of the wrong amino acids that each mutation produced along the protein chain. In other experiments, Sydney Brenner, whom we will also refer to again, found a number of mutations in phage that blocked the synthesis of the protein coat of the phage at certain points. He found that the position of the mutations along the nucleic acid chain, as revealed by genetic experiments, corresponded to the length of the protein chains that these mutant strains produced. Thus, if four mutations were found genetically to be in the order A-B-C-D, then strain D would produce the longest protein molecule, followed by C, B, and A. It is reassuring to have experimental support for the concept of co-linearity, and we can now return to the details of how the nucleic acid chain determines the amino acid chain.

Some years ago, before 1950, it was generally known that there were two distinct kinds of nucleic acid, deoxyribose nucleic acid (DNA) and ribose nucleic acid (RNA). The difference, chemically speaking, is not very great. In Chapter IX the description was that of DNA, but if an extra oxygen atom is added to the sugar in each nucleotide and if the nucleotide thymine is replaced by a similar one, called uridine (the nucleoside of the base uracil), then we have RNA. RNA can exist in several different forms with different functions, but in general, it does not exist in the form of a long double helix like DNA. Absence of the extra oxygen on the sugar makes DNA more stable chemically, and the double helix structure makes DNA a more rigid molecule. The chemical distinction between DNA and RNA was known before their respective roles in the living cell had been discovered. For some time

done a certain piece of research, it can usually be assumed—especially in the field of molecular biology—that he did not do the work alone. In the present instance, Yanofsky had four co-workers.

RNA and DNA were known as yeast nucleic acid and thymus nucleic acid because yeast was a good source for the one, and the thymus gland for the other. There was some speculation as to whether RNA might not be characteristic of plants and DNA of animals, but it soon became evident that the best distinction was in terms of their position in the cell. Nuclei contained DNA predominantly, and the cytoplasm was rich in RNA.

Let us now state the problem of protein synthesis as it appeared about 1958. Hereditary material was indubitably DNA. The key substances in metabolism were enzymes, which are proteins. Enzymes were known, in some cases, to be controlled by genes, and it was natural to suppose that DNA in the chromosomes somehow determined the synthesis of specific enzymes. RNA appeared to be implicated because it was present in all living cells, because it was so similar chemically to DNA, and because its concentration in a cell was known to change when a cell synthesized protein. Cells synthesizing large amounts of protein, like the silkworm's gland cells, are particularly rich in RNA. The problem became more absorbing when very small particles in cytoplasm, called microsomes or ribosomes, were found to consist of 60 per cent RNA and to be connected with protein synthesis. The other 40 per cent of their substance is protein.

In 1960 a Yugoslav-born biologist, Marko Zalokar, working at Yale University, performed some elegant experiments which clarified fundamental questions. He used the plant *Neurospora,* which we have had occasion to mention before. *Neurospora* is a fungus, and like most other fungi—molds, plant parasites, mushrooms, and toadstools—its body is made up of many branched tubes. There are cross walls at intervals in these tubes, and they mark off cells. Zalokar used very young plants of about one centimeter in diameter, with their tubes, or hyphae, radiating out neatly from the center. He found that if these little plants are spun very fast on a special contrifuge, each cell acts as a small contrifuge tube and there is a strong force throwing everything outward. Small and heavy particles are forced outward faster than others and nuclei and ribosomes are nicely separated; ribosomes move faster and are found all together near the outer end, and the nuclei, of which there are many in each cell, are found further in (Fig. 29). Now Zalokar wanted to know what happened in the cell to one of the building units of protein, the amino acid leucine, and to one of the building units of RNA, the nucleotide uridine. He therefore placed living *Neurospora* plants in a specially prepared leucine or uridine which contained a radioactive isotope of hydrogen, called tritium (H^3). This would put a label, so to speak, on the leucine or uridine, and its fate could be followed by its radioactivity. In a typical experiment several mycelia, or masses of hyphae, were placed in radioactive uridine and taken out one by one after varying intervals of time; then they were spun on the contrifuge, killed to stop all further chemical reactions, washed, and put on a photographic film to see in what part of the cell the radioactivity lay. It was found that mycelia killed less than one minute after they had been placed in radioactive uridine showed no radioactivity on the photographic film. Mycelia killed one to four minutes after they had been in radioactive uridine showed radioactivity in the region of each cell known to contain the nuclei. Mycelia killed eight minutes or longer after being in radioactive uridine showed radioactivity in the ribosomes. This means that uridine first goes to the nucleus and later to the ribosomes. When the same sort of experiment was performed with radioactive leucine, it was found that leucine first goes to the ribosomes and later spreads all over the cell. It is reasonable to suppose that the first place a component goes to is the seat of synthesis, and we can therefore conclude that RNA is synthesized in the nucleus and protein is synthesized in the

FIGURE 29

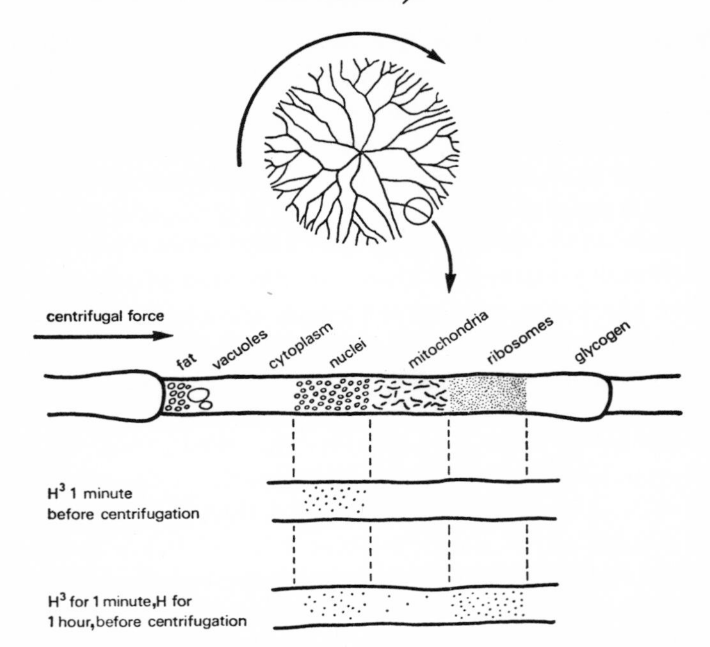

Organelles of a Cell Concerned with Synthesis. The various morphological components of a cell can be separated in *Neurospora* by centrifuging the living plant. A young *Neurospora* plant, which consists of a circular growth of branched tubular cells (hyphae), is shown at the top of the diagram. One hypha (in small circle) is shown magnified below, with the position of the various components after centrifugation. In practice they are not quite so neatly separated as shown. When one of the constituents of RNA, uridine, labeled with radioactive hydrogen (H^3), is fed to the plant, it goes first to the nuclei and later to the ribosomes, as illustrated in the lower two sections of hyphae. The bottom hypha is kept in common, nonradioactive hydrogen (H), during the period after exposure to H^3 so that additional incorporation of radioactive hydrogen will not confuse the picture. This is evidence that RNA is synthesized in the nucleus and moves out later to the ribosomes. Some of the radioactive hydrogen leaks into the mitochondria, but this does not affect the main conclusion.

ribosomes. The proteins later move to other parts of the cell, wherever enzymes are required. Newly synthesized RNA is later found in ribosomes, and this movement from nucleus to ribosomes suggests that it acts as a go-between: it carries information from DNA in the nucleus to the ribosomes, where protein is synthesized.

Zalokar's experiments are only a sample of many different and complex lines of evidence which have finally fitted together like pieces of a jigsaw puzzle into a clear picture. It would take us too far afield to discuss all these ramifications, and we will limit our account to the general picture of protein synthesis which emerges. The story will be told dogmatically and the reader must bear in mind that details may be modified even as this goes to press. It is hoped, on the other hand, that he will appreciate the satisfying nature of the hypothesis.

The idea that DNA makes RNA and RNA makes protein is a relatively old one. A Swedish chemist, T. Caspersson, and a Belgian, J. Brachet, had emphasized this in work they did before 1958, but its truth and significance were not widely acknowledged.

Most of the RNA in the cytoplasm is concentrated in the particles called ribosomes that we have already referred to, and it would therefore be reasonable to assume that DNA makes ribosomes and ribosomes make protein. But this is not the whole truth; a new idea, which proved to be very important, came from the French microbiologists François Jacob and Jacques Monod. They proposed that there was another kind of RNA besides ribosomal RNA which was responsible for carrying information from DNA to protein. They were studying in *E. coli* the kind of enzyme which is not produced by the cell unless the substrate of that enzyme (the substance upon which the enzyme acts) is present. Enzymes of this sort are called inducible enzymes; they are often produced in enormous quantities when the sugar or whatever it is they act on is present, but are almost entirely absent when it is not. The French microbiologists reasoned that if the enzymes were synthesized by RNA then, in order to be able to turn the synthesis on and off, the RNA directly concerned would have to be short-lived. If it were a stable RNA that stayed in circulation forever, it would make protein forever because it could not be easily shut off. This reasoning eliminated the RNA making up the ribosome itself, for ribosomes are very stable. By the use of radioactive labeling, it can be shown that their atomic turnover is slow. This suggestion inspired many experiments in different laboratories throughout the world, and it was proved correct.

The new kind of RNA that was found to carry the DNA protein information was called messenger RNA, or m-RNA. As Jacob and Monod had originally suggested, it has a high turnover rate. There are special cases where it is rather stable, but these do not invalidate the argument.

Another property of the RNA directly concerned with protein synthesis must be that it reflects the genetic code in the DNA of the nucleus. Messenger RNA can be distinguished from the other types of RNA, and it answers the purpose. Its base ratios are similar to those of DNA if one takes uracil to be equivalent to thymine. It can be shown, in addition, that not only are the base ratios of m-RNA similar in general to those of DNA, but in any particular organism the m-RNA can be made to form a double strand with DNA, which means that there is probably a one-to-one correspondence of nucleotides.[2] In the phage called T_2 the identification of m-RNA is particularly striking because when the bacterium *E. coli* is infected with phage the bacterium stops making its own protein and

[2] The correspondence will be to one or the other of the two complementary chains of a Watson-Crick DNA; it cannot be both. The similarity of nucleotide ratios cannot therefore be exact for each nucleotide, but the ratio of adenine and thymine to guanine and cytosine will be the same for DNA and m-RNA.

makes phage protein directed by phage genes. An infected cell would then be expected to make m-RNA corresponding to phage DNA and not to bacterial DNA. Fortunately, the two DNA's can be distinguished and the m-RNA can indeed be shown to correspond to phage DNA.

We can now state that the first step in protein synthesis is formation of m-RNA by a template mechanism from the DNA of the genes in the nucleus. Messenger RNA then passes out into the cytoplasm, and attached to a ribosome, it directs the synthesis of a particular enzyme or enzymes.

Proteins, as we have already said, are chains of about twenty different amino acids. Messenger RNA, like DNA, is made up of four different nucleotides. Amino acids bear no chemical relationship to nucleic acids,[3] and therefore a job of translation has to be done to get from RNA words written with four letters, representing the four nucleotides, to the twenty-letter amino acid words found in enzymes. The translation cannot be the simple one of substituting one nucleotide for one amino acid; several RNA letters must specify one amino acid word. There is good evidence that an RNA word is exactly three letters, or nucleotides, long. The translation is performed by another kind of RNA, transfer RNA (t-RNA), in conjunction with an enzyme. These can be though of as constituting a dictionary. One of the twenty different amino acids floating around in a cell gets attached, by the intervention of a specific enzyme, to a particular molecule of t-RNA. This t-RNA has a block of three nucleotides somewhere in its chain which is destined to fit exactly to a triplet of nucleotides in m-RNA. Thus, successive triplets along the m-RNA be-

[3] This is not altogether true. Two English workers, Professor S.R. Pele and Miss M.G.E. Welton, spent many hours fitting, in jigsaw manner, atomic models of amino acids to DNA bases. They find that there is a good fit between most amino acids and their codons (see Table 13). The significance and meaning of this somewhat embarrassing finding is not clear.

come attached to t-RNA, each with its amino acid attached in turn to it. The amino acids are then linked together by the action of other enzymes, and when the whole message is completed the new protein chain is freed from the ribosome. The complete process is shown diagrammatically in Figure 30. What role the ribsome itself plays is not well understood. It is known to be made up of two parts, referred to as the 30S and 50S units because of the speed at which they centrifuge out. Neither the 30S nor the 50S part can synthesize protein alone, but together they form an active 70S ribosome. (S values are not additive; the explanation for this is complicated.) In the synthesis of the protein hemoglobin it is known that five ribosomes associate with one m-RNA unit during synthesis.

The flood of experimental results concerning different kinds of RNA and protein synthesis has been associated with the development of new techniques. Each stimulates progress in the other. Some of the analytical techniques have been ingenious but simple. Very high speed centrifuges have been manufactured for many years now, but more recent techniques have involved refinements in their use. They can spin at speeds of 60,000 revolutions per minute, forces 100,000 times that of gravity, or more, are produced. Protein molecules are forced to the bottom of the centrifuge tube, and some idea of the size of a protein can be gained by measuring the rate at which it sediments. In these machines the boundary between two different solutions can be seen while the centrifuge is running by means of a special optical system. If caesium chloride, which is a rather heavy material, is put into the tube, it will tend to be concentrated in the bottom as it is spun and a gradient will be formed in the tube such that the solution at the bottom end is more dense than the solution at the top. If a nucleic acid is put into the tube it will settle in that part of the tube where the density of the solution is equal to its own. Two nucleic acids of different density will form two

FIGURE 30

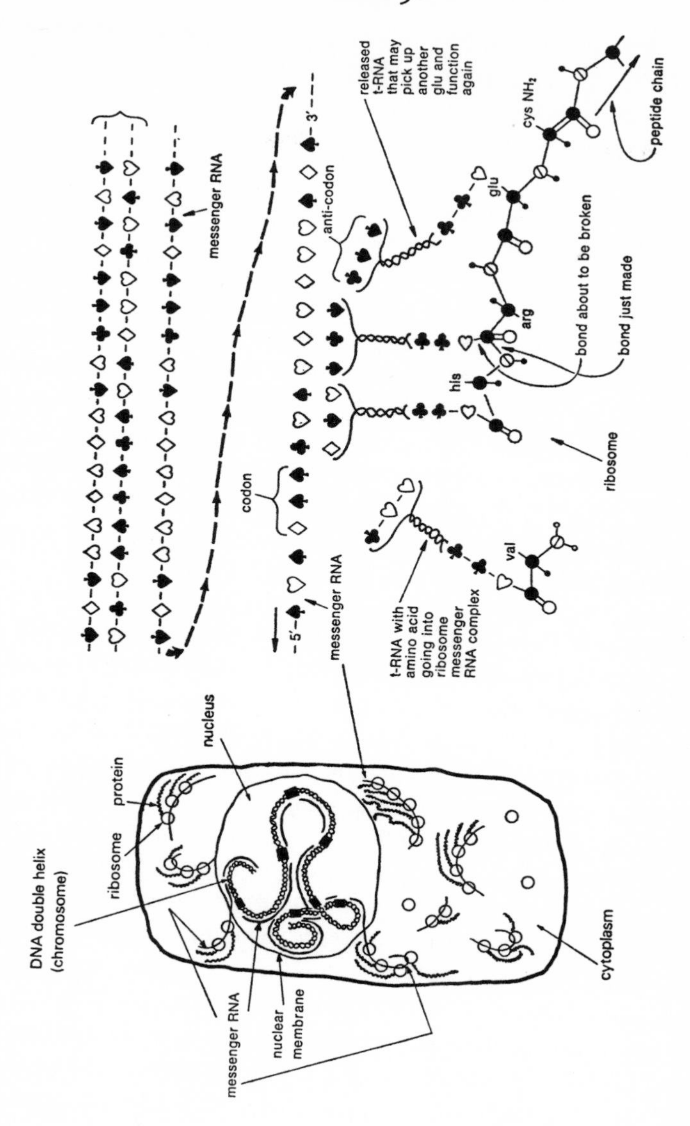
DNA double helix
(chromosome)
ribosome
protein
nucleus
messenger RNA
nuclear
membrane
messenger RNA
cytoplasm
messenger RNA
messenger RNA
5′
3′
codon
anti-codon
t-RNA with
amino acid
going into
ribosome
messenger
RNA complex
val
ribosome
his
arg
glu
cys NH_2
bond about to be broken
bond just made
released
t-RNA
that may
pick up
another
glu and
function
again
peptide chain

Protein Synthesis. On the left is a cell with a single chromosome in its nucleus. Messenger RNA is being synthesized alongside the chromosomal DNA and is itself synthesizing protein in the cytoplasm in association with ribosomes. There is evidence that from one to twenty ribosomes may be associated with a single messenger unit (see Plate 7). They may move along the m-RNA, each synthesizing a separate protein chain as it moves along. The m-RNA is then probably broken up in those cases where the enzyme it makes is inducible or repressible, but may be fairly stable and make a large number of enzyme molecules in other cases, particularly in differentiated cells, where a high output of an enzyme is required during the whole lifetime of the cell. It is not known whether the ribosomes become attached to the m-RNA as it leaves the DNA or at the nuclear membrane or in the cytoplasm. The former possibility is attractive, since the attachment of ribosomes may be a necessary condition for the m-RNA to peel off the DNA.

The right-hand side of the figure shows a very small portion, eighteen nucleotides, of DNA, the m-RNA that it will form, and the way in which amino acids are incorporated into a chain. The top three rows of symbols would be in the nucleus and everything below the arrow takes place in or on the ribosome.

The attachment of free amino acids to corresponding t-RNA by specific activating enzymes is not shown.

bands which will be at different levels. These bands can not only be seen, but can be extracted by taking the tube out of the centrifuge, puncturing a hole in the bottom, and letting the liquid drop out slowly into a succession of small tubes, changing tubes every drop or two. The different nucleic acids will be separated into different tubes. This method is so sensitive that it can separate two nucleic acids which differ only because one of them has a heavy isotope of nitrogen in place of the usual nitrogen. Labeling by means of radioactive isotopes as well as by heavy isotopes can be used in conjunction with centrifugation. Two radioactive labels can be used and measured simultaneously: one nucleic acid may be labeled with tritium, a radioactive isotope of hydrogen, and another with a radioactive isotope of phosphorus; the two isotopes emit beta rays of different energies and these can be measured separately on a scintillation spectrometer.

In the analysis of proteins the technique of chromatography has been widely exploited. This depends upon the well-known phenomenon that if one end of a strip of blotting paper is dipped into ink or a mixture of inks, the various pigments in the ink will form separate bands along the strip. If a solution of starch is made solid with something like gelatin this will act better than blotting paper, and if an electric current is passed along the strip so that one end is electrically positive and the other negative, then proteins with a positive charge will tend to move one way and those with a negative charge another. The same general principle can be used by having a long tube packed with an appropriate powder that acts as blotting paper. A mixture of proteins is poured in at the top end, and as they pass down the tube they become separated into bands. If the liquid is allowed to escape drop by drop at the bottom end and each accumulation of a few drops is collected in a separate small tube, one can collect relatively large quantities of each different protein or part of a protein in separate tubes. This is a rather tiresome process and has been greatly automated. Mechanical collectors for the separate drops have been widely used. Completely automatic machines have been developed to measure the separate amino acids in any protein. The protein is broken down into its component amino acids, these are passed through various columns, and their amounts are measured, all by a machine—while the scientist and his assistant can think of the next experiment. In actual fact the scientist and his assistant are more often to be found, screwdriver in hand, trying to repair one of the pumps or electronic components of the machine that saves them so much drudgery.

A very recent development has been the gas analyzer. This machine forms gaseous compounds of the amino acids, passes the gases through columns, and measures them. The advantages are its speed and the small quantity of material needed. The disadvantage is that the machine needs even more loving care and attention than many of the other devices. With these and other techniques, much has been learned about nucleic acids and proteins.

The three main types of RNA are very different in size. Ribosomal RNA occurs in the form of a particle 200 Angstrom units in diameter, and has about 3,000 nucleotides. These particles centrifuge out at fairly slow speeds. Messenger RNA has about 1,000 nucleotides and under some conditions is soluble. Transfer RNA has about 60 or 70 nucleotides and is characteristically soluble; it is sometimes called soluble RNA, or s-RNA.

Messenger RNA is very difficult to isolate, and even the evidence for its existence is somewhat indirect. Transfer RNA is more easily isolated, and the twenty expected types have been found. There are, in fact, more than twenty because some amino acids appear to have two or more t-RNA types to service them. One of these types, the t-RNA that attaches to the amino acid alanine, is the first nucleic acid to be analyzed completely; the complete order of nucleotides has been worked out. It is as follows: GGGCGUGUGGCGCGUAG UCGGUAGCGCGCUCCCUUGGCGUGGGAGAGUCU CCGGTUCGAUUCCGGACUCGUCCACCA. Reference to Fig. 20 will show that the structure of a nucleic acid chain has a direction determined by the position 3′ or 5′ of phosphate bond; in the above sequence for alanine t-RNA the 5′ end is at the left (the GGG . . . end) and the 3′ at the right (the . . . CCA end). The underlined letters denote modified nucleotides; the letter refers to the most similar nucleotide of the four expected ones: uridine (U), guanine (G), adenine (A), and cytosine (C). The presence of so many odd nucleotides is puzzling, as is the presence of thymidine, which is characteristic of DNA.

Transfer RNA is stable and the same molecules appear to

be used over and over again in protein synthesis. Somewhere along its length there is presumably a group of three nucleotides representing the anti-code for a particular amino acid, and this triplet is attracted to its code on m-RNA. Other parts of t-RNA must be able to attract a specific activating enzyme with its particular amino acid. All kinds of RNA—ribosomal, messenger, and transfer—appear to be transcribed from DNA of the nucleus because there is a correspondence in their nucleotide sequence with that of some part of chromosomal DNA.

The overall roles of DNA and RNA are represented in Figure 31.

FIGURE 31

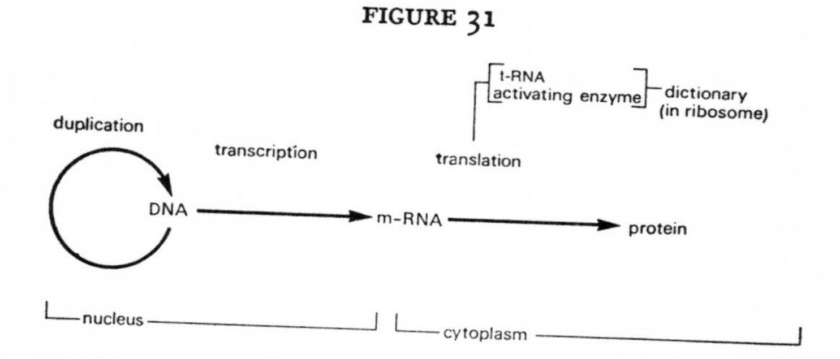

It seems obvious that t-RNA and the activating enzymes constitute the dictionary, but there was the possibility that they merely act as catalysts and that the amino acids somehow are directly related to a triplet code on the m-RNA. This idea was widely held before t-RNA was discovered. A very neat experiment conducted by collaborating workers in different laboratories has shown the idea to be erroneous. The experiment is to attach the amino acid cysteine onto its t-RNA and then change the cysteine into alanine by the action of Raney nickel, which does not otherwise disturb RNA or its attachment to the amino acid. It can then be shown, by methods that will be appreciated before the end of the chapter, that alanine now goes into the place where the cysteine ought to have gone. The system has been fooled. It means that once an amino acid is attached to its transfer RNA, it loses its identity as regards protein synthesis and takes on that of the transfer RNA. The same is true in a written dictionary; one can fool the reader by changing a word after it has been printed opposite its foreign equivalent.

As the details of protein synthesis in living cells became known and, in particular, when it was recognized that the order of nucleotides in DNA and RNA determines the order of amino acids in protein, a new problem, surely one of the most intriguing biological problems in many years, presented itself. The coding problem consists in discovering what two or three or more nucleic acids correspond to each amino acid, and how they are decoded. This is the kind of puzzle which appeals to the theoretician, the man who works with pencil and paper, and many possible codes have been proposed and examined theoretically.

Since we are concerned with twenty amino acids and only four nucleotides, more than one nucleotide must be used to code for each amino acid. As we have seen in Chapter IX, the various combinations of any two nucleotides can code for 4^2, or 16, amino acids; this is still not enough. Three at a time can code for 4^3, or 64, amino acids and this is plenty; in fact, there will be 44 possible codes to spare. A few calculations in the early days of theoretical coding showed that if the 44 spare codes are regarded as nonsense—that is, if no amino acid ever gets attached to any of them—then a code can be devised so that in a long line of nucleotides each amino acid will have a triplet code in the line but all overlapping triplets will code for nothing. Imagine the four nucleotides to be A, E, S, and T; then eleven triplet sequences make sense in English and the rest are nonsense; in the sequence ASSSEESEASETTEE-

EATTEASEETATASSSAT, the words ASS SEE SEA SET TEE EAT TEA SEE TAT ASS SAT appear at unique positions; all other sequences of three letters, such as SSS SSE EES ESE . . . , are nonsense. This constitutes a nonoverlapping code, which need not be sequentially read. Exactly twenty amino acids and no more can be accommodated by such a code. We now know, because of various experiments, that the code is nonoverlapping, but is, in fact, read sequentially; this means that some of the overlapping triplets may make sense but are prevented from being read because the code is read sequentially—first the first three nucleotides, then the next three, and so on. Evidence for this was obtained in England by Francis Crick and his co-worker Sydney Brenner (the same Francis Crick who had, with Watson, previously contributed the Watson-Crick model for DNA). The experiment began with a mutant obtained in a certain phage. The mutant could be grown as easily as the wild type on one strain of bacteria, but could be recognized because, unlike the wild type, it would not grow on another strain of bacteria. The mutant was obtained following treatment by an interesting chemical mutagen, an acridine dye which belongs to a group of chemicals which are used as antiseptics. There is evidence that acridine dyes get into the Watson-Crick helix of DNA and cause mutation by eliminating a nucleotide or adding an extra one.

From the original mutant several apparent back mutations were obtained which behaved like the wild type. Genetic analysis showed that they were not true back mutations but that they involved a second mutation near, but not exactly at, the same place as the original. The new mutations, when separated into progeny phage by crossing the double mutant with a wild-type phage, behaved just like the original mutation in their phenotypes. Thus two mutations in the same gene seemed to cancel each other out.

The explanation proposed is that the first mutation added a nucleotide and the second mutation subtracted a nucleotide, or vice versa. In the sequence of words above, if an A is added in the fifth position, most of the sequence makes nonsense when read sequentially: ASS SAE ESE ASE TTE EEA TTE ASE ETA TAS SSA T. The gene will not code for a correct enzyme and the phage will be a mutant. Similarly, if the T in the thirteenth position is subtracted, most of the words will be nonsense: ASS SEE SEA SET EEE ATT EAS EET ATA SSS AT. It must be remembered that the spaces between the groups of three letters have been inserted only to make the words more easily recognizable; no such spacing between nucleotides exists. Now, if the two mutations are both in the same organism, we get: ASS SAE ESE ASE TEE EAT TEA SEE TAT ASS SAT. There are three nonsense words near the beginning, but all the rest make sense, and in many cases a few wrong amino acids among hundreds, especially in certain places, apparently do not matter.

Third mutations were also obtained on the double mutants which behave like the wild type, and these again behaved like mutants. In all, a large number of mutants were obtained which could be divided into two groups, + and —, such that a + mutant and a — mutant together gave a wild type. In terms of our example with English words this implies that although the code is read sequentially, the overlapping words are nonsense and do not code for any amino acid; it must be realized that the argument holds just as well even if all the triplets of letters in the mutants do spell out English words; so long as the words are different from those in the wild type, they will constitute a mutant. These experiments provided a powerful argument that the code was, in fact, read sequentially from one end to the other.

The same mutants were used to provide evidence for a triplet code rather than a quadruplet or quintuplet code. It was possible to put two + mutants or two — mutants into the same phage by a cross. Such double mutants appeared mutant, but when a third + or a third — mutation was added, the phage was the wild type. Using our analogy of English words again, three — mutations, in the fourth, ninth, and thirteenth positions, would result in: ASS EES ESE TEE EAT TEA SEE TAT ASS SAT. A few words are nonsense but all the rest are all right, and the organism may well appear to be the wild type. Four and five + or four and five — mutations piled up together were found to result in a mutant type.

In all this work certain mutants are designated + and others —, but it cannot be known which contain an extra nucleotide and which a deficiency, nor does it matter in this context.

An unfortunate feature of this brilliant work is that nothing is known of the enzyme involved. The same type of experiment has, however, recently been reported in a case where the protein concerned is rather easy to study, and we will describe this later in connection with the code.

About the time of the International Congress of Biochemistry in Moscow in 1961, two laboratories, more or less independently and more or less simultaneously, obtained evidence as to which three nucleotides code which amino acid. Severo Ochoa at New York University and Marshall Nirenberg at the National Institutes of Health, Bethesda, Maryland, both used synthetic m-RNA to make, or rather to begin to make, protein. Ochoa had previously learned to make RNA chains by enzymatic action. It was not possible to make RNA with a particular desired sequence of nucleotides. What was possible was to make a long chain consisting of just uridine (poly-U) or of a mixture of uridine and one or more of the other three nucleotides in a random sequence. Owing to a technical chemical difficulty, which has now been overcome, uridine had to be a constituent of the synthetic RNA in all of these experiments. Ribosomes were extracted from living cells, and to them were added the supernatant fluid containing all twenty soluble, or transfer, RNA's, as well as the necessary activating and polymerizing enzymes and a few other ingredients of known and unknown function. The brew was then ready to make protein as soon as synthetic m-RNA and a supply of various amino acids were added. A wise investigator would probably have guessed that the experiment would fail because these synthetic and unnatural RNA's might lack many subtleties of natural m-RNA. In fact, at that time some workers in England were trying to perform the same sort of experiments with naturally occurring RNA from plant viruses. They failed, while those using synthetic RNA succeeded.

The experiments require some technical skill to perform. Conditions must be just right, addition of the right amount of simple chemicals like magnesium is very important, unwanted naturally occurring RNA in the various components must be destroyed, and the synthesis of more RNA during the experiment must be prevented. Above all, a way must be devised to detect the synthesis of protein. It might be supposed that the experiment would consist in letting the reaction go on for as long as necessary and then extracting the protein synthesized and analyzing it to see what amino acids were in it. This was not the method used and the reason is that very little protein, too little in fact to be called proper protein, is synthesized, and that the brew already contains so much other protein that it would be impossible to find the newly synthesized bits. The way in which the problem was circumvented was to add one amino acid that was radioactive, while all the others were normal. The total protein could then be extracted and tested for radioactivity. If it was found to be radioactive, then the particular amino acid that was radioactive must have been used in synthesis. For example, when synthetic poly-U was used and the experiment was repeated with each of the amino acids in turn as the radioactive one, it was found that only when the amino acid phenylalanine was the radioactive one was the protein radioactive. Thus uridine, or three uridines in a row, determines phenylalanine. On the basis of a code consisting of three nucleotides, all twenty amino acids have now been alloted nucleotide triplets (Table 13).

TABLE 13

The Genetic Code

Nucleotides	*Protein*	*Nucleotides*	*Protein*
GG–	Gly	CG–	Arg
GC–	Ala	AG (A) (G)	Arg
GU–	Val	AA (U) (C)	Asn
AU (U) (C)	Ilu	CA (A) (G)	Gln
CU–	Leu	UG (U) (C)	Cys
UU (A) (G)	Leu	AU (A) (G)	Met
UC–	Ser	UG (A) (G)	Try
AG (U) (C)	Ser	UU (U) (C)	Phe
AC–	Thr	UA (U) (C)	Tyr
GA (U) (C)	Asp	CA (U) (C)	His
GA (A) (G)	Glu	CC–	Pro
AA (A) (G)	Lys	UA (A) (G)	nonsense

This table presents the best recent genetic code showing codons on m-RNA which specify each of the twenty amino acids. The letters of the triplets represent the nucleotides adenine (♡, A), guanine (◇, G), uracil (♠, U), and cytosine (♣, C). The abbreviations for the amino acids are explained in Table 14. A twenty-first amino acid, cystine, is found regularly in proteins, but there is no code for it because it is formed from two cysteine molecules after the peptide chain has been made. Other odd amino acids that are found in some proteins may also be formed from existing ones after the peptide chain has been made. Terminal letters in parentheses are equivalent to each other; thus AA (U)(C) means AAU or AAC. A dash in final place means that any letter can be there; thus AC—means ACU, or ACC, or ACA, or ACG.

It will be seen that the third nucleotide is less specific than the first two. This code specifies amino acids for all but two of the sixty-four combinations of four nucleotides taken three at a time. It is degenerate, meaning that several different codes specify the same amino acid, but it is not ambiguous, since no code specifies more than one amino acid.

This code was derived from work done on the bacterium *E. coli*. It fits, or does not badly contradict, odd bits of information obtained from work done on viruses and blood hemoglobin and may well be the universal code for all organisms on earth, but there are some recent experiments that suggest no such thing.

"Nonsense" for UA(A)(G) indicates that these triplets may not be codons for any amino acid. When mutation to a nonsense codon occurs protein synthesis is known to stop at that point and an unfinished protein chain released. Some nonsense code may be the natural signal for the end of a protein chain. Another codon at the beginning of messenger RNA may signal the start of a protein chain, and there is evidence that some unknown codon coding for a modified amino acid, formyl methionine, is such a one. The formyl part, or the whole formyl methionine, would later be cut off. A problem would arise from the fact that this starting code might often exist, accidentally, somewhere in the middle of a m-RNA overlapping two proper codons. This would be taken as a starting point and lead to disaster. An ingenious idea avoiding this snag has been proposed by two workers at the University of Chicago, Tokumasa Nahamoto and Daniel Kolakofski. They point out that the degeneracy of the code allows a choice of codons for any amino-acid sequence such that any starting codon can be avoided.

Let us assume that the starting codon is UUG, then an amino-acid sequence phe-gly might be UUUGGU, in which case the unwanted UUG is present. If, however, the alternate code UUC for phe is taken, then the sequence UUCGGU does not contain the triplet UUG.

The actual sequence of the three nucleotides cannot be determined by the method described; valine, for instance, might be ♠ ♠ ◇ or ◇ ♠ ♠ or ♠ ◇ ♠. A new technique developed by Nirenberg's group has more recently provided evidence for the correct order. The technique depends upon the fact that a long chain of RNA is not necessary to attract or bind an amino acid and its t-RNA. Just three nucleotides are sufficient. This in itself is evidence that the code is triplet. Two nucleotides will not work; three are sufficient. The experiments consist in making molecules of two, three, or four nucleotides of known sequence. This is difficult but possible and the direction of the nucleotides, in the sense of which end has a loose 3′ bond and which a loose 5′, is known. Once it

TABLE 14

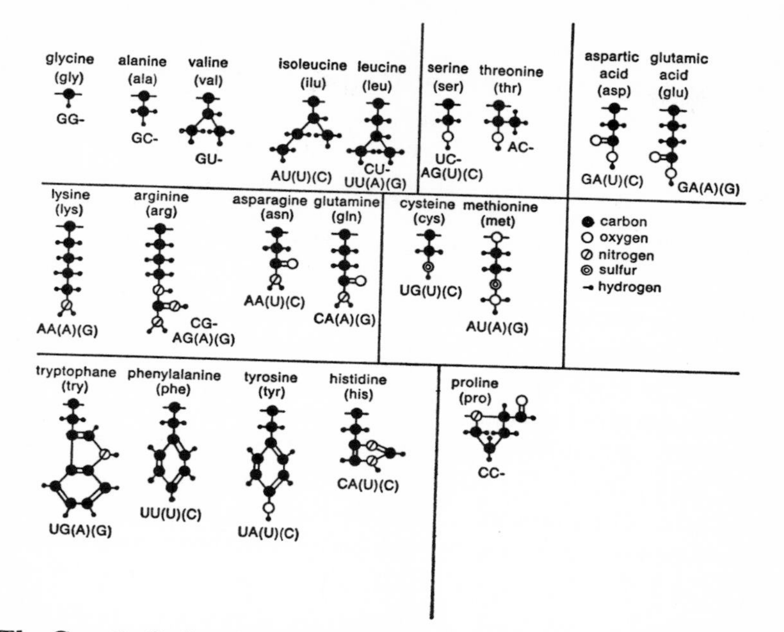

The Genetic Code—Chemical Formulae for Amino Acids. This table shows the same code as in Table 13, but with the chemical formulae for the various amino acids added.

The top carbon atom in each case is represented as part of a peptide chain, there would be a carbon-oxygen grouping on one side and a nitrogen-hydrogen grouping on the other. Proline is exceptional in that it links to the nitrogen of the chain. The structure of a peptide chain as found in proteins is shown in Figure 21.

was established that three nucleotides were the minimum required to bind an amino-acid–t-RNA complex, more than forty different triplets of nucleotides were tested against various amino-acid–t-RNA complexes whose amnio acids were labeled with a radioactive carbon atom to see which triplets bonded which amino acids. The results from the use of this technique fit well with the previous results with longer chains of randomly ordered nucleotides. They also fit, or at least do not contradict, other evidence of a different kind. In Tables 13–15 the best code, as determined by Nirenberg's group, is given, together with some of the other data that support or contradict it.

Some of these other data will now be described. H. G. Wittmann, working in Tübingen, Germany, and other workers, have induced mutations in tobacco-mosaic viruses by introducing nitrous acid, which acts rather like the nucleic acid analog that we described in Chapter X. It is believed to change cytosine to uracil (♣ → ♠) and adenine to guanine (♡ → ♢). Now the amino acid sequence in the protein of the coat of the tobacco-mosaic virus is known, and the nature of the change in a mutant can be determined. In several mutants the protein of the virus was found to have the amino acid isoleucine in the position where threonine occurs in the wild type. The mutation had thus made the change threonine → isoleucine. According to the codes for these amino acids given in Tables 13 and 14, this would mean a change ♡, ♣, ♠ → ♡, ♠, ♠. This requires the change of only one nucleotide through the action of nitrous acid and it is the right kind of change, namely ♣ → ♠. Some fifteen different mutants have been examined in this way; each occurred several times and all but three fit the code as given in Table 13 in that only one nucleotide had to be changed and the change was one of the two changes expected from the action of nitrous acid. The exceptions may mean that the code is wrong in these particular cases, or they may have been due to spontaneous mutation, or even to contaminants. Other explanations are readily available.

It may be remembered that we mentioned in Chapter IX that tobacco-mosaic virus contains RNA rather than DNA. This is a curious fact and appears to mean that in these viruses RNA can do the job of DNA as well as play its various regular roles. It does not affect the significance of the argument about coding.

Another protein whose amino acid sequence is known is human hemoglobin, and here again about sixteen mutants are known. These have not been produced by nitrous acid or indeed by any analog mutagen, to be sure, but we may nevertheless guess that most if not all of them are due to changes in a single nucleotide. If this is assumed, then the particular amino acid substitutions found in the hemoglobin of these mutants should require the change of only one nucleotide of the code. This has been found to be the case. The fact that the code, which was developed from test-tube experiments, fits what bits of information we have concerning other organisms suggests that there may be a universal code valid for all organisms. It is an intriguing possibility; it would mean that the same code is used in tobacco-mosaic virus, in humans and in the bacteria from which Ochoa and Nirenberg obtained their ribosomes, t-RNA, and activating enzymes. From other experiments it appears that the ribosomes are quite unspecific, that ribosomes from one organism work perfectly well with m-RNA and other components from a different organism.

The most recent and elegant confirmation of the nature of the code is an experiment similar to the one performed by Crick and Brenner on the phage mutants that could be sorted out into + and − mutations due to the adding or subtracting of a nucleotide. In the present case the protein concerned was known and the actual amino acid changes in a mutant could be ascertained. In one double mutant a series of five amino acids were altered as follows, the abbreviations are those used in Table 14:

-lys-ser-pro-ser-leu-asn-ala—wild type
-lys-val-his-his-leu-met-ala—double mutant

According to the code these amino acids can be as follows:

AAA AGU CCA UCA CUU AUU GC–
AAA GUC CAU CAC UUA AUG GC–

It will be seen how nicely all five changes can be explained by the subtraction of an adenine at one end of the chain by the first mutation and the addition of a guanine at the other end by the second.

A different kind of evidence which also supports the conception of the code that we have outlined comes from Yanofsky and his co-workers in California. Yanofsky has been studying an enzyme called tryptophane synthetase in *E. coli* for some years and has been able to identify the particular amino acid change in some mutants just as Wittmann has in the virus proteins. The wild type has glycine in a certain position on the tryptophane synthetase protein, and in two mutants this is replaced by valine and arginine respectively. On crossing the two mutants, he gets back the wild type with glycine and a new type which has serine in the position concerned. According to the code, valine can be GUU and one of the codes for arginine is AGA. If there were a cross-over between the first and second nucleotides the recombinants GGA and AUU would be formed. The former is the code for glycine, which was found, and the latter is for isoleucine, which was not found but might have been missed for technical reasons. A cross-over between the second and third nucleotides would give GUA (valine) and AGU (serine). Valine was not found, but serine was. A double cross-over would give GGU (glycine) and AUA (methionine). Glycine was found and there is no knowing whether it was GGA or GGU. Methionine was not found but again would most probably be missed. That some of the bacteria were of the wild type (glycine) and others had serine can thus be explained by cross-overs within the coding triplet.

The technical reason why certain replacements would be missed is that it is most difficult to detect a mutant among many wild types. Fortunately, some of the amino acid replacements in the tryptophane synthetaste protein do not make the enzyme completely nonfunctional. In these cases the mutants can be isolated from types where the enzyme does not function at all. When glutamic acid or arginine occupy the position the organism is completely mutant, but with other replacements there is a varied amount of activity of the enzyme. Besides the two mutants having valine and arginine replacements that were used in the recombination experiment, Yanofsky obtained many other mutant strains with other replacements in these positions. These mutants were obtained either directly from wild type or from other mutants. The family tree of these mutants is shown in Table 15, and on the assumption that each step involves a single base change, they fit the code well.

These experiments not only support our ideas about the code, but they have a bearing on crossing-over and on mutation. They indicate, as does other evidence, that crossing-over is not restricted to certain points between genes or even to certain points between the triplets representing code words, but that it can occur more or less anywhere along the DNA chain of a chromosome, between any of the ultimate molecule units, the nucleotides. We must add here that "crossing-over" is used in a broad sense and that "recombination" is a better term, for as we shall see in the next chapter, the way in which recombinants are formed between two close mutations in the same gene, is somewhat different from the crossing-over described in earlier chapters. The recombinants in Yanofsky's experiments occurred with a frequency of about 2 in 100,000, which means the mutation sites were very close indeed, as we would expect. One cannot get closer than neighboring nucleotides.

As regards our ideas of mutation, the experiments show that mutations can arise by recombination. They are true mutations in the sense that they make a different protein and they will breed true. They occur, moreover, with a higher frequency

TABLE 15

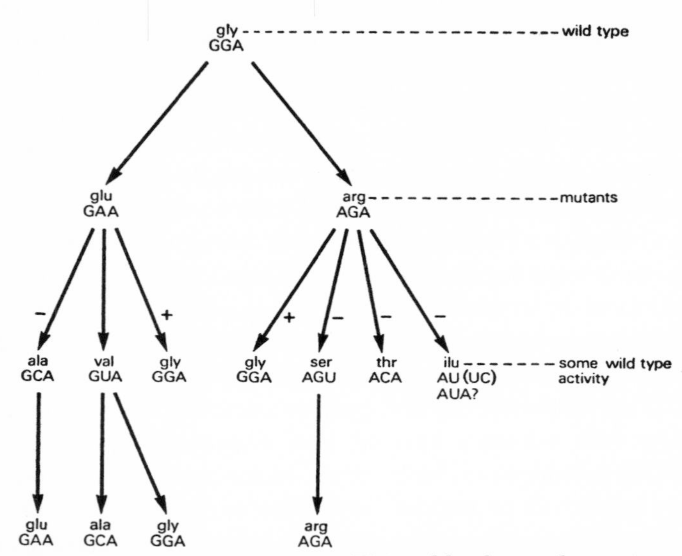

Mutations and the Genetic Code. This table shows the amino acids that have been found to replace glycine in a certain place in the tryptophane synthetase protein, as described in Chapter XI. All changes except arg → ilu can be represented as single nucleotide changes if the amino acids are given codes taken from Table 13 as indicated. Arg → ilu can be accommodated by allowing AUA to code for ilu instead of met, and there is no real reason for not allowing this except that it would destroy the order and symmetry of the code. The plus sign (+) indicates mutations that are enhanced by the use of a chemical mutagen (2-amino purine), which probably changes A to G or U to C. The minus sign (–) indicates changes that are not so enhanced. Data are not available for the others. This table represents just one example where amino acid replacements in protein are known. Other examples are virus-coat protein, human hemoglobin, and the enzyme alkaline phosphatase. All of these fit the code about as well as or better than the present case.

Some changes which technically could have been detected were not found. Thus, arg never gave rise to val or ala, and glu never gave ilu, ser, or thr. Reference to Table 13 or 14 will show that no code assignment will allow these amino acid changes to be made with just a single nucleotide change.

than the normal spontaneous mutations. They are presumably occurring all the time in any organism that is hybrid for amino acids that belong in exactly the same place in the same protein.

In Chapter VIII we were not prepared to describe the more subtle production of mutations that we have introduced here in connection with the genetic code. Let us summarize the phenomena described since then as they concern mutation. Two classes of chemical mutagens can be distinguished—the base analogs, including nitrous acid, and the acridines. The base analogs change one large nucleotide (adenine or guanine) into the other, or one small nucleotide (thymine or cytosine) into the other, but never a large into a small or vice versa. The acridines add or subtract a nucleotide. One would expect that mutations produced by base analogs could be reversed by base analogs, but not by acridines, and also that mutations produced by acridines could be reversed by acridines, but not by base analogs. Experiments have shown this to be generally true. Spontaneous and radiation mutations fall into all categories—some can be reversed by base analogs, some by acridines, and some by neither.

This chapter has been about macromolecules. The word itself is new, but has already appeared frequently in the titles of books, institutes, articles, and applications for government grants. The large molecules of heredity and protein synthesis can be looked upon as organs of the cell. Their structure can be related to their function from an engineer's point of view. The DNA chain is a very rigid structure; its double strands give it additional rigidity and also insure against loss of information because if bases on one chain are destroyed, the same information is still held in the other and repair can be effected. The differences between the subunits of DNA are slight; all four nucleotides are roughly similar, which gives the chain a simple, one-dimensional configuration that is well suited to duplication.

It will be remembered how nucleic acid, soon after its original isolation, was broken down into two kinds: DNA and RNA. Further study then analyzed RNA into several kinds: m-RNA, t-RNA, and ribosomal RNA. We can see that m-RNA is well designed for its function. It is not so long as DNA, and therefore need not be so rigid. RNA is not quite so stable chemically as DNA and it need not be, for if a particular molecule breaks down, another can soon be made from DNA. For a similar reason, there is no need for double strands. The functions of t-RNA and ribosomal RNA are not well understood. At first sight they might be thought of merely as supporting structures. The specificities involved in linking a set of three nucleotides to a particular amino acid could lie entirely in the activating enzymes. However, there are already indications that both of these RNA's may play a much more important role.

Proteins are more complex molecules. In the form of enzymes they have to induce delicate and precise reactions requiring specific three-dimensional shapes. Such molecules are unsuited to duplication or to the compact preservation of information.

Thus DNA, the different kinds of RNA, and protein all seem well designed for their functions, so far as these functions are understood. Among the things that are not clear we have mentioned the role of t-RNA and ribosomes. Another puzzle concerns the transcription of m-RNA from DNA because the two strands of DNA would produce m-RNA's with different messages. Each of these m-RNA's would produce a different protein. The answer most probably is that only one strand of DNA is copied. But how just one, the right one, is copied and whether the other one plays any informational role is unknown.

The details of DNA duplication are also in need of clarification. Although duplication, as well as the synthesis of RNA from a DNA template, has been achieved *in vitro, i.e.* in a test-tube, it is not the same process as that which occurs in the living cell. Among the differences it can be noted that *in vitro* synthesis produces branched chains and that the polymerizing enzymes work along each chain in a polarized fashion and could not work progressively along both chains from one end of a double helix to the other as is believed to occur *in vivo* (see Plate 11). The difficulty lies in the fact that the direction or polarization of the two strands of a Watson-Crick DNA run opposite to each other. The question of how far test-tube experiments duplicate nature is also pertinent to work done in breaking the genetic code. Much of the proposed code or codes is probably correct, for there is corroborative evidence from *in vivo* systems, but many subtleties may have been missed in the codes made on the basis of radioactive amino acid incorporations into protein *in vitro*.

Some of the subtleties are very likely due to built-in repair and correction mechanisms and this aspect of living organisms should not be neglected. It is noteworthy that the whole biological process we have described goes wrong only rarely. Mutations, errors of template copying, and other accidents must be occurring all the time as an egg develops into an adult, and yet, for the most part, adults are normal and function properly. There must be innumerable mechanisms to correct mistakes. We have already mentioned that the double nature of a Watson-Crick DNA chromosome insures that even if one strand is somehow damaged, all is not lost, for the equivalent information is still preserved in the other strand. Some pretty experiments have shown that there are special enzymes that can cut out certain adjacent nucleotides on one chain that become damaged by the action of ultraviolet light, and other enzymes are known that can repair the cut-out piece by copying from the other strand. In diploid organisms the fact that there are two copies of each gene means that if one mutates or is damaged in some other way the other can usually carry on. Mutated genes can also be corrected. The change in the part of the chromosome making an activating enzyme or t-RNA, enabling a wrong code to read right, will be taken up in a later chapter. There is good evidence that the code can also be changed by an alteration in the ribosome. The antibiotic streptomycin does this for several mutations, and this drug, normally so deadly to bacteria, then becomes a requirement for these crippled cells. In both cases of correction it is thought the code is not absolutely changed but only loosened up a bit. Specificity is lost. The mutated gene still makes the wrong protein, but it also makes a little of the right protein. The change in code probably means that many other genes are making some wrong proteins, but this can be tolerated. Anyone who has bought furniture in parts to be assembled at home will appreciate this point. For a perfect table each hole is drilled exactly to a specific size to accommodate a specific size of screw or bolt. Unfortunately, it sometimes happens that the wood has swollen or warped and it is impossible to push the screws into their holes. In such cases one wishes that the screw-making machine had been a little less precise and had made screws which varied more; some would then be found which could serve. *In vitro* studies on the code would miss these subtleties of the code unless specially designed to detect them. The fact that the code is degenerate must also be connected with what we can call the problem of repair and spare parts. It will be seen from Tables 13 and 14 that all amino acids appear to have at least two alternative codes and many have four. There are also known to be two or more different t-RNA's for each amino acid and two or more different activating enzymes have already been found for one amino acid.

The complete nucleotide structure of the t-RNA for alanine has been given earlier in this chapter, and one can speculate on whether and how it is folded and where the triplet codon[4] for alanine lies. A little doodling with pencil and paper will show that it can be folded in several ways which bring about half the nucleotides opposite complementary partners. The amino acid with its activating enzyme is known to attach to the right-hand end, terminating . . . CCA. As for the code, Table 13 suggests that the codon for alanine is GCU or GCC or GCA or GCG. Now if GCU is the m-RNA codon, the anti-codon will be AGC. This is obtained by taking into account not only the complementary nucleotides—G to C, C to G, and U to A—but also the polarity of the chain, using the convention that the left-hand end represents a free 5′ band and the right-hand end a free 3′ band. When chains of nucleotides pair they are presumed to do so with their polarities pointing in opposite directions. If we look along the long series nucleotides in alanine RNA, we find only one AGC triplet. There are three GGC and three CGC triplets, which correspond to the alternative codons GCC and GCG given for alanine in Table 13. All of these seven anti-codons are in the left-hand half of the t-RNA, away from the . . . CCA end. Which of these codons is used is not known, but the structure of the ribosome may well play a part in the choice. An alteration in ribosome structure could make another triplet serve as anti-codon and then alanine would be put opposite a different triplet. This would be one of the ways of changing the code to cover up accidents. All of these subtleties of the code—degeneracy, ribosomal effects, and possible t-RNA effects—are little understood, but that they come under the general category of repair and spare parts rather than anything more fundamental in an evolutionary sense is indicated by the fact that the code is, in general, universal. Ribosomes, t-RNA, and activating enzymes from organisms as different as bacteria, yeast, rats, and man can be used interchangeably, and

[4] The original code on DNA is called the anti-codon; the complementary codon on m-RNA is the codon, and that on t-RNA, the anti-codon again.

the codons in Table 13 fit information obtained from viruses, molds, and man.

We will conclude with the peculiar case of a spare, non-functional gene which occurs in humans. The higher animals are unable to make certain amino acids in the cells of their bodies. These amino acids are known as the essential amino acids; there are about ten of them, and they must be included in the diet. Among them are histidine and tryptophane. There is good reason for not making these two if one can avoid it because they are rather difficult and energy-consuming amino acids to make. The peculiar thing is that although we do not make these two amino acids in any part of our body, we have the genes for them. This is proved by the fact that human embryonic cells do, in fact, synthesize them. Evidently for the greater part of their life these genes are completely shut off, and one wonders whether, in an emergency, they could be turned on again. The subject of the turning on and off of genes will be introduced in Chapter XIII.

XII *A Pause for Reflection*

We have come a long way from the idea of a minute and perfect replica of man being transmitted in sperm to expand into a member of the new generation. Today's theories of heredity are cold-bloodedly rational compared to ancient, more romantic, one might almost say more biological, hypotheses. For the biologist is usually thought of as one who unravels intricate structural details of large and small organisms, attempting to relate them to the functioning of the organism. The beautiful accounts and drawings of the learned and pious French researchers the Tulasne brothers, on sexual organs of the cryptogams, represent a fine example of what biology was.

But as we approach fundamental issues—the mechanism of heredity and the control of cell chemistry—we find ourselves in a realm of numerical logic, of symbolic signs positive and negative, of random probabilities. Consider, say, the beauty of the hands of Audrey Hepburn, the gracefulness of Pavlova, the imaginative sensitivity of Keats. Must not the essence of these be something equally inspiring, some extraordinarily complex pattern half revealed by an extremely powerful microscope? Or more likely some force, some biological entity, never to be revealed by the apparatus of science? Well, no; as we have seen, the secret lies in a particular order of four rather small and monotonous chemical molecules strung together in a very long chain. This brings to mind the way an engineer constructs a machine or, better still, the way a computer is designed to solve complex mathematical problems. Looking back, one is tempted to suggest that the whole story of genetic mechanisms could have been worked out theoretically without any laboratory experiments: the idea of a particulate gene, linkage groups, and diploidy, and finally the genetic code duplicating by a template mechanism. A well-known German biologist, Wilhelm Roux, in 1883 did, in fact, arrive at a model consisting of linear arrays of small units from purely theoretical considerations of how exactly to duplicate a large number of units. Computers and Morse code use only two symbols, but a little reflection might well have led one to choose four in a genetic system. The thought is, of course, an absurd exaggeration, but the truth is that one cannot fail to be impressed by the mathematical beauty of the system. The words of Sir James Jeans written in 1930 in reference to discoveries in astronomy come to mind, "We have already considered with disfavor the possibility of the universe having been planned by a biologist or an engineer; from the intrinsic evidence of His creation, the Great Architect of the Universe now begins to appear as a pure mathematician."

All life on earth from the smallest virus to man himself has the same basic genetic system—information stored as DNA and expressed through RNA and proteins. The few exceptions are minor; tobacco-mosaic virus and some other viruses in which the information is stored as RNA instead of DNA, other viruses in which there is a single DNA strand instead of a Watson-Crick double strand, an odd nucleotide found in the DNA of some other viruses.

The smallest living organism is a creature of some interest. Viruses don't count because they are not free-living, they use part of the protein-making machinery of their host. The smallest free-living organism belongs to a group called pleuropneumonia-like organisms, or PPLO. It is only .25 of a micron (μ), or about .00025 of a millimeter, in diameter; an amoeba is about a thousand times bigger, a hydrogen atom about a thousand times smaller. This organism contains some 4 per cent DNA, 8 per cent RNA, and at least 40 different enzymes. It is easy to calculate that the 4 per cent DNA must represent a Watson-Crick helix of about 75,000 pairs of nucleotides. On the basis of a triplet code, 25,000 amino acids would be synthesized. If we take an average enzyme to consist of about 300 amino acids, then this organism could code about 80 enzymes. These calculations are approximate, but they fit reasonably well; the minimum number of enzymes necessary to carry out basic chemical reactions in a cell must surely be at least 100, but this figure is not too different from 80. These organisms require a complex medium to grow; they need to be supplied with many vitamins and other chemicals which they cannot synthesize themselves, that is why it is considered likely that they can get by with somewhat less than 100 enzymes. Higher organisms probably require upward of 10,000 enzymes.

If we make some assumptions, a few rough calculations can be made about the number of genes in other organisms. The average enzyme has a molecular weight of some 40,000. Taking the molecular weight of an average amino acid as 125, the average enzyme should have about 300 amino acids. If we assume that three nucleotide pairs code one amino acid, then a gene which makes an average enzyme has about 1,000 nucleotide pairs. Taking the molecular weight of an average nucleotide pair as 600, this represents a segment of DNA having a molecular weight of about 600,000, or 6×10^5. This figure fits fairly well with the average molecular weight that is found for some m-RNA molecules in *E. coli*. For *Drosophila* the haploid amount of DNA per nucleus is 8.5×10^{-14} grams, which multiplied by 6×10^{23} gives a molecular weight of about 5×10^{10}. Dividing by 6×10^{5} we get roughly 100,000 genes.

The amount of DNA in the nuclei of several organisms is known, and dividing this by 6×10^{5} will give the number of genes. The figures for a few representative organisms are tabulated in Appendix 1.

For *Drosophila* large errors have no doubt gone into these calculations. Much of the DNA in a cell may not code enzymes and may not even be genic. Using average values can also introduce errors. The number of bands seen on chromosomes of the salivary glands of *Drosophila* is about 5,100 and this would be a lower limit for the number of genes because further study might resolve what looks like a single band into two or three bands. The two estimates for *Drosophila* are, nevertheless, tenfold apart, which is somewhat more than trivial.

Proteins and nucleic acids are found in all organisms down to the very smallest, and it looks very much as though they play a basic role in all living organisms, at least on earth. It is natural to speculate on whether they also played an important role in the most primitive organisms, in the original evolution of life from nonliving chemicals. Now that our species can travel in space and is contemplating trips to the moon and planets, serious thought and research is being devoted to the origin of life and the possibility of life on other planets. The primitive earth as it cooled down some five billion (American and French billion, 10^{9}; not British billion, 10^{12}) years ago is now generally thought to have consisted of reduced as opposed to oxidized chemicals. Carbon was present in the form of methane gas (CH_4), nitrogen in ammonia (NH_3), oxygen in water (H_2O). There were undoubtedly many free hydrogen molecules, and various other molecules, including some with phosphorus. Now if these chemicals were allowed to react together at random, it would be very unlikely that a protein molecule or a nucleic acid molecule or a living cell would be formed—much less likely than drawing a bridge hand consisting of thirteen spades. A great deal of energy in the form of ultraviolet light and other radiations would help, but other factors would have to play a part. If, after several million years, a few amino acids and a few nucleotides were formed eventually, the chances of further evolution would be increased if they could be taken out of circulation so that they would not be broken down again. It would also make the development more credible if these molecules could multiply or at least increase the chances of their own formation by autocatalysis. And lastly, evolution toward a living cell would be more likely if these rare molecules were brought together in small packets so that they could react together.

There is good reason to believe that all these factors did play a part. It has been shown by Stanley Miller and Harold Urey in Chicago that if a mixture of the gases methane, ammonia, and hydrogen is exposed to repeated electric sparks, and if a method is devised of separating off any nongaseous molecules that may be formed, then small amounts of amino acids, including glycine and alanine, can be detected. It has also been shown that the nucleic acid adenine is formed. Oxygen prevents much ultraviolet light from reaching the earth; if there was no oxygen in the primitive atmosphere of the earth, then there must have been strong ultraviolet radiation. If water was constantly evaporating, condensing, and falling as rain, it would bring down amino acids and other nongaseous molecules with it and they would remain in the water below, where their concentration would increase, protected from the destructive effects of radiation. Schemes have been suggested whereby certain molecules might catalytically enhance their own formation, and Oparin, a great Russian authority on the origin of life, has proposed various ways in which further molecular evolution might take place. He suggests, in particular, that the important molecules might be further concentrated and brought into close contact by adsorption onto clay particles in a wet environment.

Evolution of the final sequence, DNA → RNA → protein, no doubt took a very long time, and we must suppose that particles having the attributes of life existed with more primitive chemical systems. There is a great deal of room for speculation as to which evolved first, nucleic acid or protein. Perhaps they evolved more or less simultaneously. It is a curious fact that the amino acids which are produced from simple gases in a Miller-Urey type of experiment are precisely those which are the most abundant in proteins.

The basic chemicals used in all forms of life on earth are, therefore, very much the same. To be more accurate, the chemical building units—just five nucleic bases, of which the thymine of DNA is equivalent to the uridine of RNA, and just twenty amino acids out of the several hundred that exist —are used almost universally to form nucleic acids which constitute the basic hereditary machinery, and proteins which constitute the basic metabolic machinery. Some further minor exceptions may be added to those that are known, but the general uniformity will nevertheless remain impressive.

On earth—but what about life on other planets? In a different environment, or even in a similar environment, could a form of life evolve that was based on different chemicals? One's imagination is strained by such a thought. One solid point of departure in flights of the imagination is that the chemical atoms throughout the universe are the same, so we have to think in terms of known molecules or of molecules that could be made with the ninety-odd atoms at hand. The goal, life, can best be defined in terms of a genetic system.

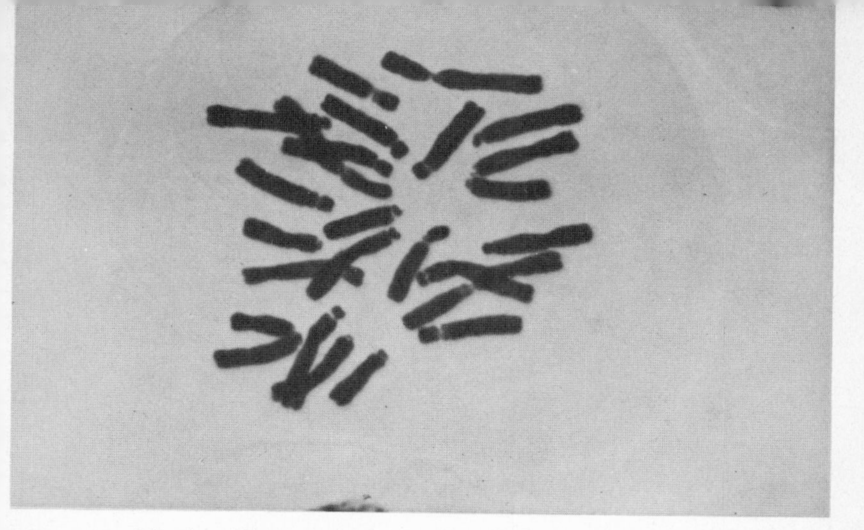

PLATE 1.—*Mitosis.*—Photograph of a cell halfway through mitosis (metaphase) in a particularly favorable material, root cells of the lily, *Lillium regale.* The number of chromosomes is twenty-four; some have constrictions (centromeres) near the ends, and two pairs of chromosomes have constrictions near the middle. This material was actually treated with colchicine before killing, sectioning, and staining. Colchicine interferes with the division process in such a way that better chromosome preparations can be made. Magnification x 2,400.—*J. MacLeish and Brian Snoad, Innes Horticultural Institute*

PLATE 2.—*Meiosis* in the organism shown in Plate 1.—This is an early stage (diplotene) in the first division of cells which are to give rise to pollen grains. Similar (homologous) chromosomes have paired and are held together at points of chiasma. Between these points the chromosomes tend to separate, forming loops. The number of chromosome pairs (bivalents) is twelve. Magnification x 1,700.—*J. MacLeish and Brian Snoad, Innes Horticultural Institute*

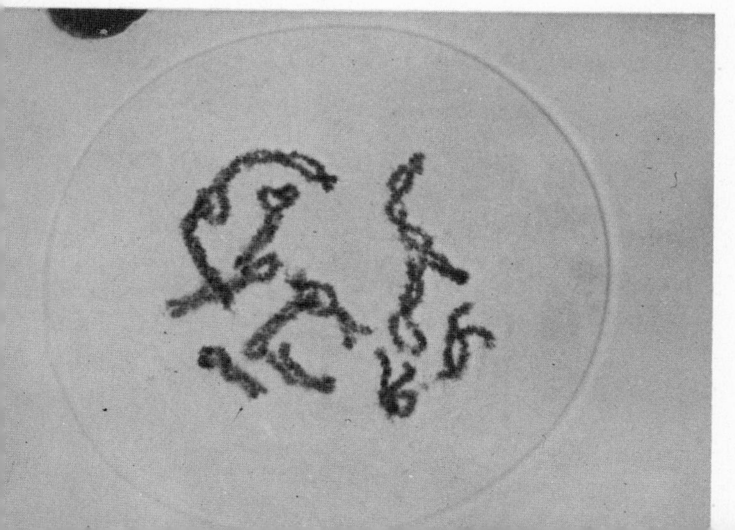

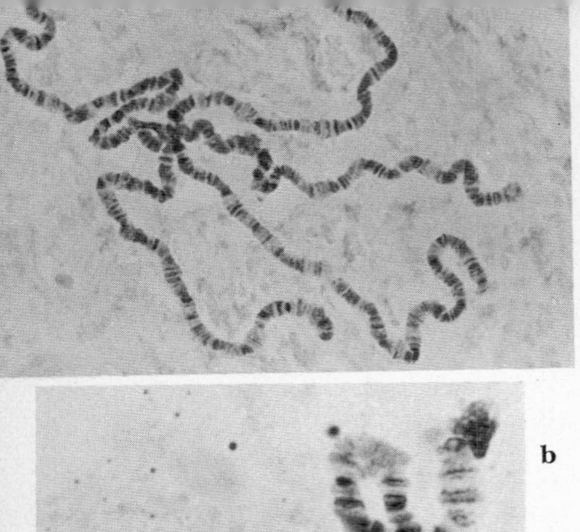

a

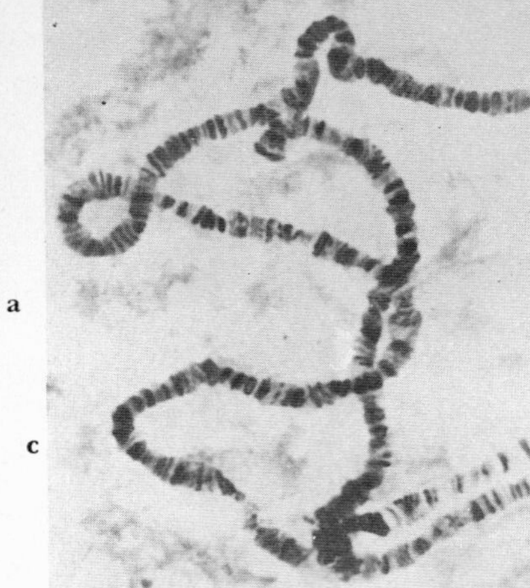

b

c

PLATE 3.—*Salivary chromosomes*.—The chrom somes in the cells of the salivary glands in female larva of *Drosophila melanogaster*, the vin gar or fruit fly.

a) Complete set of normal chromosomes. *D. me anogaster* has three pairs of chromosomes plus se chromosomes. In the salivary glands, homologo chromosomes pair together and appear single; als all chromosomes join at their centromere region In two of the chromosomes (designated 2 and the centromere region is near the middle, and the chromosomes thus have two arms, left (L) and right (R). Starting with the chromosom near 11 o'clock and proceeding in a clockwise direction, the chromosomes are 3R, 2R, 2 3L, X (the two sex chromosomes), and 4 (very short). The distance across the photograp from 3R to 3L is about 250μ, or ¼ of a millimeter.

b) A chromosomal rearrangement as seen in the salivary-gland chromosomes. This rea rangement was obtained by exposing male *Drosophila* flies to X-rays and mating them t normal females. Although fertility was low, some eggs and larvae were produced. Many the surviving larvae were heterozygous for chromosomal rearrangements which could be see in the enormous chromosomes of the salivary glands. In this case there has been a transloc tion of a piece of chromosome from one part of the right arm of chromosome 3 to anoth part. The first part therefore shows a deficiency as compared the normal, and the other part an addition. If the origin chromosome had regions A-B-C-D-E-F-G, then the order the rearranged chromosome is A-C-D-E-F-B-G, and t normal and rearranged chromosome pair as follows (show also in the photograph).

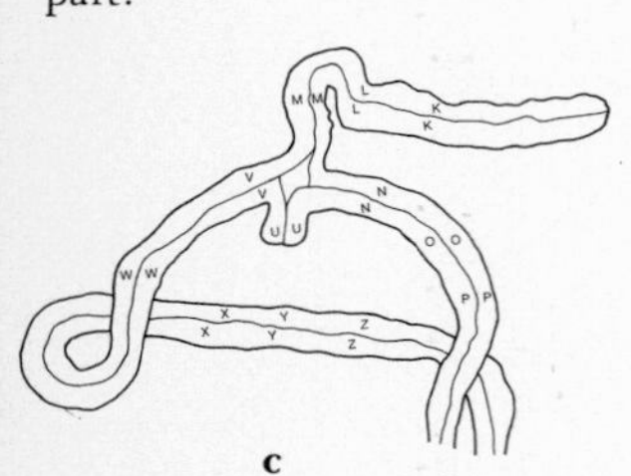

c

c) Another rearrangement as seen in the salivary chromosomes; in this case the larva was heterozygous for a translocation between two chromosomes. The two chromosomes involved in the translocation are 2L (K-L-M-N-O-P) and 3R (U-V-W-X-Y-Z). The two new chromosomes formed by the exchange can be represented as K-L-M-V-W-X-Y-Z and U-N-O-P. The four chromosomes K-L-M-N-O-P, U-V-W-X-Y-Z, K-L-M-V-W-X-Y-Z, and U-N-O-P will pair as follows (shown also in the photograph).—*Kaufmann, U. of Michigan*

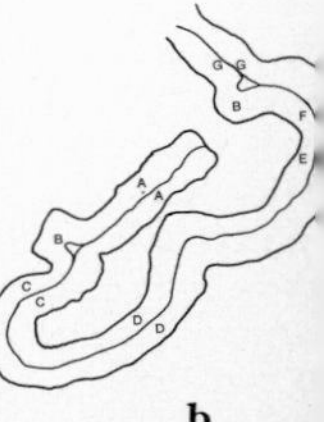

b

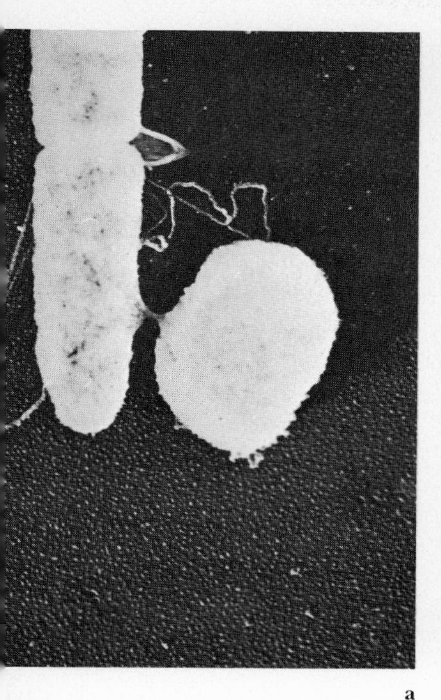

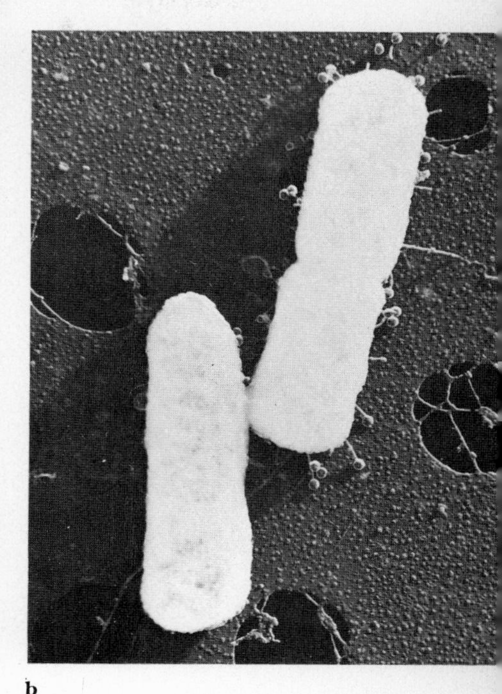

a b

LATE 4A AND B.—E. coli *cross.*—Electron-microscope photographs of the intestinal acterium *Escherichia coli* in the process of sexual mating. In each case the male Hfr) and female (F^-) organisms can be distinguished. In **4a** the female is of a utant type which tends to be round rather than rod-shaped. In **4b** the female is om a species which is sensitive to a phage (virus), the male being immune. Phage articles, resembling round-headed pins, can be seen sticking into the female partner. n both photographs there is a clear cytoplasmic bridge between the male and female acteria. This was thought, when these photographs were first obtained, to be the ridge through which the male chromosome passes. It now seems more likely that the hromosome passes through a much finer hair, of which three or four are to be found n male cells. These so-called pili can be likened to the tail of a phage, through which e phage chromosome passes into a bacterium.—*Anderson, Philadelphia*

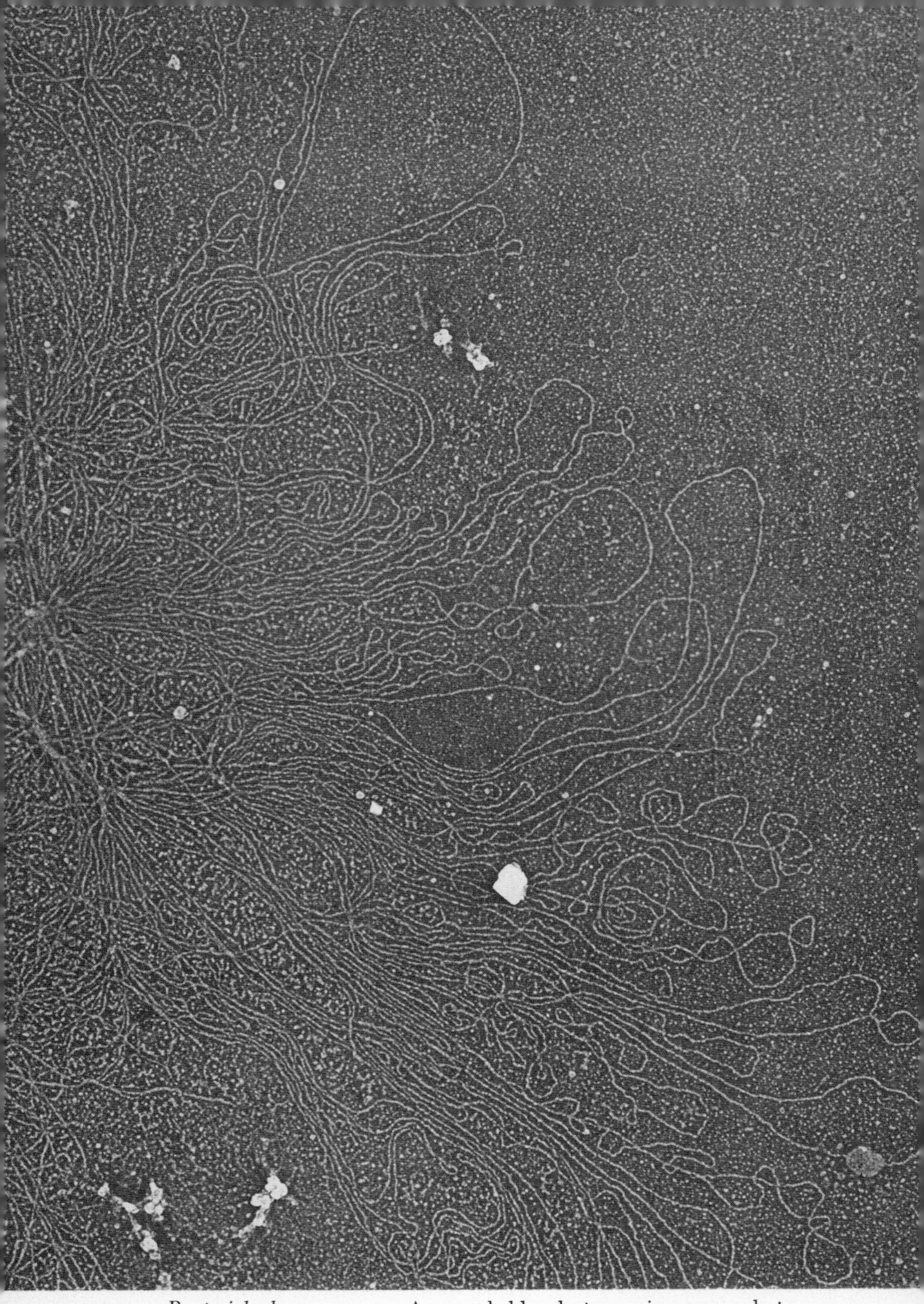

PLATE 5.—*Bacterial chromosome.*—A remarkable electron-microscope photograph of a bacterial chromosome. This may well be a Watson-Crick double helix of DNA. The organism is *Micrococcus*, but the chromosome of *E. coli* is presumably similar, and it is such an object that must pass, single file, from male to female in a mating, as shown in Plate 4. Magnification x 52,000. —*A. Kleinschmidt & D. Lang, Frankfurt*

LATE 6.—*Watson-Crick model.*—Photograph of a model of a DNA double elix made by M. H. F. Wilkins. Symbols for atoms are shown at left. Scale ı Angstrom units is shown at right.—*M. H. Wilkins, King's College*

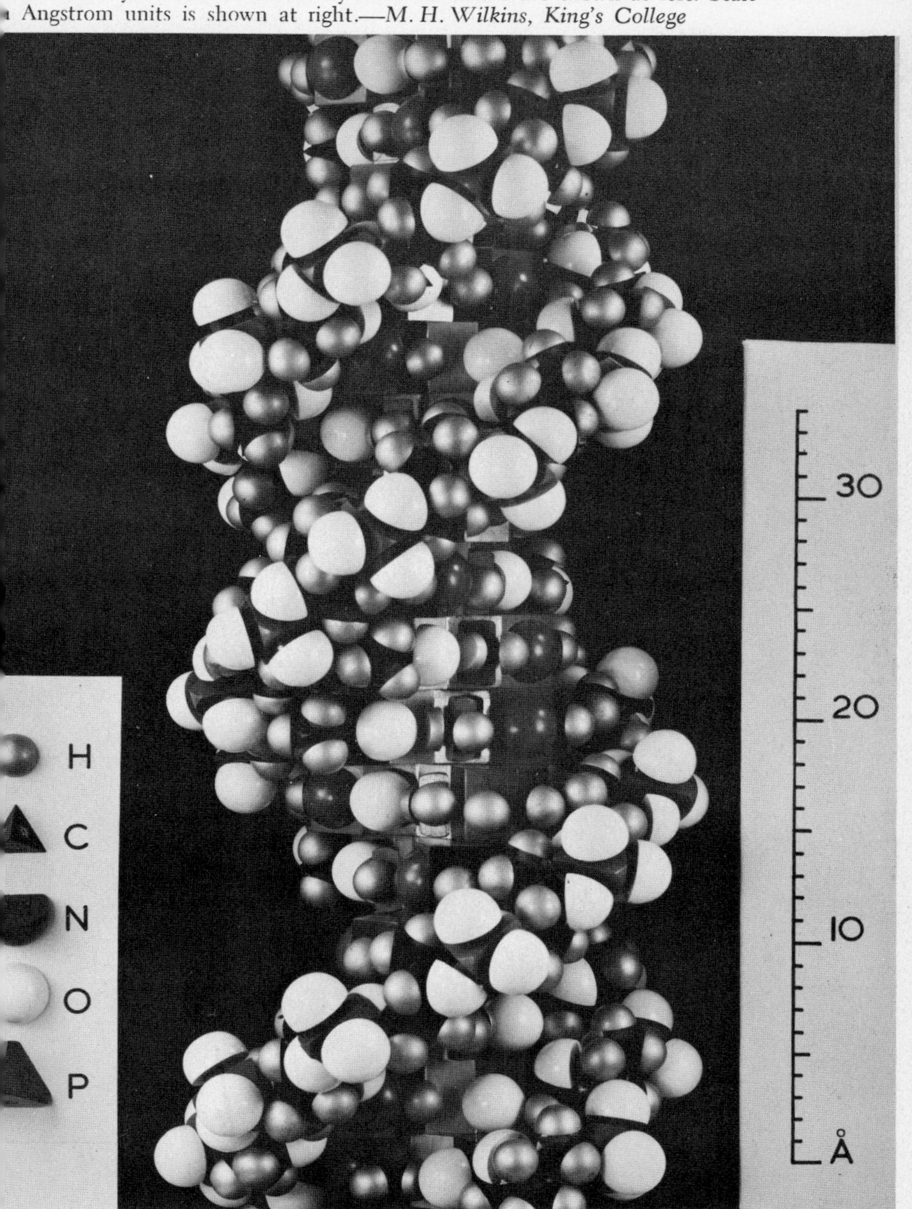

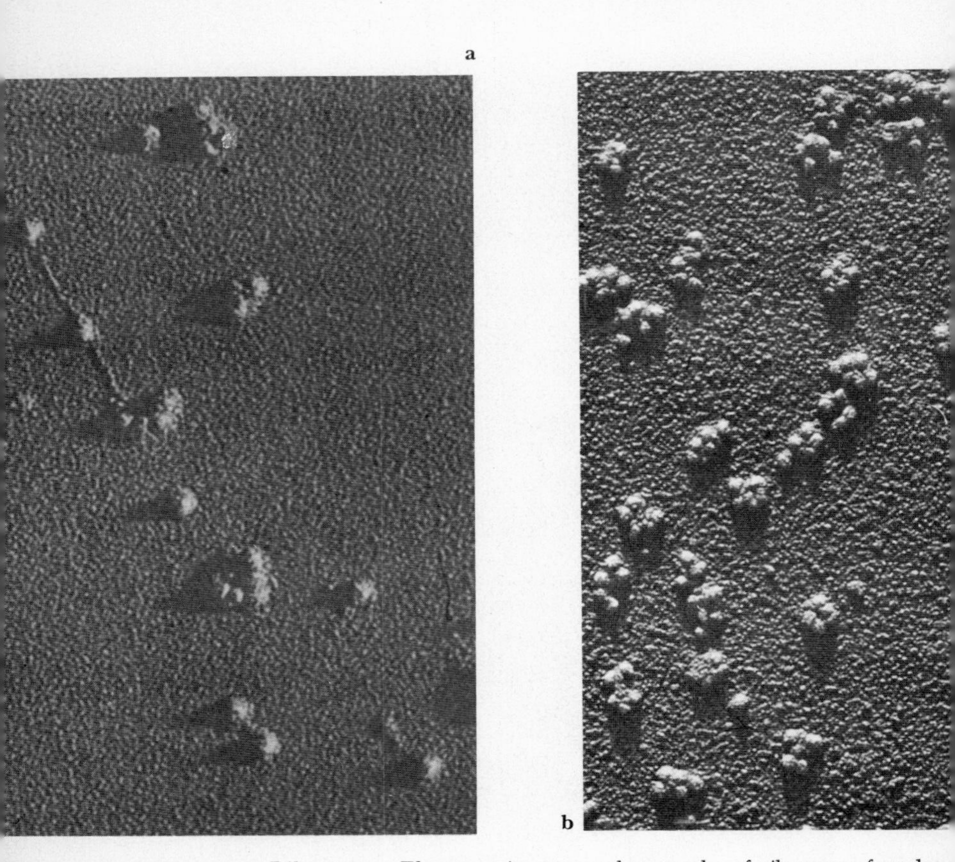

PLATE 7.—*Ribosomes.*—Electron-microscope photographs of ribosomes found in reticulocytes which make the protein hemoglobin.

a) A group of three ribosomes which are connected by a thread which may be messenger RNA or tape.

b) Ribosomes aggregated in clusters of five or six. It appears likely that active ribosomes are always so aggregated.—*Warner, Rich & Hall, MIT*

LATE 8.—*Myoglobin*.—Complete chemical structure of the rotein myoglobin. The backbone of the polypeptide chain is iown by the thick thread which winds its way through the omplex structure. There is an atom at the end of each ick and at each juncture of sticks.
'wo spheres can be seen near 12 o'clock, the larger gray phere represents an atom of iron and the smaller white one a iolecule of water. The two ends of the peptide chain are iarked "C terminal" (near 11 o'clock), representing the acidic nd—COOH, and "N terminal" (near 7 o'clock), repre-nting the basic end—NH_2.—*J. Kendrew, Inst. Molecular iol., Cambridge*

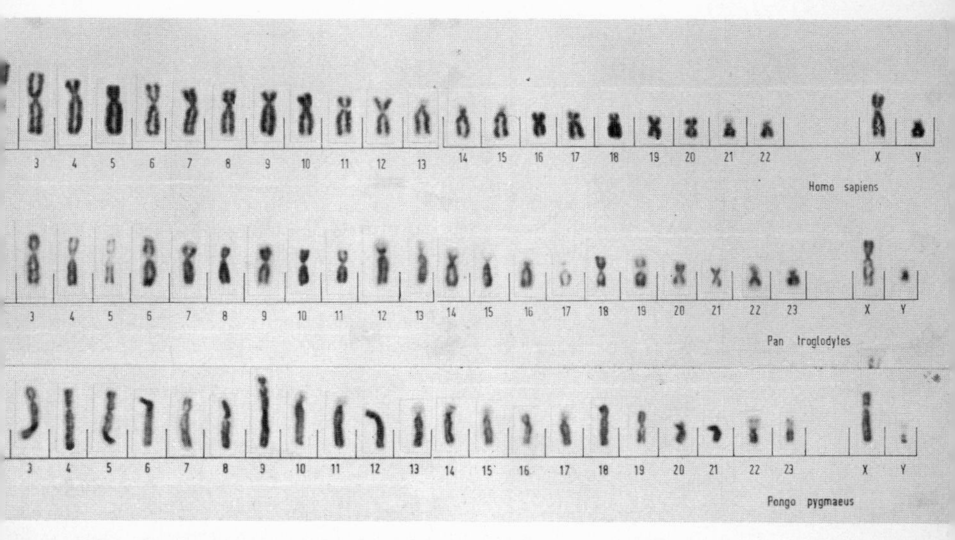

ATE 9.—*Chromosome sets compared*.—Photograph of the complete set of male human romosomes and a comparison with those of the chimpanzee Pan and the orangutan ongo. The photograph of each individual chromosome has been cut out of the original cture and repositioned in line for better comparison.—*B. Chiarelli, Pavia*

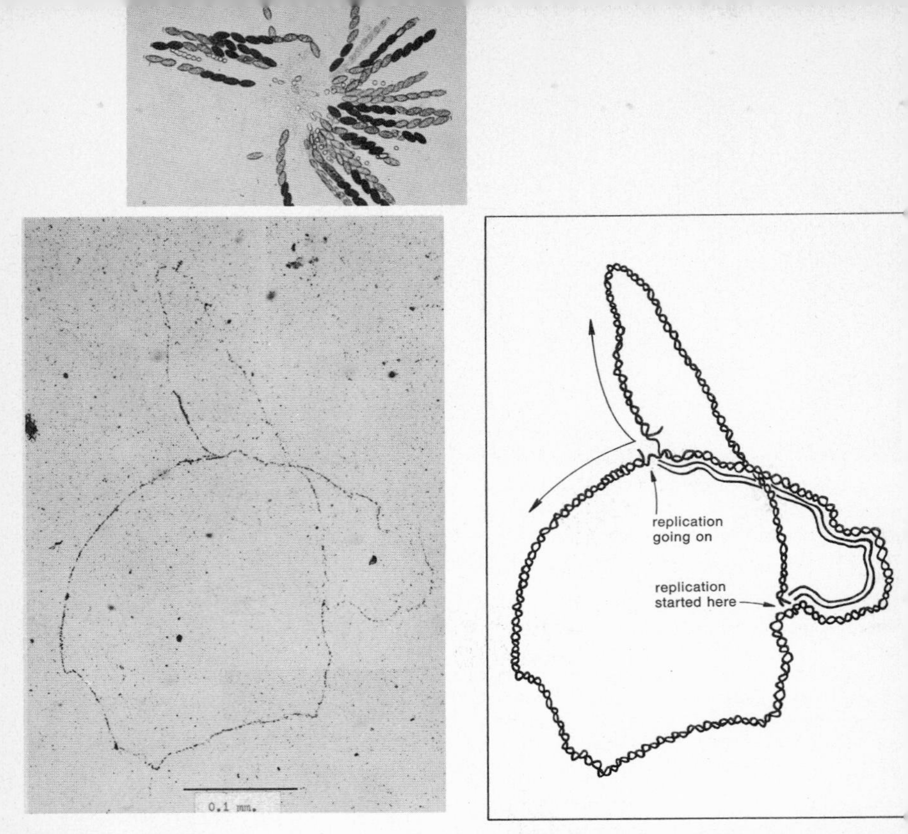

PLATE 10.—(*Top*)—*Segregation in Neurospora.—Neurospora* and other microorganis provide a beautiful demonstration of Mendel's law of segregation. The character invol here is white spore, as against the usual black spore. According to theory, if one parent black-spored and the other parent white-spored each meiotic division should produce exa two white and two black spores. A peculiarity of *Neurospora* and some other fungi (Ascomycetes) is that each product of meiosis divides once again before spores are form this results in eight spores from each meiotic division. Each group of eight spores remains a row, and about twenty of such rows can be seen in the photograph. Most groups of ei show exactly four white and four black spores, which is in agreement with theory. Three four appear to consist of eight white spores, and these exceptions may be due to sev things, the most likely being that four of the spores have not yet developed the black pigm but will do so later. In other words, they are white for environmental rather than gen reasons. Mutants producing white spores that remain white and germinate easily can be tained in an allied mold, *Podospora*.

The color difference of spores shown in this photograph can only be seen at a certain stag development; later all spores become black.—*D. R. Stadler*

PLATE 11.—*Chromosome of* E. coli *during replication.*—The bacterium was grown on trients containing radioactive hydrogen (tritium) atoms which were used by the bacterium synthesizing the DNA of its chromosome. The bacterial cell walls were then dissolved a the rigid chromosome allowed to escape and lie on a photographic plate. The radioactiv of hydrogen atoms in the chromosome then produced black granules on the plate, outlin the shape of the chromosome. By counting the number of granules along different parts the outline and knowing how many cell generations the bacteria had been in radioac nutrient, this photograph can be interpreted as showing a DNA helix replicating at point shown by the arrows in the diagram; the double lines indicate that part of the ci lar chromosome that has not yet replicated. This photograph provides evidence that the *coli* chromosome is circular and that the DNA of which it is made replicates according the ideas of Watson and Crick.—*J. Cairns, Cold Spring Harbor*

We should not insist on familiar properties such as movement or respiration or intelligence, but only on an evolving complexity, chemical complexity. This requires storage of information, duplication of information, and a certain amount of change, random or directed. Evolution to more complexity by the process of natural selection will follow of necessity. Chemists can speculate as to whether these requirements can be met by systems other than nucleic acids and proteins and whether such systems are possible at very high or very low temperatures. With or without water. In oxygen or devoid of oxygen.

Many of us may live to know the answers to some of these questions.

XIII *Cells Are Not Made by Enzymes Alone: The Regulation of Activity*

A great deal is known, as the preceding chapters have attempted to show, about the way in which genes make specific enzymes. But how far does this take us in understanding how animals and plants grow and develop? Enzymes are large, complex, and versatile molecules; they control precisely and delicately all the important chemical reactions in a cell. But a list of the several thousand enzymes in a cell would not tell us much about what that cell was going to become.

To put the matter more strongly, imagine that we knew all the enzymes present in the fertilized egg of a frog. If we put a mixture of all these several thousand enzymes in a solution of some mixture of salts, vitamins, and the like, would a tadpole develop in the test-tube? Of course not, and one reason is that in a developing zygote each enzyme is in the right place at the right time and in the right quantity. There may be other fundamental properties of a living cell of which we are at present unaware. We know little about the position of enzymes in a cell; this is a problem of morphology, and apart from the importance of membranes to which enzymes are attached within the cell, there is nothing of interest now known. As regards the amount of each enzyme and also the activity of the enzymes, there is much recent speculation which deserves attention.

The picture that the reader should have in mind at this point is of a long string, or a small number of long strings, of DNA, the chromosomes. Alongside these, short segments of messenger RNA are synthesized. Each segment of m-RNA passes out into the cytoplasm, where, in conjunction with a few ribosomes, it synthesizes a protein molecule.

There is reason to believe that many genes, that is to say, many segments of the long DNA chain, are concerned with making molecules other than enzymes. There is also evidence that the DNA thread may not be a monotonous series of nucleotides, but may be interrupted by nodes consisting perhaps of something different from DNA or, at any rate, by regions that have special functions or behavior different from that of the parts of DNA that code amino acids. A line of evidence that seemed at one time to point in this direction concerns the phenomenon of conversion. The experiments to be described can be interpreted as showing discontinuities along the DNA chain with respect to crossing-over, the phenomena can also be explained another way, but the subject is of interest in other respects as well. Better evidence for discontinuities will be described in connection with regulation of DNA and m-RNA synthesis. The idea of conversion is that one allele of a gene can change another allele of that gene into itself. In a heterozygote *Aa*, conversion would produce AA or *aa*. Before recombination had been explained by crossing-over, or rather before this concept had been established and accepted, some geneticists proposed that all recombination was due to conversion. This was a development of the sort of thing Bateson had suggested to account for the different proportions of combinations of alleles that he found. Conversion would explain recombination as follows. Consider two haploid parents, *AB* and *ab*, in which the characters *AB* and *ab* are linked so that offspring usually have these two characters in the same combination. Now, if in a heterozygous zygote *AB*/*ab* the gene A converts the gene *a* to A, then the cells resulting from the meiotic division of this zygote will be *Ab* and *AB*. *Ab* is a recombinant and could be erroneously considered to have resulted from a cross-over. A distinction between the two events can readily be made if all four products of meiosis are collected, as will become clear.

The theory of conversion had been discarded for some time when C. C. Lindegren revived it in 1953. He worked with yeast and claimed that during the analysis of quads he found genes that segregated 3:1 or 4:0 instead of 2:2. That is to say, when he crossed a cell with a character A with one having *a* and dissected the four cells formed after meiosis, he found that three might have the character A while only one had *a*. This went directly against accepted theory and was rejected by many, or perhaps most, geneticists. It was pointed out, quite rightly, that there could be other more acceptable reasons for getting a 3:1 segregation. For instance, the character might be controlled by two similar genes, AA, such that one would be sufficient to give the character he was testing for. His cross would then be AA x *aa* and he might get a quad (the four cells being respectively AA, A*a*, *a*A, and *aa*) in which each gene had segregated 2:2, but the first three cells nevertheless would show the character A, and the fourth, the character *a*. As it happened, the objections were overruled by further tests, and other workers using other organisms began to get corroborating results. Literature prior to 1950 had, in fact, recorded 3:1 segregations, but these had not attracted attention; it may be suspected that more recent workers had also encountered them but had rejected them as experimental errors. Soon an old theory, due originally to a brilliant American cytologist, J. Belling, was revived and given a new name, "copy choice." This supposes that there is no real conversion of one allele into another, but that there is an error during duplication, one new gene being formed from the wrong template. Let us elaborate by giving an example. If we have three genes on a chromosome, a cross of *ABC* with *abc* will normally duplicate during early meiosis, as shown on the left in Figure 32. An error in

FIGURE 32

		A B C			A B C
A B C			A B C		
		A B C			A B C
	→			→	
		a b c			*a* B *c*
a b c			*a b c*		
		a b c			*a b c*

duplication might proceed as shown on the right in Figure 32, resulting in a 3:1 segregation for the gene *B*. The copy-choice theory becomes more complicated when examined in detail and in terms of Watson-Crick double helices. It is more difficult to explain 4:0 segregations on a copy-choice model, but then the evidence for 4:0 segregations is not nearly so solid as that for 3:1 segregations.

Before describing these phenomena in more detail, let us review the definition of a gene. Earlier work, mostly with *Drosophila,* which led to the construction of genetic maps was done with genes which were relatively far apart. If 5 per cent of the offspring were recombinants, the genes concerned would be regarded as rather tightly linked and close together on the map, although there would most probably be several genes in between them. The sophistication of later work consists in counting more flies, millions instead of thousands, or of using microorganisms in which the counting is easier. When large numbers of progeny are observed, the genetics of regions within a gene can be analyzed, and this, at first, caused some confusion in terminology. Since words are so intimately related to thoughts, it also meant that the thinking of many was confused.

A gene was defined in 1925 by T. H. Morgan as "any particle in a chromosome that is distinguishable from other particles by either crossing-over or mutation." Several other writers have defined it in terms of a unit of physiological action. For some time these two definitions, the genetic and the physiological, coincided. The physiological test was to put two mutations together in a hybrid. If the latter looked like the wild type, the two mutations must have affected two different genes; if it looked intermediate in type, then the two mutants represented two alleles of the same gene. In a diploid organism, if two genes *A* and *B* were involved, then one mutant might be *a*/*a*, *B*/*B* and the other A/A, *b*/*b*. The F_1 hybrid would be *a*/A, *B*/*b* and wild type. If a single gene were concerned, the mutants might be *a*/*a* and *a'*/*a'* and the F_1 hybrid would be *a*/*a'* and probably intermediate in appearance. The genetic test would be to breed the hybrids among themselves and see if a wild type appeared in the F_2 progeny. If two genes were concerned, then nine-sixteenths of the F_2 would be wild type, *A*–*B*–, one-sixteenth being of the true-breeding homozygous wild type, *A*/*A*, *B*/*B*. If a single gene were concerned, then no wild type could be recovered in the F_2, which would be one-quarter *a'*/*a'* like one mutant, one quarter *a*/*a* like the other, and one-half *a*/*a'* like the hybrid. The same would be true in a haploid organism except that genetic results would be obtained one generation sooner. The physiological test in the haploid organism cannot ordinarily be performed by making a heterozygote, but the equivalent can be done, as we shall see in Chapter XIV, by having nuclei of the two mutant types in the same cells. Confusion arose when some pairs of mutants or groups of mutants, which were thought to be alleles of the same gene because they affected the same character and because the hybrid was intermediate, were found to give rise to occasional wild types in their progeny.

One of the early clear-cut cases of crossing-over occurring within a gene was discovered by the author in the genes which determine sex in mushrooms. These well-known genes, which have multiple alleles, were mentioned in Chapter III. It was found that two alleles, say A^1 and A^2, can, by recombination, produce two new alleles, say A^3 and A^4. In this case the frequency of recombination was fairly high and so the new alleles could be isolated in a quad. Furthermore, the two new alleles, A^3 and A^4, could be crossed to give back the original alleles, A^1 and A^2. Unfortunately, nothing is known about the gene product or about the nature of the sex reaction in these haploid mushrooms. It may be that these genes do not code for proteins; nevertheless, two strains such as A^1 and A^2 can be defined as alleles of a single gene because they affect the same character; yet when crossed they give new types, which would indicate that they are alleles of different genes.

A gene—or, at any rate, most genes—can now be defined as that segment of DNA in the chromosome which determines the production of a protein molecule functioning as an enzyme. To be more precise, we should perhaps say "polypeptide chain" instead of "protein molecule" to take care of those cases where an enzyme is made up of more than one polypeptide chain. We can also say that a gene, or perhaps a small number of related genes, is the segment of DNA which produces a molecule of messenger RNA. The reservation "most genes" is made because, as we have hinted, many genes may not make enzymes at all, and because in some viruses, (see Chapter XII) the genetic material is RNA. The best examples of characters controlled by single genes are concerned, as we have seen, with biochemical deficiencies in microorganisms.

It is in these that recombination within a gene has been studied. In both *Neurospora* and the bacterium *E. coli* it is rather easy to produce a number of mutants which cannot grow unless the amino acid tryptophane, for instance, is added to the medium. If two different mutants with this deficiency are crossed and if enough progeny are tested, a few will be found that can grow without tryptophane and are, therefore, wild type. Finding rare wild types is easy with these systems because if millions of spores are spread on media without tryptophane, none of the parental mutants will grow and anything that grows will be one of the rare wild types. The fact that several different mutations of the same gene can be obtained and that they will give back the wild type by recombination is not surprising in view of the structure of chromosomes. The chromosome segment representing the gene for tryptophane would consist of a chain of about 843 nucleotide pairs in terms of the Watson-Crick model. The various mutants would be mutant because somewhere along the line there was a wrong nucleotide pair. Each individual mutant, excepting rare coincidences, would have a wrong nucleotide pair in a different place, and thus, if two mutant segments were brought together in a cross, a complete correct segment could be obtained from correct parts of each parent.

The frequencies with which wild types are obtained from crossing two mutants of the same gene is low, usually less than 1 per cent. It therefore requires a lot of work to observe the event by dissecting quads. When this has been done, it has been found that the wild type nearly always represents a conversion, not a reciprocal cross-over. The situation is represented in Figure 33. Numbers represent nucleotide pairs and *x* represents the position of the wrong nucleotide pair. In the first conversion Pair 3 has made an extra copy; in the second conversion Pair 6 has made an extra copy.

Georges Rizet, working in Paris, has recently found a way

FIGURE 33

Mutant 1	1 2 x 4 5 6 7	reciprocal	1 2 x 4 5 6 7	Mutant 1
Mutant 2	1 2 3 4 5 x 7	cross-over	1 2 x 4 5 x 7	Double mutant
			1 2 3 4 5 6 7	Wild type
			1 2 3 4 5 x 7	Mutant 2
			1 2 x 4 5 6 7	Mutant 1
		conversion	1 2 3 4 5 6 7	Wild type
			1 2 3 4 5 x 7	Mutant 2
			1 2 3 4 5 x 7	Mutant 2
		or		
			1 2 x 4 5 6 7	Mutant 1
		conversion	1 2 x 4 5 6 7	Mutant 1
			1 2 3 4 5 6 7	Wild type
			1 2 3 4 5 x 7	Mutant 2

of analyzing this phenomenon in greater detail. He works with a mold, *Podospora*, which is very similar to *Neurospora* but is especially suitable because it produces white-spored mutants. Many hundreds of thousands of spores resulting from a cross can be examined in their asci, the sacs enclosing the products of meiotic divisions (see Plate 10), and the rare white spores can be spotted. When one is spotted, the whole ascus in which it is found can be dissected and each spore of its quad examined by further breeding. It is unfortunate that nothing is yet known about the enzymes produced by these genes for spore color, but several genes and some two thousand mutants have been identified. By analyzing a large number of crosses, Rizet has found that the gene can be divided into one or perhaps a few so-called polarons. Within a polaron, recombination is inevitably due to conversion. Reciprocal crossing-over is restricted to regions between polarons. The word "polaron" was suggested by the fact that in a sense there is a polarity: on a copy-choice model one has to imagine that duplication always proceeds from one end of the polaron to the other.

Further work has somewhat clouded the issue. The phenomena described by Rizet have not been confirmed in other organisms. It is clear, nevertheless, that irregular quads are generally very rare when one is examining recombination between two genes some distance apart, but are frequent when the two mutations are within the same gene, which means that they are relatively very close together. Unfortunately for the researcher, mutants very close together recombine very rarely, and experiments in which the progeny of a cross were spread, several millions, on minimal medium and the rare wild types that grew were analyzed, do not, unfortunately, give any indication as to whether conversion or crossing-over is involved; the analysis of quads is necessary for that.

Innumerable models have been drawn and published to explain reciprocal crossing-over and conversion, many rather sophisticated mathematical treatments have been devised, but the most promising attack is the chemical one. This has already shown convincingly that in the phenomenon of transformation in bacteria described in Chapter IX, and in other special recombinations in bacteria, an actual piece of DNA is inserted into another length of DNA; it is not a matter of synthesizing a new piece of DNA by using first one template and then another, as the theory of copy choice would have it. As regards crossing-over and conversion in organisms other than bacteria, the chemical approach suggests that certain enzymes may cut DNA chains and other enzymes may break up lengths of one of the cut ends in such a way that when synthesizing enzymes repair the gaps, parts of strands may be copied from a different partner. The process is too complicated and not well enough established to describe more fully here, but the general idea will probably turn out to be true. That idea is that all recombination is a process which involves complicated happenings over a short region, giving rise to various odd ratios that we call conversions, but outside this region a regular reciprocal cross-over is observed. If a boy scout took two pieces of rope, one red and one blue, and cut and spliced them, red to blue and blue to red, the result would be clear for most parts of the rope, but in the short sections of splice there would be a complex pattern of red and blue strands. The experiments of Rizet would indicate that the splices in this analogy never occur at the boundary between genes, but on the other hand if the splice involved only a very short region, then the chance of such a region's falling on a boundary would be very slight.

Other evidence for discontinuity along the chromosome involves the important matter of the regulation of gene action, and this will now be described.

As far back as 1899 it was known that certain enzymes are not present all the time, but are only produced when the substrate, the chemical on which they act, is present. Enzymes of this sort, mentioned in Chapter XI, are known as adaptive or inducible enzymes; the economic advantages of the system are obvious. A cell can have a dozen enzymes which it may not need in large quantities, depending on the substrate it finds around it. To produce all of them all the time would be wasteful; better far to wait until a particular substrate is present and then take this as a signal to produce the appropriate enzyme and produce it in very large quantities. Five per cent or more of the total protein of the cell can be produced as a single enzyme in many cases. The production of an adaptive enzyme by a chemical, usually its substrate, is known as enzyme induction, and its study has proved complex, but at the same time more interesting than was at first suspected. Jacob and Monod and their associates at the Pasteur Institute in Paris have formulated a neat theory embracing many items, some of which have been lying around in laboratory notebooks for many years. Among the major things that it explains besides induction is a phenomenon called repression. Some enzymes which are not adaptive enzymes are nevertheless controlled, in this case by having their production stopped. The chemical that does this is usually a product of the enzyme. This action again makes sense, for when there is enough of the product, the enzyme is no longer necessary. The theory calls the genes which code for enzymes structural genes. It supposes that at one end of a structural gene there is a special region called an operator. The operator works like a switch which turns on and off. When it is on, the structural gene works and produces messenger RNA which produces enzyme; when it is off, it does not. Now, operators are turned on and off by regulator substances which are made by other genes, not necessarily close to the structural gene and operator. Finally, the regulator substance, which some workers suspect to be a protein, reacts with the inducer or repressor (Fig. 34). The whole scheme was originally conceived with another fact in mind, namely, that one repressor or inducer often affects more than one enzyme, and when it does so, it affects them always to exactly the same extent. Usually the genes for the production of several enzymes affected are adjacent on the chromosome where the same operator turns all three structural genes on and off. In other cases, the several structural genes may be far apart and each then has its own operator which reacts to the same regulator substance. The theory is an attractive one and will be firmly established when the regulator substance has been chemically identified. But even if wrong, we can agree with Thomas Huxley that "consecutive wrong thinking is the next best thing to right thinking." There is room for modification in the theory, and no one will be upset if, for instance, the regulator substance is found to act on the translation of m-RNA as well as, or instead of, on the transcription of DNA producing m-RNA.[1]

[1] This would make sense if production of m-RNA, attachment to ribosomes, and translation into a protein chain took place simultaneously in an interconnected system such that the whole process, including the production

FIGURE 34

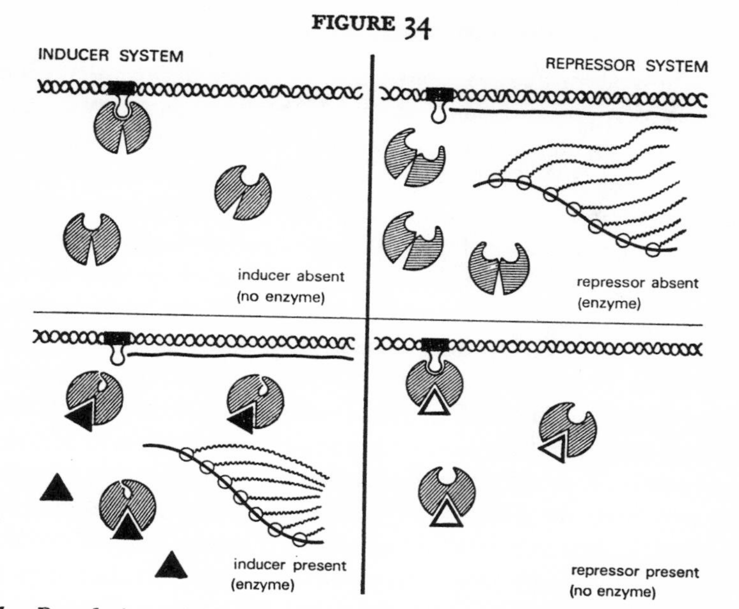

The Regulation of Enzyme Production. On the DNA double helix (thick spiral lines at the top of all four quadrants) there is a special region, the operator (black rectangle with white knob below). When the operator is free, messenger RNA (straight line under DNA) is formed and this then moves away and forms protein in association with ribosomes as in Figure 30.

When the operator is blocked, no m-RNA is formed and therefore no protein (enzyme) is synthesized. The operator is blocked by a regulator substance (shaded circular shapes) either alone (inducer system) or in association with a repressor (triangle in repressor system). In inducer systems, where the operator is blocked by the regulator alone, an inducer (symbolized by black triangle) can associate with the regulator substance and prevent its association with the operator. The shapes in the diagram are fanciful, but for those who conceive of the regulator as being a protein the circular shapes may represent allostearic proteins in which the inducer or repressor attached to one side of the molecule changes the shape of the other side, which attaches to the operator.

The regulator substance is shown here to attach to the DNA partly in order to simplify the diagram. A rather more attractive idea is that it attaches to m-RNA produced by the DNA and prevents the formation of protein by the m-RNA. The end result would be the same and intermediate results might also be similar because as m-RNA began to pile up there would be a feedback effect which would prevent further synthesis of m-RNA.

The system as presented will only work if the m-RNA is short-lived, producing one or two or perhaps as many as five enzyme molecules and then breaking down or becoming inert (see Chapter XI). Some cases are known where the m-RNA must be long-lived, for instance in blood reticulocytes, where there is no nucleus, but proteins are nevertheless synthesized abundantly. But instances of this sort do not mean that all m-RNA is long-lived. In cases where the regulatory system works, each m-RNA may make only four or five protein molecules, but other enzymes in other organisms may not be so regulated in this way and the m-RNA in those cases may be stable and produce many hundreds or thousands of enzyme molecules. Detailed evidence for the regulator-operator theory has not been presented and will not be here; let it suffice to say that it depends on the behavior of various strains which, according to the theory, represent mutations of operator gene and regulator gene. These are strains of *E. coli*, and a description of their behavior would take us too far into the complexities of *E. coli* genetics. The system has not been conclusively demonstrated in organisms higher than *E. coli*, but the fact that enzymes are induced and repressed in higher organisms leads some geneticists to believe that the theory will be found to apply to other organisms also.

We mentioned previously that not all genes necessarily make enzymes and here we have an example of such a gene, the gene making the regulator substance. There may be as many as one or more of these for each structural gene.

This theory was mentioned as showing that there is a discontinuity of the chromosome. The segment of chromosome

---

of m-RNA, would be blocked if protein synthesis ceased. In higher organisms these processes would take place at the nuclear membrane, perhaps the nuclear membrane breaks down at this point. Only one protein chain need be produced while the complex is adjacent to the DNA chains; further protein synthesis could take place anywhere in the cytoplasm by free m-RNA and ribosomes.

from the operator to the end of the structural gene or genes which it controls must have some special feature that marks the beginning and the end. If there were no end marker, an operator would switch on and off all the genes right to the end of the chromosome.

This is only one theory of gene regulation; there may well be other mechanisms also at work which remain to be discovered. One particular phenomenon which is well known but for which there is no explanation concerns "position effect." It is well-known that in *Drosophila* and in corn when a chromosome rearrangement is made, a translocation or inversion, as described in Chapter V, genes can change their effect. Rearrangement means that genes near the ends of the rearranged pieces are brought next to different parts of a chromosome and this change in position of a gene evidently makes a difference to the expression of the gene. The gene itself is not changed, not permanently at any rate, because when rearranged back again the gene expresses itself as it originally did.

The bar-eyed and double bar-eyed *Drosophila* flies mentioned in Chapter V form a well-known case of position effect. *Drosophila* being a diploid organism, the wild type (females) should be designated *B/B*, and the bar-eyed female flies, *BB/BB*. *BBB/B* heterozygotes are double bar-eyed flies. Thus, bar (*BB/BB*) and double bar (*BBB/B*) have the same number of bar genes, namely four, but their position on the chromosomes—two on each, or three on one and one on the other—makes a difference to their expression.

An interesting feature of the position effect is that it is most obvious when genes are moved, by chromosome rearrangement, next to heterochromatic parts of the chromosome. We have not yet mentioned heterochromatin, and little is, in fact, known about it. It represents another discontinuity along the chromosome. Heterochromatic regions are regions which stain deeply before or after the rest of the chromosome stains.

No interesting chemical differences have been found in heterochromatic regions and their different staining properties may be due to the fact that the DNA strands coil up and are perhaps synthesized differently or at different times in these regions. It would be very good to know if heterochromatic regions are made of the same DNA as the rest of the chromosome and if so, whether there is anything special about the proportions of nucleotides in these regions. In comparing the genetic and chromosome maps of *Drosophila* it is noteworthy that heterochromatic regions contain few, if any, genes.

This chapter has dealt with two topics—the regulation of enzyme production, and discontinuities along the very long DNA thread of a chromosome. A closing remark must be made about each of these topics. About the regulation of enzymes it must be realized that the mechanism described here is only one of many regulatory devices in the cell. Some other mechanisms are known, and there are undoubtedly many that have not yet been discovered. We have already mentioned that m-RNA may be very stable in some cases, but must be short-lived in others. The stability of m-RNA may itself be an important factor in regulation and may or may not be under direct genetic control. Similarly, there is evidence that particular enzymes are destroyed in a controlled manner when in too high a concentration. The proteins that are always associated with nucleic acid in higher organisms can be mentioned as one other mechanism of control. Histones, protamines, and other proteins form, with nucleic acids, the nucleoprotein that was mentioned in Chapter IX. They occur in fairly large quantities; about half of a nucleoprotein is protein. Some experiments have shown that DNA with its associated protein does not synthesize as much enzyme as the naked DNA from which the protein has been removed. Little is known about the specificity of this inhibition, but the finding nurtures the thought that genes not wanted in a certain tissue or at a certain time may be shut off by those proteins. This would represent a long-term and in some cases, perhaps, an irreversible regulation.

Concerning continuity and discontinuity along the DNA strand, we must point out that recent work has made the picture a great deal simpler than it was. One might imagine, a priori, that there were three different genetic units: the gene proper, which is the functional unit, or cistron, as some call it; the unit of recombination, which is the smallest unit that can be exchanged by recombination, perhaps because of special break points in the chromosome; and the unit of mutation, which would be the smallest piece of chromosome that could be changed in a stable way. In Chapter X we saw that the unit of mutation is the base pair, which is also the basic chemical unit. The experiments of Yanofsky, described in Chapter XI, provide good evidence that the unit of recombination is also the base pair, since recombination can occur between any adjacent base pairs. It is most satisfactory to have evidence that the basic chemical discontinuity is also the fundamental discontinuity as regards both mutation and recombination. The discontinuities concerned with regulation and with reciprocal recombination that were discussed above are of a secondary nature, superimposed upon the basic nucleotide discontinuity.

XIV *Enterprising Enzymes: The Return of Complexity*

Previous chapters have described the genetic material, the way it duplicates and is transmitted, the way it directs the composition of proteins.

A discussion of discontinuities along the nucleic acid chain introduced the subject of regulation. This was regulation at the production end: regulation of the amount of enzyme produced. But enzymes are subtle, complex molecules, and they are themselves subject to regulation after they are produced. In this chapter we shall describe some recent ideas about the structure and function of enzymes.

Enzymes were described in previous chapters as proteins, which are long chains of amino acids. Each particular enzyme has a particular sequence of amino acids which is determined by a gene. This aspect of an enzyme is sometimes called its primary structure, but this is only half the story. The long chain of amino acids is coiled up in various intricate ways, called secondary and tertiary structure or conformation (Plate 8). On top of all this, two or more units of coiled-up amino acid chains, called the monomers in this context, may be loosely attached to each other as a dimer, tetramer, or other polymer, in what is called aggregate or quaternary structure.

It is a remarkable fact that genetic techniques are providing information about the aggregate structure of enzymes. The work to be described was done originally with *Neurospora* by Norman Giles and his associates at Yale. The initial experiment was to put together two *Neurospora* mutants of the same gene. For example, mutants which would not grow without the nucleic acid base adenine would be put together on medium that lacked adenine. Although the two plants might fuse and form a heterokaryon (in which nuclei from both strains are present in the same cells), one would not normally expect the heterokaryon to grow. In fact, procedures like this used to be considered a test, in a *Drosophila* fly heterozygous for two mutants, or a *Neurospora* plant heterokaryotic for two mutants, of whether the two mutations came from a single gene (allelism) or from several. If the heterozygous or heterokaryotic organism was wild type, then the two strains were regarded as mutants of different genes; if it was not, then they were assumed to be two alleles of the same gene (see Chapter XIII). On the basis of genes making enzymes this makes sense because if, in a diploid or heterokaryon, the two mutants affect different enzymes, then the cell will still have a complete set of enzymes and will appear normal, but if they are mutants of the same gene, then each mutant will produce a blemish on the same protein, and the cell will lack that particular enzyme completely.

The experimental results were unexpected; in many cases the heterokaryon did grow. This could only mean that two faulty alleles of the same gene, even when they were in different nuclei, could produce a good enzyme. Two possibilities could explain this: either the two faulty messenger RNA's can somehow undergo a recombination, similar to sexual recombination in DNA, or two faulty proteins can make a good enzyme. The latter now seems to be generally the correct interpretation, and in some cases it has been possible to extract the two faulty proteins, put them together in a test-tube, and demonstrate the presence of a good enzyme.

The mutual repair of faulty parts of two enzymes is usually thought of in terms of their aggregate structure. If two monomers, both faulty but faulty in different places of the amino acid chain, come together to form a dimer, the dimer can evidently work as a good enzyme. This, by itself, is a most interesting observation, but it is not the end of the story. When a large number of mutants of the same gene are obtained and all the combinations of pairs are tested, some pairs will be found to grow and others will not. Let us construct a simple table consisting of five mutants. If we mark those pairs that grow with a + and those that don't with a —, the table may look like Table 16.

TABLE 16

Mutants	1	2	3	4	5
1	—	+	+	—	+
2	+	—	+	—	—
3	+	+	—	+	—
4	—	—	+	—	—
5	+	—	—	—	—

At first sight this may not appear significant, but a little rearrangement will reveal that if each mutant is considered as a faulty segment of a line such that where the faulty portions overlap there is no growth, but where they do not overlap there is growth, then we can diagram the five mutants as in Figure 35.

If any mutant were found which did not grow with 1 and 3 but did with 2, the scheme would be destroyed, but in practice, no such mutants are found in most systems. This means

FIGURE 35

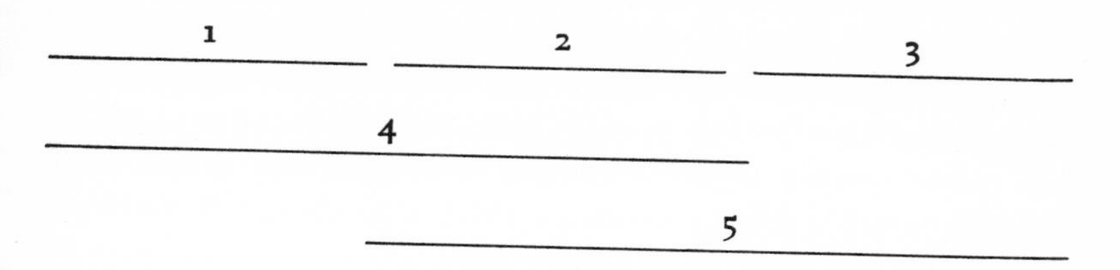

that the model fits the data and that the mutants probably represent damaged segments in the linear polypeptide chain of an enzyme.

In the case of mutants requiring adenine, over forty different strains were tested and the data fell correctly into a table consisting of seven segments along a linear array. The reasoning used in constructing these "complementation maps" is the same as that used to map a series of large and small deletions of chromosomes. In the case of chromosome deletions, the equivalent test is to make crosses of mutant organisms and look for wild-type progeny. If the two deletions overlap, no wild type can be expected, but if they do not, then a complete chromosome can be produced by crossing-over.

The complete amino acid sequence is only known, at the time of this writing, in three proteins, two of which—hemoglobin and insulin—are not enzymes, although the former might just qualify as one. The manner of coiling and the structure of the aggregate is well known only in myoglobin (Plate 8). The fact that some complementation maps turn out to be linear, like the example given above, is of interest. If we grant that the dimer or tetramer which constitutes the enzyme is arranged in such a way that a defect in one part of one monomer can be corrected by a correct part in the same place in the other monomer, then this correction mechanism must, in these cases, rely upon a simple linear basis.

A satisfying aspect of these complementation maps is that

the maps which have been constructed from data about the growth or nongrowth of heterokaryons correspond very well to the genetic maps for the same genes. Not much can be said about distances because there is no way of measuring distance in a complementation map, but the order of the mutants in the genetic map and in the complementation map is the same. The fit is not perfect and there are a few obstinant mutants which will not fit in their right places.

More recently some complementation maps have been found to fit into the shape of a circle instead of a straight line. And in one or two of these, when the complementation map is compared with the genetic map, all mutants fit into place if the complementation map is considered as a spiral. The aggregate enzyme might then consist of two monomer spirals, one on top of the other, as in Figure 36.

FIGURE 36

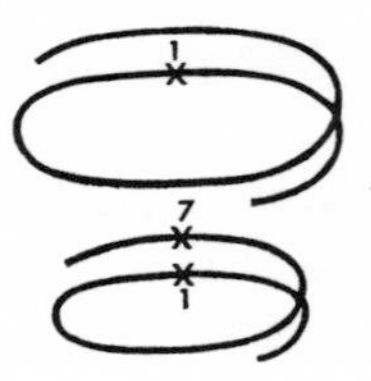

A defect, say at 1 in the top monomer, cannot be remedied by a defect at 1 in the bottom monomer, nor even by a mutant having a defect at 7 in the other, because although they are at different positions on the peptide chain, they lie close together when the chain is folded. In other words, 1 and 7 act in the same way. How the monomers of the enzyme actually fit together to allow complementation in these systems is not known. The whole subject is very new and present ideas are tentative. There are not even many ideas about what constitutes a defect. Many of the mutants dealt with are presumably defective for only one amino acid, but as regards complementation the data indicate that the defect must spread over a longer region.

There is a great deal yet to be discovered about the structure and function of enzymes. An innocent might regard them as specific catalysts in which the special order of amino acids exactly determines the way in which a chain coils up and this, in turn, specifies exactly what reaction the enzyme can catalyze. It is beginning to look as though the amino acid sequence does, in fact, determine where and how it coils up, but it is also beginning to look as though only a small part of the enzyme is actually concerned with its catalytic powers. One of the functions of the rest of the enzyme may have to do with regulation. This should not be confused with repression, described in the last chapter. The regulation referred to here is called inhibition and acts on the enzyme itself, not on the production of the enzyme. Many enzymes are inhibited when a large amount of what they produce is present. This is a virtuous economic device. It prevents the wasteful and possibly harmful production of too much product. It may be thought of as a blocking of the enzyme by the product at the exact position on the enzyme where the product is formed. If an enzyme be represented thus 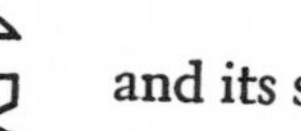 and its substrates thus then the enzyme may join the two substrates to form a product thus:

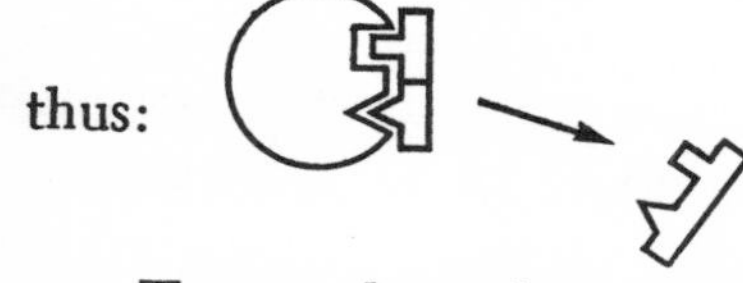

Too much product in the vicinity may tie up the parts of the enzyme into which the substrates fit because the product will be as likely as, or more likely than, the substrate to get into position.

In many cases this is no doubt the explanation of inhibition, but in others it turns out not to be. In cases where it is not, a chemical quite different from the substrate may inhibit the enzyme. Several examples are known where there are sequences of enzymes in which the product of one is the substrate for the next, as in the examples given in Chapter VII. A sequence can be represented thus:

$$A \xrightarrow{\text{enzyme a}} B \xrightarrow{\text{enzyme b}} C \xrightarrow{\text{enzyme c}} D \xrightarrow{\text{enzyme d}} E.$$

It is found in these cases that the product (E) of a late enzyme, suppresses the first (a), or sometimes all earlier a,b, c, and d) enzymes. This is an even more economical and less dangerous device than blocking just one enzyme by its product because it eliminates the accumulation of intermediate products.

In a few cases there is real evidence that the inhibitor acts on a different part of the enzyme from that to which the substrate is attracted. We thus have the picture of an enzyme having one part concerned with the substrate and one or several others concerned with inhibitors.

To inhibitors we should add activators, because some sites may accommodate substances which promote, or are necessary for, enzyme activity. The word "allosteric" has been coined to indicate a protein with several interacting sites. The nature of the interaction is not well understood, but opinion, and some evidence, seems to favor the idea that when an inhibitor or an activator occupies a certain site on a protein, then the folding of the peptide into a tertiary structure may be altered in such a way as to inhibit or promote enzyme activity.

The aggregate structure of proteins offers further possibilities of inhibition and of changes in specificity. In one well-studied example, the enzyme called glutamic dehydrogenase, which has to do with synthesis of the amino acid glutamic acid, was found to be inhibited by steroid hormones, especially by the most active female sex hormones in mammals. Glutamic dehydrogenase is an aggregate of four parts, it is a tetramer. The hormone works by breaking up the aggregate structure into its four parts. These parts cannot work on glutamic acid like the original enzyme, but curiously, they can act on another amino acid, alanine, and they thus represent another enzyme, alanine dehydrogenase. There is reason to believe that in this interesting enzyme the four parts are themselves made up of smaller parts.

Another enzyme studied in mammals and birds is lactate dehydrogenase. This enzyme is also probably a tetramer. Refined study of this enzyme from various sources has shown that there are five slightly different varieties of the enzyme. All five, called isozymes, are found in the same individual. The interest of this story is that when the five enzymes are broken up into their four parts, it turns out that they are all made up of only two different monomers. The difference between them lies in the proportion of the two parts, or monomers. Thus, if we call the two kinds of monomer A and B, the five isozymes can be represented thus: AAAA, AAAB, AABB, ABBB, BBBB; the second isozyme (AAAB), for instance, is made of three monomers of A and one of B. Isozymes are quite common—perhaps most enzymes exist in several slightly different forms—and so the work on lactate dehydrogenase may be of wide significance.

Unfortunately, very little is known of the genetics of this system because it is not easy to get in a mammal the mutants necessary for the required genetic analysis. One cannot employ selective techniques as one can with microorganisms. Presumably the two monomers are made by two distinct genes, which would mean that we have an enzyme coded by two genes. The five isozymes have slightly different properties, and this means, in effect, that with the two genes concerned one can get five different, albeit only slightly different, enzymes. What decides which of the five will be made is not known, but it may depend merely on how much of each monomer is present, since proportions of the five isozymes follow random aggregation laws. If this is so, it means that regulation of the quantity of protein made by a gene may determine the quality of enzyme produced. Surely a nicer example of the change of quantity into quality than Marxists have dreamed of.

One more class of factors which influences the activity of enzymes must be mentioned; these are the suppressors.

Experiments are often made to restore a given mutant to wild type. This is a good way to measure mutation rates of a particular gene because it is easy to select for wild type among the millions of mutants that cannot grow on a simple medium. When such experiments are performed, however, many of the wild-type organisms that are collected prove to be different from the original wild type. The mutant gene has not mutated back to wild type, but a second gene has mutated and this has canceled the effect of the original mutant, thus allowing the organism to grow on simple medium. The second mutation is called a suppressor because it suppresses the action of the original mutation. There are now known to be several kinds of suppressors. Some of them probably knock out some other enzyme, and their doing so, for peculiar metabolic reasons, restores growth to an approximately normal rate. Others are known to restore the very enzyme damaged by the original mutation, and these are more difficult to interpret. One interesting suggestion is that the second mutation concerns the part of the chromosome making t-RNA or the activating enzyme; in other words, the second mutation changes the dictionary which reads the code in such a way that it makes a wrong triplet read right. Here again, as was described in Chapter XI in connection with the effect of streptomycin on ribosomes, the change in activating enzyme or t-RNA may be more in the nature of a loosening up of specificity. This would forestall the calamity of all other enzymes being damaged while one was restored.

Equally interesting are other suppressors, which can be shown to lie within the same gene but at a different site, a different nucleotide pair, from the original mutant. Here again there is more than one way in which they may act. Sometimes their action may be due to the addition or deletion of nucleotide pairs. If the first mutant deleted or added a nucleotide pair and the second mutant, close to it, added or deleted a further pair, then most of the code would read right, as is the case of the acridine-induced mutant mentioned in Chapter XI. In the case of the enzyme tryptophane synthetase, which is one of the most studied enzymes, it is known that a change in a second amino acid of the enzyme can restore activity. How this works is not known, presumably it has to do with the way the protein folds up. The original mutant, changing one amino acid, prevents it from folding correctly; the second amino acid change allows it to fold more or less correctly again. It should be added that study of this enzyme has also shown that many amino acids can be changed without affecting the activity of the enzyme (see Chapter XI and Table 15).

In general, it can be said that enzymes are complex protein aggregates which catalyze specific reactions. Their action can be regulated in several different ways. These regulatory functions are related both to the structure of the gene that lays down the amino acid sequence and to other genes which may be far away on the genetic map, as well as to the metabolic state of the cell. It must be borne in mind that although the sequence of amino acids in a protein has been worked out in some cases, the aggregate structure of an enzyme is a very difficult and delicate object to study. Pitfalls are plentiful; not only is it difficult to know how many polypeptide chains there are in an aggregate, but several cases are now known in which one large protein aggregate seems to carry out two or three or perhaps five different enzymatic reactions. This contrasts with DNA, where although the sequence of nucleotides is difficult to determine, the Watson-Crick structure of the whole molecule seems well and universally established. The structure of the chromosomes of higher organisms is, of course, another matter which may reveal unforeseen complexities.

XV *Morphogenesis: The Development of Structure*

After a rather detailed account of how genes determine the production and regulation of enzymes, it would be proper to end Part Two with a picture of how enzymes determine the development of an organism from egg to adult. Unfortunately, apart from establishment of the word "morphogenesis," not much progress has been made in this direction. Many interesting but isolated observations have been made and we will have to limit ourselves to a description of some of these.

We will begin by describing some elegant experiments, performed many years ago, which show that the nucleus produces some substance or substances which determine shape. J. Hämmerling, who initiated this work in the 1930's in Germany, used an alga called *Acetabularia,* which is most beautifully designed for the purpose. It consists of a single cell and at one stage of its life cycle has a single nucleus near the base. There is a long stalk and an umbrella-shaped cap on top. The whole plant is about five centimeters tall, with a cap about one centimeter in diameter. There are several species which can be distinguished by the shape of their caps. The remarkable and fortunate fact is that the base part of one species containing the nucleus can be grafted onto the stalk section of another species, and a new cap will regenerate. The type of cap regenerated corresponds to the species of the nucleus, not to that of the stalk. The conclusion drawn from many experiments of this kind is that the nucleus produces a substance which travels up the stalk and determines the shape of the cap. There is some evidence that the substance is RNA, and there is anticipation that it is messenger RNA. More refined experiments have been performed in which the basal nucleus is pushed out and the nucleus from another species pushed in. These plants sometimes produce a cap corresponding to the cytoplasm at first, but after one or two caps have been cut off, the subsequent caps that develop always correspond to the nucleus. Experiments of this sort have shown that the substance, m-RNA or other, must be very stable; it can still determine the shape of a cap after several months, at least if it is not active during the waiting period. This stability would contrast with the instability of the m-RNA's that have been studied in microorganisms. None of the substance is made in cells treated with actinomycin D, which is a specific drug that stops all transcription of RNA from DNA. There is some evidence, rather ambiguous, that the substance does not become active until light has fallen upon it. If it is indeed m-RNA, this would be a novel and interesting control mechanism. Experiments in which the stalk section alone regenerates a cap or basal root system suggest that there are two chemical substances, one of which determines growth of a cap and the other growth of a root. Something could also be said about the concentrations of these substances in a newly cut stalk. Unfortunately, it has not been possible to isolate them, so nothing is known of their chemical nature. It is also unfortunate that *Acetabularia* is a poor organism for genetic experiments a generation takes several years and sexual crosses are difficult.

There are scattered bits of evidence that within the nucleus visible changes occur in the chromosomes of some specialized tissues. We have already mentioned the fact that the chromosomes in the salivary glands of *Drosophila* are about a hundred times as large as normal chromosomes. They contain about a thousand times the normal amount of DNA. Oversized chromosomes are found in many other flies besides *Drosophila* and in other tissues besides salivary glands. The prevalent opinion is that they represent many duplications of the original DNA strand, together with an unfolding or uncoiling which gives them their enormous length. The cells in which they are found are specialized and do not normally divide.

In the single-celled protozoan *Paramecium*, there is also something like this. *Paramecium* has two nuclei, the micronucleus and a large macronucleus. The macronucleus is belived to be made up, like the salivary-gland chromosomes, of numerous duplications of the chromosomes. The interesting thing about *Paramecium* is that the hereditary qualities lie in the micronucleus, but the physiological functions appear to be carried out by the macronucleus. During sexual reproduction the macronuclei of the parents are lost and new ones are formed for the offspring.

There is more to be said about large chromosomes. C. Pavan, working in Brazil, has found a large fly, common in South America, which has even more enormous chromosomes in several tissues of the body. He has observed that in certain tissues, at certain stages of development, a part of the chromosome, representing perhaps a single gene, swells up and appears diffuse. Exactly what these swellings signify is not known, but it would seem to be in some way a visible expression of a gene in action: it is known that a great deal of RNA, perhaps m-RNA, is made in these regions.

There is hope that these so-called puffs may lead to more

interesting discoveries. One lead is provided by the fact that an insect hormone, ecdysin, makes the puffs appear. Ecdysin has a dramatic effect on the metabolism of insects and so the relation between puffs and metabolism may be studied by the use of this substance.

After these brief items about the nucleus and chromosomes, we turn now to a subject the importance of which is difficult to judge. While evidence for the role of the nucleus and chromosomes has been accumulating, some well-established cases of cytoplasmic inheritance have appeared. The first extensive work on this was done with the green chloroplasts of plants. It was found that some albino mutations are not transmitted in a Mendelian manner, but that the progeny nearly always resemble the female parent. This is due to the fact that the egg carries much more cytoplasm than the pollen, which carries little or none at all. In the cytoplasm of the egg there must be hereditary units which develop into chloroplasts, or determine the production of chloroplasts. These units cannot be made from information contained in the nucleus, but only from duplication of units already present in the cytoplasm. If an egg has none of these units or has defective units, the plants will have albino or defective chloroplasts even though the genes brought by the pollen are normal. This does not mean that genes have nothing to do with the formation of chloroplasts—we know that they do; but it means that some differences between the chloroplasts of plants are not due to genes or to the environment, but are due to genetic units in the cytoplasm.

Another case of cytoplasmic inheritance, which has been well analyzed, was found in yeast by Boris Ephrussi, working in Paris. There is no difference in size between male and female yeast gametes, so the test of reciprocal crosses cannot be used in this case. The character studied was "petite," the development of a minute colony, looking very similar to a bacterial colony, as opposed to the normal, rather large colony. Various experiments indicate that the petite character is due to the absence of some particles in the cytoplasm which cannot be made from genes but have to be there originally. When two petites are crossed, only petites are found in the progeny; when a petite and a normal are crossed, all the progeny are normal because the normal parent carries enough particles to satisfy all the progeny. The particles must, like chloroplasts, be capable of duplication. The character petite has been found to be related to respiration in yeast. Two enzymes, present in normal cells, are absent in petite cells. An interesting feature of this work is that the same petite character can also be due, in other mutants, to a gene. In the latter cases the character segregates in a perfectly Mendelian way.

In the petite character of yeast, the cytoplasmic particles are present in the normal cell and absent in the mutant. In another example, this time in *Drosophila*, the presence of particles is harmful and they are found in the less efficient organism. The character, studied by Philippe l'Heritier in France, is susceptibility to carbon dioxide poisoning. It had been the practice in some laboratories in France to anesthetize flies with carbon dioxide rather than chloroform. Some flies were found which did not recover from a standard dose of carbon dioxide. The inheritance of this character has proved to be complicated, but in general, when reciprocal crosses are made, the progeny resemble their mother. In other words, the character does not obey Mendel's laws, but is cytoplasmic.

A particle which multiplies by itself in the cytoplasm and has a harmful effect on the host comes close to what we mean by a parasitic virus. If we call the carbon dioxide factor in *Drosophila* a virus, then why not call the yeast factor a special kind of beneficial virus? And what about the chloroplast case which we mentioned first? Most people would balk here. A chloroplast is a chloroplast and not a virus. If pressed to make a distinction, they might say something to the effect that one is a normal component of the cell and the other is a parasite introduced from outside. A distinction based on origins may not satisfy the questioner, but let us not pursue this line of reasoning any further. It does not lead anywhere and was mentioned only to show the relation that can be made between a virus and a so-called cytoplasmic factor.

The carbon dioxide factor in *Drosophila* is of particular interest because the determining particle, which reproduces autonomously in the cytoplasm, sometimes gets attached to a chromosome, where it resembles an ordinary gene. This peculiar behavior has been found to be true of some other cytoplasmic particles and they have been given the name "episomes" by the French school. It is interesting to note that some viruses would come under the definition of an episome since some phages may reproduce freely in the cytoplasm of their host bacteria, or may become attached to the bacterial chromosome and divide in step with it. The phenomenon is known as lysogeny and was described in Chapter IX.

The slipper-animalcule *Paramecium,* which we have described as having two nuclei, has also proved to be a favorable organism for the study of cytoplasmic inheritance. For many years Tracy Sonneborn and his colleagues at the University of Indiana investigated a cytoplasmic particle named kappa, which is responsible for the production of a substance that is toxic to other *Paramecia.* It is similar in many ways to the cytoplasmic particle causing the petite character in yeast. A feature of kappa is that it cannot divide and persist in a cell unless a certain gene is contained in the nucleus. The gene cannot create kappa *de novo* but is necessary for its maintenance. It appears to do this through the intermediary of yet another particle, called a metagon.

Some antigenic characters of *Paramecium* depend on the temperature. At one temperature they show one antigenic character, at another temperature, another. At an intermediate temperature this character depends on past history, on the temperature at which the *Paramecium* was kept previously. There is no evidence of a particle associated with this antigenic character, but there is good evidence that it is controlled by the cytoplasm.

More dramatic recent experiments of Sonneborn raise the question of the inheritance of acquired characteristics, about which more will be said in Part Three. Dramatic experiments are often simple, and in this case, the experiment consisted of damaging a section of the mouth parts of *Paramecium*. The damage was found to persist in the progeny of the damaged cell. *Paramecium* is a ciliate—its outer coat and mouth are covered with cilia, or microscopic hairs. The wavelike motion of cilia enables *Paramecium* to swim and to engulf food. At the base of each cilium there is a special body which is believed to be self-duplicating. If some of these bodies are damaged, they may not be able to divide, and they cannot be created *de novo*. This may explain the persistence of the damage in the progeny.

The direct way of investigating the role of cytoplasm and nucleus is to put identical nuclei in different cytoplasms and different nuclei in identical cytoplasms. This has been done by J. F. Danielli in England and more recently in the United States. Using a micromanipulator, Danielli pushed the nucleus out of an amoeba and pushed the nucleus from another species of amoeba into it. He found that many characters, such as shape, size, and longevity, were determined more by cytoplasm than by nucleus. Other characters, such as the amount of certain amino acids, were determined wholly by the nucleus. We will describe later similar experiments involving one species of a higher organism but different cells of that organism.

Before we leave the subject of cytoplasmic inheritance, let us introduce another thought which may already have occurred to the reader. When we write of a character being determined by the cytoplasm instead of by the nucleus, what exactly is meant? Obviously, all characters are determined by the nucleus and the cytoplasm together and also by the presence of water, oxygen, and various other factors in the environment of the organism. An isolated nucleus or isolated cytoplasm will not produce any organism or any character of an organism. Actually, if one wished to be contrary, one might consider the cytoplasm as more important than the nucleus. An *Acetabularia* plant with its nucleus cut off can produce a whole new cap, but the isolated nucleus can do nothing. A little thought will resolve this paradox; what we are really writing about, and what a geneticist is nearly always dealing with, is the difference between organisms. Does the difference between two organisms depend upon a difference in cytoplasm or a difference of nuclei, or, to broaden the subject, on a difference in the external environment?

There is one category of cytoplasmic chemicals which are not self-duplicating and yet could, by a stretch of theoretical imagination, be regarded as accounting for hereditary differences between organisms. These are the activating enzymes. Together with transfer RNA they constitute the dictionary which determines what amino acid belongs to what triplet of DNA nucleotides. A change in the specificity of an activating enzyme, either in the part that bonds to an amino acid or in the part that bonds to t-RNA, would be a change in the code. Imagine that the activating enzyme which translates three uridines (UUU) into the amino acid phenylalanine has phenylalanine in a certain position in its molecule. Suppose that replacing phenylalanine by tyrosine in that position changes the specificity of the activating enzyme, and furthermore, changes it in such a way that UUU now codes for tyrosine instead of phenylalanine. With exactly the same nuclear DNA, a cell with this new activating enzyme will make more of the new enzyme; the change will be self-perpetuating and may have diverse effects on other enzymes where phenylalanine is replaced by tyrosine. This a fanciful notion, and the evidence points in the opposite direction, namely, that the genetic code is universal and the activating enzymes are more or less the same in all organisms.

At a higher level on the hierarchy of factors that have key roles in morphogenesis are the hormones. Many hormones, including the sexual hormones, are steroid substances and are presumably made by enzymes controlled by genes. Insulin, which controls the metabolism of sugar, is a hormone which is a protein, and it would be interesting to know whether it is made by a template mechanism, like enzymes, or is built up amino acid by amino acid, each step catalyzed by a specific enzyme. A mutation is known in the mouse which affects the pituitary hormone and produces a dwarf mouse. In corn there is a gene which produces "lazy corn," plants which lie prostrate instead of growing erect. This characteristic has been found to be due to the lack of a plant hormone, an auxin. Apart from these instances very little is known about the genetics of hormones. Even diabetes, the disease resulting from insulin deficiency, has not proved amenable to detailed genetic study.

It is known, on the other hand, that many hormones act by stimulating the genes to make more RNA. This can be demonstrated by the use of a special chemical, actinomycin D, which can prevent RNA being made from DNA but does not otherwise injure the cell. These hormones do not work in the presence of actinomycin D. In other experiments it has been shown that estrogen, the female sex hormone increases the production not only of m-RNA, but also of t-RNA and ribosomal RNA. It must, therefore, act on several different parts of the chromosomal DNA. One of the effects of estrogen in hens is to stimulate the liver to produce many of the proteins that go into the yolks of hen eggs. Cocks have no use for these yolk proteins, but if they are given estrogen they do, unnaturally, form yolk proteins in their livers. It is interesting that whereas estrogen stimulates the liver to produce yolk proteins, it stimulates the uterine cells in females to produce quite different proteins which are the cause, presumably, for the growth and changes of the uterine tissues that occur when the estrogen level increases. This shows that the hormone is not specific for certain genes in all cells, but is specific for one set of genes in liver cells and another set of genes in uterine cells.

The hormone responsible for all the extraordinary changes inflicted upon an insect as it undergoes metamorphosis is called ecdysin; it was mentioned earlier in this chapter as the cause of puffs in certain places along the giant chromosomes of a South American fly. This is another example of a hormone, also chemically a steroid, stimulating a gene to make RNA. An added feature of the ecdysin story is that at a low concentration it stimulates the formation of one new puff and at a higher concentration, another. In the natural state the concentration of ecdysin gradually increases just before metamorphosis, and the various concentrations at different times may be a way of causing various specific genes to produce the required proteins at those times. Work with ecdysin has been tedious because it is very difficult to obtain in large quantities. Very recently the synthetic production of ecdysin was announced, and we can look forward to accelerated work on this interesting subject.

Experiments on a water mold by an American botanist, John Raper, have shown that the sexual organs of this organism can be produced by putting a drop of the correct hormone into the water in which the mold is growing. The amount of hormone needed is extremely small; although the hormone has never been completely purified or identified, the best preparations cause male sex organs to grow when only one part hormone in 10^{12} is added.

One worker claims that changes can be brought about in cells by adding RNA from other cells. He extracted RNA from liver and treated other cells, growing in tissue culture, with it. He found that the latter began to make several enzymes peculiar to liver cells and continued to make more and more of these enzymes for some time. It is not at all clear what role the RNA plays, whether it should be considered m-RNA, or an inducer, or as some other kind of trigger, but the results are interesting and may lead to further discoveries.

In Chapter VII we described how the snail mother determines the direction of coiling of the shells of her offspring. This character is determined very early in development; in fact, it can be traced back to the first few divisions of the zygote. What is it, present in the material cells around the zygote, which is responsible? It may be a chemical substance comparable to a hormone, or it may be the shape of the surrounding cells, the gradients of various substances in them, or some other forces.

Drastic changes in shape are often produced by different growth rates. The American geneticist and lay theologian Edmund Sinnott has studied the genetics of the shape of gourds and has found that many of the very drastic differences in shape are controlled by genes which influence the relative growth rates in different directions. The genes concerned appear to control a growth ratio—the ratio of longitudinal to radial growth, for instance—and the duration of growth at this fixed ratio. It has also been found that growth is due mainly to cell division rather than cell enlargement. How a gene controls whether, and how often, a cell divides one way rather than another is not known.

In *Neurospora*, several mutants are known which have many more branches than normal plants. Some of these mutants present a very striking appearance to the naked eye.

Tatum and his associates at the Rockefeller Institute in New York have found that the branching is caused by a weakening of the cell wall. The cell wall of *Neurospora* consists of fibers of protein joined by a "glue" made of a starchlike substance. These mutations affect the latter, and it is found that the same chemical change can be brought about by putting the sugar sorbose into the medium or by treating the plants with various other chemicals. The treated plants then resemble the mutant plants.

The examples of shape in gourds and *Neurospora* are relatively simple, but what of the pattern of fingerprints, whose main features are known to be genetically controlled? What about the very precise shape of facial features, concerning which Blaise Pascal wrote, "If the nose of Cleopatra had been shorter, the whole face of the earth would have been changed"?

We have not said much about the structures within cells, but they are numerous and intricate. Some are probably self-duplicative; among these are the mitochondria which contain the chemical machinery concerned with energy transformations, the centrioles concerned with nuclear division, and the basal bodies concerned with cilia. Others are presumably created *de novo* from genic information. An important category of structure within cells is formed by the membranes, which play a vital role. There are membranes around each cell and membranes around each nucleus, and the electron microscope has revealed in the cytoplasm an intricate network of membranes called the endoplasmic reticulum. The latter is especially well developed in cells that secrete proteins, and in them the ribosomes are attached to the endoplasmic reticulum. Most probably the reticulum has to do with the transport of protein, made in the ribosome, out of the cell. Each kind of membrane has its own peculiar structure—related, no doubt, to its role of keeping out those substances which should be out, of keeping in those which should be in, and of contributing to the transport of those which should move out or in or along. A morphological item which is far removed from the gene in the hierarchy of enzymes, regulator substances, master hormones, and lesser hormones, is the intricate shape of a spider's web. This is probably under genetic control, since different species constantly build the same shape of web. This shape must be determined in the first instance by instinct, by the structure or at least the function of the spider's brain. We must suppose that the order of nucleotides contains the information about the web, but what a job of decoding there must be between the genes and the web!

And what of the intricate morphology of the brain of man? One might first conceive of the brain as perhaps something like a telephone exchange, with every nerve connected at each end to exactly the right other nerve or nerves, just as are the electric wires of a telephone exchange. Each nerve might be controlled by a separate gene. But this first idea fades upon reflection. There are about ten billion (10^9) nerve cells in a man's brain, which would surely represent more than a fair share of his genes. Other considerations also argue against it, especially the increasing information that is becoming available about the role of specific chemical substances in the working of the brain. An extreme view in the other direction would be that connections between the nerves are random, that a very large complex but random network of nerves is laid down, and that other factors use this as a structure upon which the working of the brain is built.

Another aspect of morphogenesis is the problem of differentiation. As the zygote cell of an organism divides into two, four, eight, and more cells, the cells are different from the zygote and different from each other. Eventually some cells form nails or hair, some muscle, some blood corpuscles, some skin, and so on for all the tissues of the body. The rule, in developing embryos, is that a cell never divides into daughter cells which are exactly like it and like each other. What is the basis for this difference? The chromosomes in most cells of the body look similar; presumably the DNA and its sequence of nucleotides is similar. One of the first practical questions that can be asked is whether the difference is due to a difference in nucleus or in cytoplasm. It is this question that makes the examples of cytoplasmic inheritance, described above, interesting.

A direct approach to this question has been attempted in two laboratories, one in England, the other in America. The experiments are technically difficult, and failures far exceed successes. The trick is to remove the nucleus from a zygote and put in its place the nucleus from a cell of a developing embryo. The most suitable organism for these experiments is the frog, and the results show that in general the nucleus from a cell of the embryo can make a complete and perfect adult frog. Certain experiments seem to show, however, that in some cells of an older embryo the nucleus has been changed in some rather permanent way that cannot be reversed and it no longer acts like a zygote nucleus. Any change in nuclei almost certainly does not involve a change in DNA. The nucleotide composition of DNA from various tissues of the same species has been found to be similar, and on general grounds it seems most unlikely that differentiation involves a change in nucleotide sequence in the DNA.

Differentiation, then, presents us with the general question of how cells with the same genes can come to be different. The most obvious influence is the environment—factors external to the cell. Gravity is one such factor, and the point of entry of the sperm is another. These two alone could determine gradients which would make every point in a zygote unique, except for a bilateral symmetry. External gradients of O_2, CO_2, and other substances would do the same. When the zygote divides these could determine a difference between daughter cells lying north, south, east, and west. Another aspect of environment is constituted by neighboring cells and tissues themselves—their surface structure and their excretions, both soluble and particulate. There is experimental evidence from tissue-culture work that excretions play some part, for it is commonly found that a small inoculum does not differentiate into characteristic tissue, but a large inoculum of many cells will. Chemical substances can diffuse out and away from a small group of cells faster than from a large one. They can diffuse away faster than they are made and no high concentration can be built up within the group. Furthermore, in a large group the concentrations of various substances will be different near the middle of the mass and near the periphery. In the particular case of muscle cells it has been found that the juices from a large group of cells will promote differentiation in a small group that would not differentiate without treatment.

When we think in terms of environmental factors, we have to think of the organism as a whole, with less emphasis on the cell. More important, no doubt, are the autonomous processes within cells. These processes are autonomous in the sense that something has changed in the cell and that if the cell could be returned to the old environment it would still remain in the changed condition. When it divides, the daughter cells may also be in the changed condition, which would mean that the change is hereditary—hereditary with respect to cell lineages, not in the broader sense of individual lineages. There is experimental evidence in the case of muscle cells and some other specialized cells called fibroblasts that single cells, if isolated and grown under appropriate conditions, will differentiate into the right kind of cell. In other words, the change in these cells is not caused by the environment, but determining factors must be latent in the cells themselves.

Mechanisms which may play a part in changes of cell heredity are not difficult to imagine. The loss of a self-duplicating cytoplasmic particle would qualify. The addition of a self-duplicating particle, or a change in one, might also take place. The blocking of gene function by histones, protamines, or some of the nonbasic proteins found in the nucleus is another possibility, to which we have already referred; this would probably involve some mechanism that made these proteins self-duplicating in a broad sense.

The regulatory devices which have been described can also lead to a more or less stable metabolic change. Let us use as an example a system of repressors. Imagine two different metabolic pathways, A → B → C and D → E → F. The substances A and D may be derived from some common precursor further back, but the two paths lead to the production of two different substances, C and F. Now suppose that substance B acts as a repressor of the enzyme which catalyzes D → E and substance E does the same for the enzyme acting on the reaction A → B. The situation will be as shown in Figure 37.

FIGURE 37

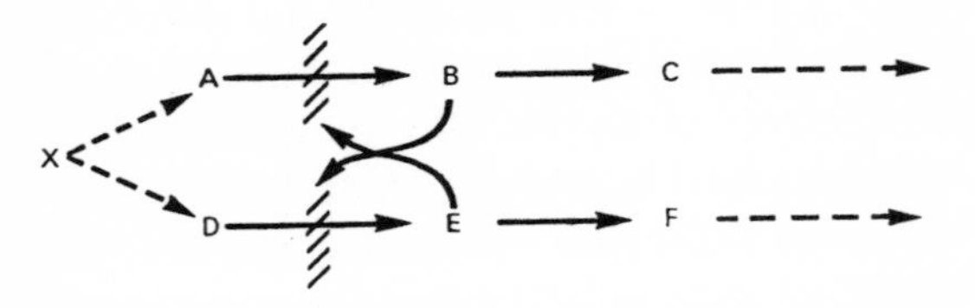

If either pathway gets a slight advantage it will dominate completely. For if pathway A → B → C has a slight advantage, there will be more of substance B, which will inhibit pathway D → E → F. This will cut down the amount of substance E, which will allow pathway A → B → C to function with even less inhibition, increasing the amount of substance B, and so on until pathway A → B → C is completely predominant. It is a case of nothing succeeding like success. More complicated schemes can be built up on the same principle. There may be inhibition of an enzyme rather than repression of the synthesis of an enzyme. The overall effect is that two cells with identical genes may have different metabolic patterns. Once something has given a slight push in one direction, the cell will accentuate that direction, which will be maintained even through cell division.

We have now covered all of the ground having to do with the genetics of individuals. Most of the interesting recent work has come from scientists who study microbes, and it is pertinent to ask how useful these ideas will be in the study of higher organisms. The microbiologist is, of course, an optimist in this matter and the embryologist or nonmicrobial geneticist a pessimist. Let us conclude, therefore, with an imaginary dialogue between these two.

MICROBIOLOGIST. In the words of two eminent microbiologists, Jacob and Monod, "Two cells are differentiated with respect to each other if, while they harbor the same genome [genes], the pattern of proteins which they synthesize is different." We have learned a lot about how genes make specific proteins and also about how the rate of production is controlled. Of the controlling factors there is good experimental evidence for the "operator hypothesis" and also for the control of enzyme activity by specific inhibitors. These two factors alone are sufficient to account for the "pattern of proteins" produced by a cell. Since the manner of production of proteins in the sequence DNA → m-RNA → protein is almost certainly universal, why not assume, at least a working hypothesis, that these principles apply to higher organisms?

EMBRYOLOGIST. Before tackling the question of differentiation, let me raise an old and more fundamental question. Does the nucleus really determine important differences between species? I will grant that the Mendelian laws are valid and also that the structure of genes and the method of their inheritance is well known and universal throughout the animal and plant kingdom. But what evidence have we that fundamental characters are determined by genes in the nucleus? Wide species crosses cannot often be made, but in at least one study, in moss plants, crosses between different genera showed inheritance of important characters to be maternal—to follow the parent contribution cytoplasm. I refer to a very old and mostly forgotten work of the eminent German botanist, F. Von Wettstein. I suggest, therefore, somewhat facetiously, that only trivial characters obey Mendel's laws, that this is an evolutionary device to test out trivial characters, but that once an evolutionary line is committed to a certain basic pattern, that pattern is governed by the cytoplasm, not the nucleus.

MICROBIOLOGIST. I am glad you are being facetious. This argument is dead and has been properly buried. Any textbook, and even the present volume, will be found to describe the overwhelming evidence that, apart from some trivial cytoplasmic factors, all hereditary determinants lie in the nucleus, in the chromosomes. However, since the subject has been raised, let me add that the operon hypothesis provides a basis on which cytoplasm could be a determinant. You will remember that the hypothesis involves specific repressors for the genes that code for enzymes. You will also remember that schemes can be devised whereby the metabolism of a cell can be put into two or three different pathways, depending on which gets a head start. The head start is gained by the pathway least affected by repressors. In this sense the amounts of the various repressors in the zygote could conceivably determine which way the zygote would develop. They could also determine the concentration of repressors in the next-generation zygote.

EMBRYOLOGIST. I see you have conceded the point. I have always thought enzymes to be rather dull; very much the same enzymes are found in all animals. What is important is not the kind of enzyme, but how much enzyme and how it is inhibited or stimulated. Now, the repressors as well as the inhibitors and stimulators are all in the cytoplasm, hence the importance of this part of the cell.

May I return to the question of how far the ideas developed by studying microbes can be used with regard to higher organisms. Bacteria and viruses are really fundamentally different from higher organisms. The two major divisions of living organisms are usually stated to be the plant kingdom and the animal kingdom, but I would say that a far more logical division would be between the bacteria and viruses, with a few other odd groups like blue-green algae, and the higher organisms. The basic differences between these two groups have been well summarized recently by a microbiologist, Roger Stanier. I will list some distinguishing items.

Higher organisms have a nucleus surrounded by a membrane; the nucleus contains several rod-shaped chromosomes and divides by mitosis; the cytoplasm is permeated by a network of membranes known as the endoplasmic reticulum; chemical processes involved in the energy of the cell take place in special organs in the cytoplasm—mitochondria or chloroplasts; proteins are associated with the DNA of the nucleus. In bacteria and viruses none of these occur; they generally have a single circular chromosome, and genes concerned with the same metabolic pathway are often clustered together.

In view of these differences I would doubt that metabolism is controlled by the same mechanism in both. I would grant, however, that the control, whatever its nature, acts on enzyme production rather than on the inhibition of enzymes already produced. This I would argue on grounds of efficiency—that if enzyme production is stopped, only one molecule of m-RNA or its equivalent DNA need be blocked; whereas many enzyme molecules would have to be inhibited if control acted on the enzyme once made.

Microbiologist. There are, of course, vast differences

between bacteria and higher organisms, but since the sequence DNA → RNA → Protein is the same in both, why should not a good control system evolved for the one be retained in the other? In any case, should one not stick with a hypothesis that has some basis rather than fumble around with none?

EMBRYOLOGIST. It is indeed better to work with some hypothesis than with none, but it is also bad to strain a hypothesis to make it fit data that do not naturally fall into place. There are many odd phenomena in higher organisms that would seem to require a different hypothesis. One of these is position effect (Chapter XIII). Why do genes act differently according to their position on the chromosome, especially when next to heterochromatin? How do you explain the position effect in bar-eyed and double bar-eyed *Drosophila* flies? The inactive X chromosome in females, described in Chapter VII, seems to become heterochromatic, but how do you explain this?

In corn a great deal of work has been done on certain elusive factors which seem to float about from one position to another on various chromosomes. These factors affect the functioning of the particular gene they happen to be on or near. The factors are themselves influenced by other genes, and ingenious, as well as laborious, experiments are necessary to study them. One of the discoverers of these peculiar phenomena has enthusiastically likened them to the regulator system in bacteria, but I would suggest that this is a good illustration of the hypothesis being strained. It may turn out to be fruitful, but it may lead us up the garden path and blind us to the real explanation.

Your recent ideas about repression are very interesting and are certainly in the current limelight, but if you look at its role in the life of bacteria you will see that it is mainly concerned with preserving an equilibrium. It is designed to maintain the *status quo*. The bacterial cell, after all, is a bit of an anarchist; it grows at full speed, like a cancerous cell, when food is plentiful and only stops when food runs out. The control mechanisms you study insure that it will be able to grow at full speed most efficiently, with no waste molecules.

In higher organisms the controls needed are quite different. Cells divide only a limited number of times, and then most of them settle down to a particular differentiated life where they work but do not divide. Each cell is attached to other cells and each cell must play a specialized role that, in cooperation with other cells, leads to the harmonious functioning of the individual. It is not sufficient, in such a situation, to cut off the manufacture of new enzyme molecules. It is necessary to inactivate or destroy the enzymes already there. In the case of rapidly dividing bacteria, on the other hand, unwanted enzymes, whose manufacture has ceased, are eliminated by dilution.

I would also like to question your statement at the beginning of our discussion that differentiation is a matter of proteins. By proteins you obviously mean enzymes, and to me this is a narrow view of differentiation. Differentiation and morphogenesis, as I study them, consist of changes in the shape of cells as well as changes in the shape of things within the cell; they involve precise movement of cells from one place to another and of chromosomes within the cell. Morphogenesis is a matter of shape and movement, not of substance. Enzymes are concerned with the synthesis of substance and this is not readily related to shape and movement. Two bricklayers may have exactly the same assortment of bricks, but they can each construct a very different house.

Microbiologist. What you say is well taken. Thank goodness you are a progressive biologist and not an ultraconservative of the kind so commonly found in the botany and zoology departments of our colleges. You have, I see, followed the brilliant discoveries of microbiologists who, I expect you have noticed, are now calling themselves molecular biologists or biophysicists. You may try to downgrade these new theories by saying that they cannot apply to more important matters, but at least you are aware of them. In this respect you are so much better than the peasants who attack us blindly without knowing what they attack or, on the other hand, try to jump on our bandwagon by borrowing from our popular streamlined vocabulary and thereby debase these new words.

EMBRYOLOGIST. Let us not talk about new words. I do not mind your calling yourself a molecular biologist, a radiobiologist, or a biophysicist; this is excusable if it gets you a better job. I am irritated, however, when you fool yourself into thinking that the new name implies a new approach or a new principle. Most of the great contributions of the past were made by men who were just as familiar with molecules or physics or radiation as you are, but they were content to call themselves biologists or chemists. I remember a time when colloids were in vogue—indeed, the secret of life was believed to reside in the mysterious properties of colloids—but people did not call themselves colloidal biologists; there were no departments of colloidal biology.

MICROBIOLOGIST. Well, I will let you in on a secret. I personally agree with you that the "molecular" approach is a phoney. The words are really political. Life in the older botany and zoology departments became intolerable to the more ambitious young men and women. We could not take over these old departments because of political inertia. So we aggregated into brand-new departments and soon got brand-new buildings. For this it was necessary to have a new name. And so I say that although our current ideas may not prove fruitful in the study of higher organisms, I do believe that the people in these newer departments will be the ones who contribute most to future progress in the understanding of embryology and morphogenesis. I also have a secret hope that as the new departments and institutes mature, some of the nostalgic pleasures of botany and zoology may return—the mysteries seen under an old-fashioned oil-immersion microscope, the students' botanical forays in the spring and fall, the handling of whole animals and whole plants. Maybe it is just the buzz and hum of my shakers and centrifuges, of the air-conditioning unit and the fluorescent lamps that oppress me.

EMBRYOLOGIST. I sympathize with you. Your recently erected institute of "molecular, biophysical, and radiobiological microbiology" is built like a beehive without the honey. It must be a horror to live and work in. The speed and economy with which it was built have surely guaranteed that the personnel as well as the building have built-in obsolescence. Let us look forward to a time when we both benefit from each other's knowledge and experience, working in pleasant surroundings which have more in common with monastic than with penal or industrial architecture.

Part Three

XVI *Survival of the Fittest: If You Survive You Are Fit*

The idea that our ancestors were apes was repulsive to people living in 1858, the year in which Darwin presented his theory of evolution. It was a scientific theory that had profound social and philosophical implications. In this respect, the theory of evolution can be compared to the theory that the earth is round rather than flat and to the theory that the earth revolves around the sun. It was not accepted lightly, for it upset deep and old ways of thought. As Theodosius Dobzhansky has said, "Evolution was about as popular in seventeenth and eighteenth century France as communism is now in the U. S. A. or capitalism in the U. S. S. R."

On the other hand, the theory of evolution is a fundamental concept which brings order into a number of different biological fields. In the middle of the nineteenth century many biologists must have been ready to think seriously about evolution. The time was ripe for the theory to be widely and seriously discussed. In the discussion, those biologists who accepted it defended it as enthusiastically as other people fought it and ridiculed it. The discussions were not always temperate. In England and Germany they led to considerable political and social upheavals. Curiously, the impact of the theory on Latin Catholic countries was far less dramatic. Gradually, in the years following the publication of Darwin's *Origin of Species*, more and more biologists were won over to the evolutionist point of view.

The idea that species are not fixed, that they were not created in the beginning exactly as they are today, had occurred to many people before Darwin. The eminent French zoologist Jean Lamarck and Charles Darwin's grandfather Dr. Erasmus Darwin, among others, had expressed the view that all animals are related to each other in some way and that species do change in time, albeit over long geological periods.

The striking similarity in basic structure of various animals and plants must suggest this to any imaginative taxonomist. The thought was well expressed by the English dramatist William Congreve, who was imaginative but no taxonomist, when he wrote in a letter dated 1695, "I confess freely to you, I could never look long upon a monkey without very mortifying reflections."

Taxonomy, the science devoted to classifying animals and plants, benefited perhaps the most from the theory of evolution. It was recognized that species were not discrete and unrelated units that could be classified by any arbitrary character that the taxonomist chose, but rather were definitely related in some way to other species and that the job of the taxonomist was to reveal this relationship. A classification based on real affinities or relationships was called a natural classification, as opposed to the more artificial classifications of the ancients. To take an extreme example: in classical times animals had been classified according to their habitat—animals that swim in the sea, animals that live on land, and animals that fly in the air. Closer study showed that in reality some flying animals, birds, are more closely related to reptiles than to the flying insects and that some swimming animals, whales and porpoises, are mammals rather than fish. Systems of classification were built up, in particular by the great Swedish botanist Carolus Linnaeus (1707–1778), which were believed to reflect natural affinities; the nature or cause of these affinities, however, was obscure. The theory of evolution provided an answer by stating that there exists a blood or filial relationship. The forms of life which lived in past geological times and were preserved as fossils could also be better understood in an evolutionary framework. The geographical distribution of animals and plants and the peculiarities of forms found in isolated regions, such as Australia or the Galápagos Islands, also fitted into the theory of evolution, which gave a new basis for the study of such forms.

Darwin dealt at length with all these matters and used them as evidence for evolution. It was, in fact, the mass of detailed evidence rather than any one particular clear scientific proof that won people over to the new concept. The alternative view was that each species had been created from scratch, fossil species as well as living ones. This meant that there must have been innumerable cataclysms throughout the history of the earth, for the fossil record shows that at different geological times different species existed. Now, if a new lot of species were to be created after a cataclysm, there is no good reason for using the basic structure of the old species in designing the new. The conspicuous fact is that the same basic structure is common to fossil as well as contemporary species. A basic structure consisting of a segmented backbone with two pairs of limbs is common to all vertebrates. The length and shape of various bones have been modified to produce the wings of birds and bats, the long legs of horses, and the arms of erect man. It is apparent that if each species were created *de novo*, the creator must have been singularly conservative and unwilling to use new basic designs. This conservatism would have had to extend even to the preservation of useless vestigial structures, such as the appendix in man and the pelvic girdle in some whales.

The cataclysmic theory of special creation was probably felt to be weak by many men before Darwin. Evolutionary ideas were being entertained not only by biologists, but also by geologists, to account for the complex structure of the earth. A major obstacle to the idea of biological evolution was the lack of a reasonable theory as to the manner or mechanism by which evolution might take place. Some mechanisms had been proposed before Darwin, notably by Lamarck, whose ideas about the inheritance of acquired characters will be examined in Chapter XVII. Other writers took evolution to be a law of nature, without showing much hope that the workings of the law could be studied in a scientific manner.

The theory of natural selection, arrived at independently and announced jointly by Charles Darwin and Alfred Russel Wallace, was undoubtedly a major factor in winning the scientific world to the idea of evolution. The concept of evolution by natural selection is simple, but it was very unorthodox at the time, and it is an extremely potent idea.

The argument of the theory starts with the self-evident fact that offspring of a family are not absolutely identical, but vary in a number of characters. In human families some children will be taller, some shorter; some will have more hair on their heads, some less; some will have larger vermiform appendices, some smaller. In a family of oak trees, some offspring will produce leaves of one shape and some of a slightly different shape. In a family of peppered moths (*Biston betularia*), some offspring will be dark-colored, some light.

The variability among offspring will mean that some individuals will be superior to or better adapted than others in the sense that their particular characters will allow them to live longer and to leave more offspring. The peppered moth spends much of its life on trees, and until recent years, the trunks of trees in the central parts of Great Britain were of a light color, being often covered with lichens. A dark moth is more conspicuous on a light background than a light one and birds might be expected to be able to catch dark moths more easily and hence more often than light ones. The light moths would, therefore, have a longer life expectancy and be able to enjoy a longer period of reproductive effort; they would leave more offspring for the next generation.

The next step in the argument is not quite so self-evident and was not at all well understood by Darwin. It says that the offspring of parents of a particular type will resemble that type in general but vary from it in both directions. Thus, six-foot-tall parents will tend to have tall children, but some will be five feet ten inches and some six feet two inches, and so on. If we denote variations in a character numerically, so that, for instance, in the offspring of a family a trait may range from 10 to 15, then the ten offspring of one family may be represented by 10, 10, 10, 11, 11, 12, 13, 13, 13, and 15. All these individuals may leave offspring, but let us say that those with the high-numbered variations of the character are superior or fitter and leave more offspring than those with the low-numbered variations. Ten children from a 13 individual may range from 10 to 16, and ten children from a 15 individual may range from 12 to 18. In the following generation the high numbers may again be fitter and some of their offspring will be represented by numbers even higher than 18. In this way a character can change by small steps through many generations, but the extent of the change will be unlimited, given enough time. Complex characters can evolve from simple ones, the only condition being that the complex character be fitter than the simple one. Notice that the variation among offspring is random. In each family some will be fitter, some less fit, than the parents. But there must be a hereditary basis to the variation; tall parents must tend, on the average, to have tall children.

Darwin recognized the necessity of continual hereditary variation for his theory and developed the idea of pangenesis, described in Chapter II, to account for it. The phenomenon of mutation, discovered later, is now accepted as providing the basis of variation for evolution. One further condition for evolution to take place by natural selection is that parents leave more offspring than are necessary to maintain the population. An organism that reproduces uniparentally, as bacteria and amoebae usually do, must produce more than one offspring before death, and organisms that reproduce biparentally, like man, must produce more than two.

The word "superior" or "fit" in the argument conceals more than is apparent. It is defined as meaning merely that proportionally more offspring are produced which survive to a reproductive age. This, however, may be for a number of different reasons. A very large number of eggs may be produced early in the life-span, as in mushrooms and fishes, or the offspring may be few but well cared for, as in mammals. The reproductive life-span may be short and intense or long and meager. Fitness will also depend on the environment; the same animal may be considered very fit in the Sahara Desert but quite unfit in Iceland. A light-colored peppered moth may be fitter and better adapted on a light tree, but less fit on a dark tree. The example of *Biston betularia* has been specially chosen because it represents a case where the actual course of evolution by natural selection has been studied in detail. This was possible because the environment changed rather rapidly in recent times and the moths evolved to become adapted to the new environment within a reasonable period of time. When the Industrial Revolution bloomed in the Midlands of England, the countryside became covered with soot. The light-colored trees became dark, and the light-colored moths evolved toward darkness. According to theory, some moths were always darker than others and when the trees became dark the darker moths avoided being caught by enemies and so left, on the average, more offspring than lighter moths. But, until it was actually shown that there was variation in color and that light moths were killed preferentially, the theory lacked a solid foundation. This was provided by H. B. D. Kettlewell, who showed, by painstaking field work, that birds do eat these moths in quantity and eat significantly more light-colored moths where there are dark, soot-covered trees and more dark-colored moths in areas where the trees are light-colored. The advantage of dark moths in sooty areas is about 30 per cent and the same is true of light moths on cleaner trees. Accurate information about selection is required, since there is evidence that in some species of moths the melanic, or dark, forms are better able to survive conditions of poor feeding. It could be that a mere relaxation of selection by predators would favor the dark forms because of their generally superior stamina.

The evolution of melanic forms of moth has been studied extensively, mainly because of the dramatic changes that have occurred in a short time. The first melanic peppered moth was recorded in 1850. It must have been a rarity at that time. In some populations of moth a change to melanism can occur in as little as fifty generations. But this very fast rate of evolution to melanic forms is due to the fact that only a single gene change is required and the melanic allele is dominant. This does not illustrate the slow evolution of a character by progressive selection of many genes, mostly recessive, that we have described earlier. It puts it rather under the category of what are called polymorphisms, which will be elaborated upon in Chapter XVIII.

A special and attractive form of selection, which was made much of by Darwin, but is thought to be less important today, is "sexual selection." Darwin argued that besides the "struggle for existence" with the cruel elements and predacious enemies, there is also a struggle for the favors of the opposite sex. A male who is able to disable other males of his species by superior pugilistic skill, or to attract females by his fairer complexion, will succeed in fertilizing more females. Darwin believed that this would be especially true of polygamous species and would explain the fact that in polygamous animals such as the peacock and lion, the sexes differ more than in guinea fowl, partridge, or terrestrial carnivora other than the lion. Sometimes, according to Darwin, it is not so much a matter of attracting or even catching the female as of avoiding the female's lethal clutches. He quotes De Greer, who saw a male spider that "in the midst of his preparatory caresses was seized by the object of his attentions, enveloped by her in a web and then devoured, a sight which filled him with horror and indignation." An evolutionist today would not be convinced by a single observation of this sort, but would require evidence that males with certain characters are preferentially devoured. Darwin's quotation from the Reverend O. P. Cambridge is not much more convincing, "M. Vinson gives a graphic account of the agile way in which the diminutive male escapes from the ferocity of the female, by gliding about and playing hide and seek over her body and along her gigantic limbs: in such a pursuit it is evident that the chances of escape would be in favor of the smallest males, whilst the larger ones would fall early victims, thus gradually a diminutive race of males would be selected, until at last they would dwindle to the smallest possible size compatible with the exercise of their generative functions,—in fact probably to the size we now see them, i.e. so small as to be a sort of parasite upon the female, and either beneath her notice, or too agile and too small for her to catch without great difficulty." Darwin does not discuss the other side of this coin: How did the female spider evolve toward such shocking habits?

Another example of sexual selection, this time in humans, concerns evolution of a female character toward an increase in size. Darwin writes, "It is well-known that with many Hottentot women the posterior part of the body projects in a wonderful manner; they are steatopygous; and Sir Andrew Smith is certain that this peculiarity is greatly admired by the men. He once saw a woman who was considered a beauty and she was so immensely developed behind that when seated on level ground she could not rise, and had to push herself along until she came to a slope. Some of the women in various Negro tribes have the same peculiarity; and, according to Burton, the Somal men 'are said to choose their wives by ranging them in a line, and by picking her out who projects farthest *a tergo*'."

Darwin may be right in presenting this as a case of sexual selection, but we should be alert to alternative explanations. It could be, for instance, that steatopygy has a nutritive function, the buttocks serving as a storage organ for fat or water, as a camel's hump was once thought to serve. Such a character might be of value to women whose menfolk spent considerable periods of time hunting and brought in the food only after long intervals. It would be both unnecessary and encumbrant in men. Tribes that developed steatopygy for the above reason might consequently develop an appreciation, through necessity, of the character. These examples show that it is very dangerous to accept the most obvious explanation for any particular example of evolution, but this caution should not distract us from accepting in general the theory of evolution by selection. The process has been firmly established in a few cases, like the case of melanism in moths that has been studied in detail, and in general, the theory offers a framework in which many calculations can, and have, been made. These calculations allow us to predict what should result in populations with given characteristics after a given number of generations.

The theory of evolution by selection explains the creation of an object as complex as a man without recourse to anything beyond the known laws of chemistry and physics. If this sounds too strong a statement, let it be said that it in no way eliminates the mystery of creation, nor, furthermore, does it explain the evolution of man in detail; it only points the way to an explanation.

The theory can be thought of as presenting a mechanism that produces the improbable. An animal is a very improbable collection of atoms. If a large number of atoms were to be mixed together at random they would be very unlikely to produce an amoeba, much less a man. The more complex an animal, the more unlikely it is that he should be produced by chance. Left to themselves, exposed to random change, things generally settle into more likely states, so evolution appears to be going against the grain. It does so, according to the theory, by throwing away, or stopping the reproduction of, the more probable states and multiplying the less probable. Selection is the sieve, screening out the simple and retaining the complex.

In the game of bridge, a hand consisting of thirteen spades is a remarkable event. It will only occur about once in every 635,013,559,600 times a hand is dealt. If one wanted to get many such hands by random deals, a prohibitive number of hands would have to be dealt; they would cover the surface of more than five hundred planets the size of the earth. To make a crude analogy with the theory of evolution, one could suppose that a few hundred hands were dealt first, and then all those with less than four spades were burnt but the rest were reproduced to make up a hundred hands. Next, a few cards were exchanged at random between some of the hands and a large pool of cards. To proceed to a second generation, all hands with less than five spades were burnt. The process of reproduction and exchange was repeated until all hands with less than eleven or twelve spades had been burnt. At this stage the population of a hundred hands would include a fair number consisting of thirteen spades. Thus, the exchange of cards was random all along, with spades not deliberately picked from the pool, yet by reproducing the hands after an exchange and by destroying those hands with few spades, a population of a hundred hands could eventually be built up that would have a fair number of hands with eleven, twelve, or thirteen spades.

This analogy is poor in many ways, but it illustrates the factors which are of importance in evolution: the population size, or number of hands; the mutation rate, or number of exchanges of cards made at each step; the selection pressure, or the rigidity with which unfit hands are thrown out.

A complex and fit organism can be represented by a hand with some eleven or more spades, and the deleterious effect of most mutations is illustrated by the fact that most random exchanges with other cards in a hand of eleven or more spades will be likely to reduce the number of spades in the hand. Evolution uses the rare beneficial mutations. A lowering of selective pressure, or allowing hands with fewer spades to reproduce, will have a degrading effect. The process is common in evolution; a good example can be seen in the loss of eyes among cave animals. The eye is a highly complex character and is not of much use in a cave where there is no light. The selection for eyes in cave animals is therefore weak and this lowering of selection pressure tends to eliminate the eye. Such a loss is commonly observed in cave animals.

In our artificial model, as well as in real biological cases, successful evolution depends upon a balance between mutation rate, selection pressure, and population size.

Entertaining arguments may be enjoyed on the topic of evolutionary progress, of what is meant by a higher organism or a more complex organism. One may question whether the evolution of some parasite to a more and more reduced form is progress or not; one may challenge the definition of "higher" and question whether a mouse is really more complex than *Paramecium,* whose complexities are especially apparent when it is viewed under the electron microscope. We will not indulge in such sophistries, but will take the dogmatic position that man is a higher form of life than the amoeba and that the main line of evolutionary progress has been toward the more complex forms.

XVII *The Heredity of Acquired Characters: The Final Answer*

From the time of the announcement of the theory of evolution to the present day, there have been individuals and schools of thought that disliked the randomness of mutations. They would not swallow the idea that variation is haphazard, without direction or purpose.

In recent years the most powerful of these groups was to be found in Soviet Russia, and the attitude of Trofin Lysenko, the leading figure of this school, is illustrated in the following quotation from his presidential address to the V. I. Lenin Academy of Agricultural Sciences in the U. S. S. R., 1948:

"Unable to reveal the laws of living nature, the Morganists have to resort to the theory of probabilities, and, since they fail to grasp the concrete content of biological processes, they reduce biological science to mere statistics. It is not for nothing that statisticians, like Galton, Pearson, and latterly Fisher and Wright, are also regarded as founders of Mendelism-Morganism. Probably, that is also the reason why academician Nemchinov has told us here that, as a statistician, he had no difficulty in mastering the chromosome theory of heredity."

The question of whether acquired characteristics are inherited is of less interest today than it was in the past. It is no longer a good question to ask. It is impossible to say that acquired characteristics are never inherited, but it can be confidently said that inheritance of this sort is not of widespread occurrence and is not of importance in evolution. Nearly all the experiments which have been put forward as demonstrating the process have been shown later to be in error or not repeatable.

In its crudest form, the inheritance of acquired characteristics means that if a limb is cut off, perhaps repeatedly throughout several generations, then offspring will be born without a limb—the lack of a limb will be inherited. Not many biologists have made this extreme claim. It is evident that operations such as cutting off dogs' tails, and circumcision among Jews, Arabs, and upper-class Englishmen, have been performed for many generations in particular families without any appreciable effect.[1] This crude form of the inheritance of acquired characteristics can be dismissed at once, or nearly at once, for one curiosity is of some interest. It happens that in one organism just such inheritance is found. The organism is a protozoan called *Difflugia corona* and the experiments were performed by H. S. Jennings of Johns Hopkins and published in 1937. The work represents a kind of trick, it is not of fundamental importance and it in no way challenges contemporary theories, but it makes one think a bit and be careful of

[1] However, Charles Darwin did manage to muster contrary evidence. He writes, "Circumcision is practiced by Mohammedans, but at a much later age than by Jews; and Riedel, assistant resident in North Celebes, writes to me that the boys there go naked until from six to ten years old; and he has observed that many of them, though not all, have their prepuces much reduced in length, and this he attributes to the inherited effects of the operation." (*The Variation of Animals and Plants under Domestication*, 1868)

one's language. *Difflugia corona* is a protozoan with a shell made of chitin in which siliceous particles are embedded. There is a circular opening in this shell which forms the mouth, and it is surrounded by a number of teeth. The number of teeth in any particular strain is constant. Jennings extracted teeth from *Difflugia* and observed the progeny for many generations. Generally, he found that the original number of teeth was restored after three or four generations, but in some cases it was not, and in these he had created a new strain with one less tooth. We must admit this is a genuine case of the inheritance of an acquired, or rather a lost, character; but it is a trivial case, for the mechanism is clear and it does not involve a change in genes.

Difflugia reproduces by budding, and the bud appears in the mouth region. After a certain amount of protoplasm has been extruded, the shell of the baby bud is formed and its mouth is formed next to the mouth of the parent shell. Teeth in the bud are formed to fit next to the teeth of the parent. The number of teeth can thus be regarded in part as environmental and the pertinent environmental factor is the number of teeth in the mother (Fig. 38).

This method of forming teeth can be viewed as a template mode of reproduction, the mother's pattern of teeth stamping out the progeny's teeth. The fact that the original number of teeth is, in most cases, restored shows that the genes are probably also a determining factor and usually predominate.

The more serious claims for the inheritance of acquired characteristics involve cases in which a character is really acquired by an individual. P. Kammerer, a young Austrian zoologist and a vigorous adherent of the theory, mentioned Japanese long-tailed cocks. These birds have tails some six to nine feet long. It is customary to perch them in a tall cage and attach weights to their tails. This treatment stimulates their tail-feather follicles to produce much more feather than they normally would. It was claimed that this treatment changed the hereditary makeup of the breed so that longer tail feathers were produced naturally. To prove this one would have to show that there was no selection of birds which had naturally long tails, irrespective of whether they were pulled or not. This has not been done.

FIGURE 38

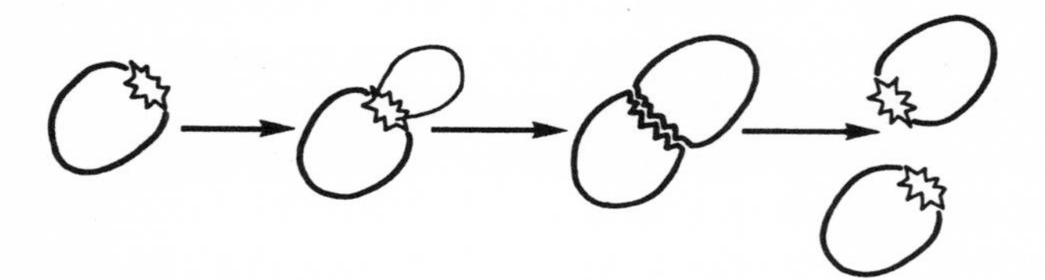

The Peculiar Case of Difflugia Corona. The number of teeth in the mouth region of this organism are inherited through a sort of template mechanism of the most superficial kind. The daughter *Difflugia* (upper organism) has the same number of teeth as the mother because they form on the pattern of the mother. Four stages in the production of a daughter are shown from left to right. This character presents a true but superficial and trivial case of the inheritance of acquired characteristics.

The idea that traits developed during the lifetime of an organism can be passed on to the children has led to some amusing ideas; it has been held, for instance, that older and therefore wiser men would beget wiser children than young green men. One scholar, John F. Kendrick by name, went so far as to write, "The delusion that the eldest son should be the crown prince has been the historical *damnum fatale* of royalty and has left the word 'king' without dignity except in a poker game." He favored succession by ultimogeniture rather than primogeniture.

The inheritance of acquired mental traits has interested several biologists. An English psychologist working at Harvard

University reported in 1927 that he had taught rats to choose a dark platform when given the choice of a dark or a light one and that the children of these rats inherited this imposed knowledge. Unfortunately, it was shown later that his results were almost certainly due to selection of more knowledgeable rats in mixed broods.

Perhaps the most sensational claim was made by the aforementioned Kammerer concerning a species of the amphibian *Alytes*. This particular species, unlike some other amphibians, does not have certain dark pads, known as nuptial pads, on the forelegs. Kammerer induced the formation of nuptial pads on some individuals by changing their environment during mating, and he claimed that these pads were then inherited. Many eminent scientists saw the specimens of *Alytes*, and opinions differed strongly as to whether they were good evidence or not. The climax in the controversy came when G. K. Noble, at the American Museum of Natural History, was allowed to cut sections of the pretended pads and examine the dark pigment in them. His conclusion was that the pigment was India ink which had been injected into the skin. The reply of one of Kammerer's supporters was, "The only possibility we can think of is that someone has tried to preserve the aspect of such black nuptial pads in fear of their vanishing by the destruction of the melanin through exposure to the sun in the museum case." The ink may have been injected in good faith with the intention of merely accentuating, not distorting, scientific truth. But it caused serious doubt, and this chapter of genetics ended disastrously. Kammerer shot himself a few weeks later and is said to have bequeathed his collections to the Soviet Academy of Sciences.

Among other claims in this general category is the Russian claim of turning winter wheat into spring wheat by moistening and cooling the seeds. The end result of this experiment was that a field of winter wheat would produce, after a few generations, a field of spring wheat. We can accept the result, but in an experiment of this kind it is vital to eliminate any possibility that some spring wheat was already present in the original winter wheat and that this was, in fact, selected during the experiment. Such a possibility was not eliminated nor even fairly entertained by the people who made the claims.

A similar objection can be made to more recent experiments in France and in Russia on ducks and chickens, respectively. Blood from a bird of one color pattern was injected into a bird which was colored differently and a permanent hereditary change was said to have been made in the recipient bird. In this case, there is a possibility that mutant types were picked up among the birds that were injected and that injection had nothing to do with it. But if one is satisfied that proper controls were used to rule out this possibility, then one must look for a possible explanation for the phenomenon along the lines of accepted genetic theory. It might be, for instance, that DNA in the blood of the donor reached the gonads of the recipient and there transformed certain genes in the same manner that DNA transforms pneumococcus cells. Such an occurrence would be surprising, but not too surprising. Apart from these two cases, transformation seems to be a phenomenon restricted to the bacteria. Even in lower plants such as *Neurospora,* attempts to demonstrate transformation have been negative, probably because an adequate length of DNA cannot get past all the barriers of membranes and destructive enzymes that are present in eukaryotic organisms between the cell surface and the nucleoproteins of the chromosomes in the nucleus.

The most critical phenomenon which might be taken to demonstrate the inheritance of acquired characteristics concerns the production of drug resistance in bacteria. It is well known that since the introduction of penicillin, strains of staphylococci have been found which are resistant to this drug.

Resistance has also developed to many other drugs, and by other bacteria; it represents an important medical challenge. Resistant strains are particularly abundant in hospitals, where the use of antibiotics is naturally frequent, and in some English hospitals the widespread use of antibiotics as sterilizing agents has been discontinued in favor of less sophisticated disinfectants on this account.

The production of drug-resistant strains of bacteria can be demonstrated in the laboratory. It is only necessary to grow a large number of bacteria in a medium containing the appropriate concentration of the drug; after a number of bacterial generations, the culture will be drug-resistant. The process can even go further; strains can be produced that are not only resistant to the drug, but are actually dependent upon it. They grow well if the drug is present, but will not grow if it is absent.

The medical lesson to be learned from this phenomenon is that antibiotics should not be used indiscriminately for minor complaints or for long periods in small doses as a prophylactic. The theoretical interest of the phenomenon lies in the question of whether the antibiotic has induced a hereditary change in the bacteria or whether spontaneous mutations have been favored by an environment containing the antibiotic. According to the first possibility, the resistant cells are not formed unless the antibiotic is present; according to the second possibility, they are. Remember that in order to test a culture for sensitivity or resistance, one must try to grow it on penicillin medium. Several ingenious experiments have been devised to distinguish between the two possibilities, and more critical thought has been concentrated on this problem than on any other example of the apparent inheritance of acquired characteristics.

One of the simplest experiments to perform is illustrated in Figure 39. A number of plates are inoculated with a large

FIGURE 39

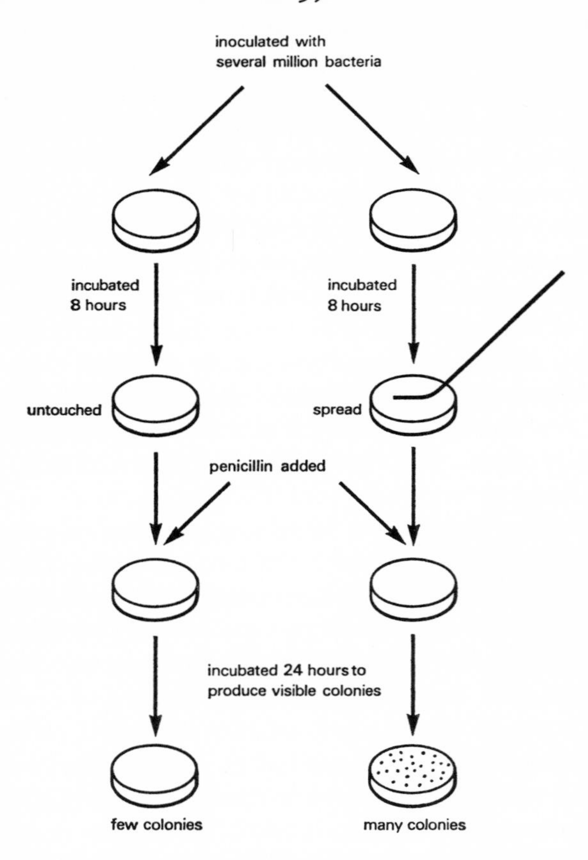

Inheritance of Acquired Characteristics—Spreading. This simple and dramatic experiment indicates strongly that resistant strains of bacteria arise by selection of random variants. See the text for an explanation.

number of bacteria and incubated for a short period of time, during which about eight divisions occur and each original cell produces a small microcolony of about 256 cells. The plates are then divided into two groups. The first group is left untouched, but the cells in the second group are spread with a sterile glass rod. The antibiotic is then added to plates in both groups equally, and they are all incubated again. Any bacteria that are resistant to penicillin will grow during this second incubation and will produce visible colonies. When an experiment like this is performed, it is found that there are more colonies on the plates where the cells have been spread than on the plates where the cells have not been spread. This is evidence that the resistant bacteria arose spontaneously and were not induced by the antibiotic. The reasoning is as follows: If the antibiotic induces the change in the few bacteria that are able to grow up into visible colonies, then spreading the bacteria around before the antibiotic is added should not affect the number of colonies that results. The critical change in the bacteria occurs after they have been spread. If, on the other hand, spontaneous mutations to resistance are occurring all the time, then one or more mutants may be present in the original inoculum and more will occur during the first eight hours of growth. Since we are considering a hereditary change, these resistant mutants will multiply during the first eight hours of growth to produce small bunches, microcolonies, of resistant cells. If, for the sake of argument, there are exactly eight bacterial generations, so that each cell of the original inoculum produces 256 cells after eight hours, then any cell that was already a mutant in the inoculum will produce a microcolony of 256 resistant cells. A mutation that occurs just after the first generation on the plates will produce a microcolony of 128 cells. A mutation after the second generation will produce a microcolony of 64 resistant cells, and so on. A mutation just before the last division will produce a pair of resistant cells. Since mutations will be occurring at random in time, both groups of plates will consist of a large number of microcolonies of sensitive cells and a few, perhaps one or two, microcolonies of anything from 2 to 256 resistant cells. In the plates in which the bacteria are not spread, these one or two resistant microcolonies will grow up into large visible colonies after the antibiotic has been added and the plates have been incubated.

In plates belonging to the other group, the cells in the one or two resistant microcolonies resulting from the first incubation will not be left together in a cluster, but will be spread as single cells all over the surface of the plate. Each single resistant cell will then grow up into a visible colony after the antibiotic has been added and the plates have been incubated a second time. The second lot of plates will thus contain from 2 to 256 times as many visible colonies at the end of the experiment as the first lot. This simple experiment provides very good evidence that the resistant cells are due to random mutations and not to induction by the antibiotic. The two alternative possibilities are sometimes referred to as instructive and elective, indicating that in the first case the antibiotic contains some information which is translated by the bacteria into the pattern or processes which constitute resistance, whereas in the second case the antibiotic merely elects those bacteria which already have the information for resistance.

This simple experiment is, as we said, a very good test, but objections can nevertheless be raised. It might be that spreading the bacteria after eight hours' growth predisposes them to change when the antibiotic is added. Spreading puts cells onto fresh parts of the medium. It could be that in this different environment they are more apt to be induced to resistance by the antibiotic. This may seem a rather strained objection, but it was considered by Howard B. Newcombe, who first described the procedure. He almost completely eliminated such a possibility by comparing the results of different experiments in which the times of incubation before spreading were varied.

An experiment which makes the same kind of test can be

performed in liquid medium in test-tubes (Fig. 40). A liquid culture of bacteria is divided into two parts. One part is incubated in a single container with normal medium, and then plated out onto, say, a hundred plates containing antibiotic. The other part is divided up into a hundred small tubes with the same medium and incubated similarly. The contents of each small tube, or a known portion of each tube, is then plated onto an antibiotic plate. In this experiment the total number of colonies growing up on the antibiotic plates will be the same in the two groups, but the distribution of colonies will be different if the process is elective. In the first group there will be roughly the same number of colonies on each plate, but in the second group there will be some plates with no colonies and also some plates with a large number of colonies. The distribution of colonies in the two cases can be analyzed in more detail. Actually, the statement that in the first case there will be roughly the same number of colonies on each plate, is itself rough. When we know the average number of colonies per plate, which is merely the total number of colonies divided by the number of plates, we can calculate their theoretical distribution. This theoretical calculation will tell us how many plates we should get with no colonies, how many with one colony, how many with two colonies, how many with three, and so on. The distribution, known as a Poisson distribution after the French mathematician Denis Poisson (1781–1840), is given by $\frac{1}{e^m} \quad \frac{m}{e^m} \quad \frac{m^2}{2!e^m} \quad \frac{m^3}{3!e^m} \quad \ldots$ where m is the average number of colonies per plate.[2] The first term of this series gives the number of plates we would expect with no colonies, the second term gives the number of plates we would expect with one colony, the third term the number of plates with two colonies, and so on. If automobile

[2] The expression 3! denotes $3 \times 2 \times 1$; e stands for a mathematical constant, 2.718. . . .

FIGURE 40

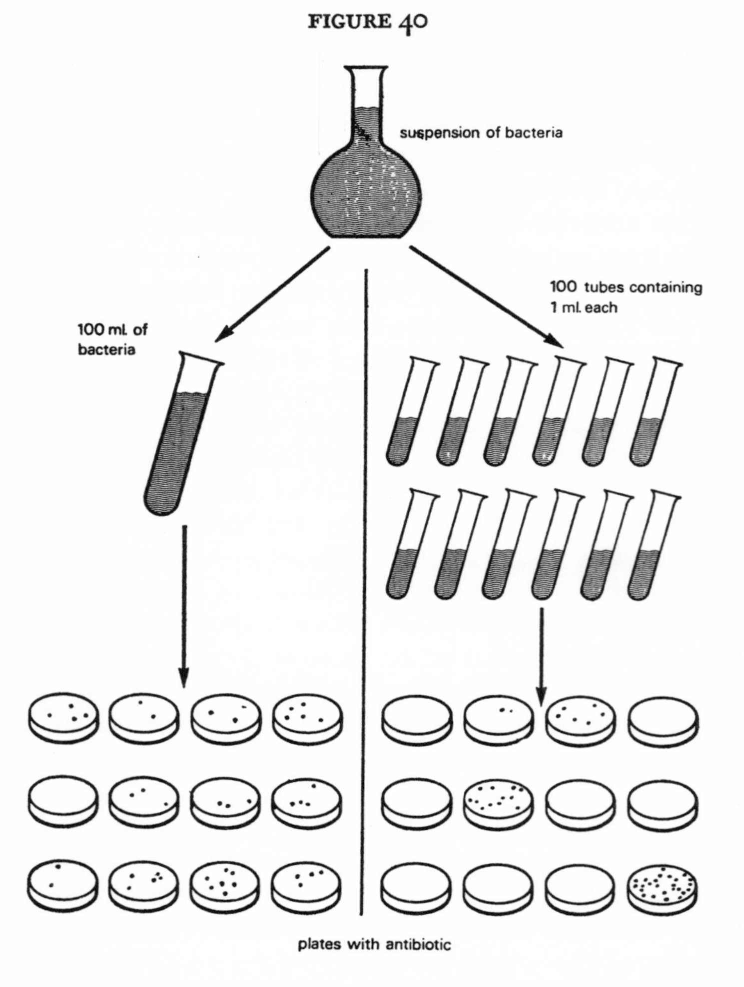

Inheritance of Acquired Characteristics—Fluctuation. The Luria-Delbruck fluctuation method. This experiment, originally applied in 1943 to the production of bacterial strains resistant to certain viruses (phage), can also be applied to antibiotic resistance. It is a rather more laborious but also more sophisticated method than that illustrated in Figure 39. The explanation is in text.

accidents occur at random and are independent, then if we know the average number of accidents in a day, the Poisson distribution will specify how many days in the year one would expect with no accidents in a town, how many days one would expect with two accidents, how many days with three accidents, and so on. If earthworms occur at random in a field, *i.e.* they do not attract or repel one another, then if we divide the field up into squares of the same size and determine the average number of worms in a square, the Poisson distribution will tell us how many squares we may expect to find with no earthworms, how many squares with one earthworm, how many squares with two earthworms, and so on. The theoretical distribution that one would expect in the second group of plates is much more complicated, but was calculated by the British radiobiologist D. E. Lea. It will not be given here, but the fact that both distributions are known means that statistical tests can be made to judge how far a particular experiment confirms the existence of one or the other process. This means that it is possible to say not only whether resistant bacteria arise by an instructive or by an elective process, but also to what extent both processes may occur. In all cases, with the possible exception of a curious drug-resistant character in *Chlamydomonas* which is non-Mendelian, the results agree rather well with the theoretical distribution expected of an elective process.

One final experiment, which approaches the problem from a rather different point of view, will be described. This experiment was described by the young American, Joshua Lederberg, who won the 1958 Nobel Prize in physiology and medicine for his discovery of sex in bacteria. He introduced the technique known as replica plating, which has proved of great value in many different kinds of experiment. In replica plating, a piece of sterile velvet is stretched over a cylinder which is just a bit smaller than a Petri dish. A dish with a growth of bacteria can then be pressed onto this velvet and a part of the bacterial growth will stick to the velvet. A virgin dish can now be pressed onto the same velvet and the bacteria will be transferred to it.

The particular experiment we are concerned with consists in inoculating a dish containing normal solid medium with bacteria and incubating it for a few hours to produce a good overall growth. This plate is then replicated, by means of a velvet pad, onto an antibiotic plate. Care is taken to mark the plates so that there are points of reference on the two plates which correspond. One or two colonies may grow up on the antibiotic plate, which indicates that they were derived from a small group of resistant cells on the normal plate. The velvet will not have picked up the whole of this group of resistant cells, and the rest of them, or some part of the rest of them, can be picked up subsequently with a needle. This is possible because their position on the normal plate can be found by reference to the position of the colony on the antibiotic plate. Surrounding sensitive cells will also be picked up by the needle, but there will be a good proportion of resistant cells. These are then inoculated into liquid medium and incubated, and a portion is then spread on a new plate with normal medium. The whole operation is then repeated, and it is found that this time there are about a hundred times more colonies growing up on the antibiotic plate. After four or five repetitions of the whole process, a pure culture of resistant cells can be obtained on the normal plates (Fig. 41).

The experiment consists essentially in growing the original culture on a normal plate, picking off a portion of this and inoculating it into liquid medium, then inoculating a new plate with this liquid growth, and repeating the cycle several times. The important point is that at no time is this culture line exposed to antibiotic. Antibiotic plates are inoculated indirectly from the velvet and are used only to tell us where

FIGURE 41

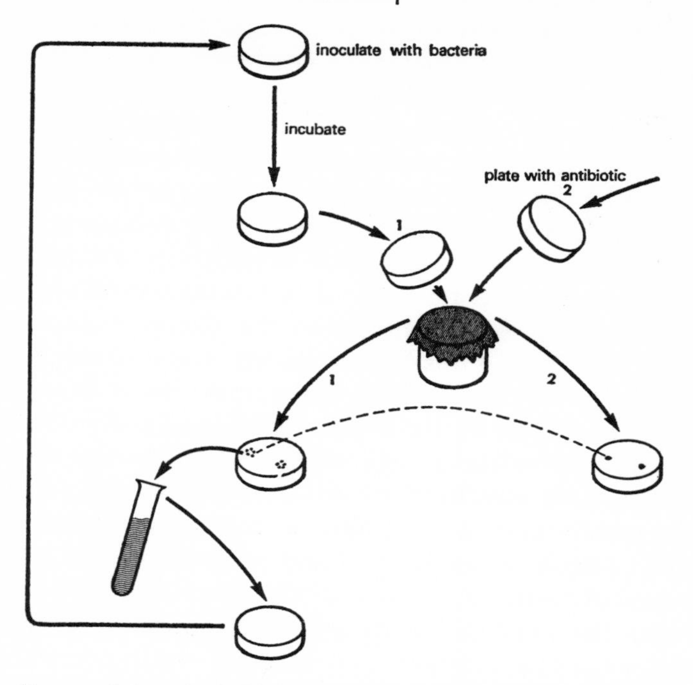

Inheritance of Acquired Characteristics—Replica Plating. The Lederberg technique of replica plating is shown. The plate containing antibiotic is used as an indicator to show where the mutant bacteria lie. The bacteria in a corresponding position on a normal plate are then cultured in a test-tube, and the whole process is repeated.

to pick off the colony for each generation of liquid cultures. The overall operation changes a sensistive culture into a resistant culture without any of the cells involved being exposed to the antibiotic.

In conclusion, we can say that there is some diverse and hazy evidence that acquired characters may be inherited, but that all the more critical work, especially that concerned with the most likely organisms, the bacteria, has shown that random mutation and selection are responsible. We said at the beginning of this chapter that the question of the inheritance of acquired characters is no longer a good question. A few years ago, when the chemistry of the gene was unknown and it was generally believed to be a very large and complex molecule or group of molecules, it was of interest to know whether genes had some of the properties of their phenotypes; whether, say in a bacteria, the gene which controlled the fermenting of a certain sugar had some chemical similarity to the enzyme which performed this function. If it did, then some acquired characters might be inherited and the phenomenon might prove to be a fruitful line of research into the structure of the gene. Today we know that genes consist essentially of an array of four different nucleotides. This array bears no structural similarity to the protein which the gene makes except, as we have seen, that the total length of the amino acid chain of the protein must be a certain fraction—perhaps one-third—of the length, in amino acid and nucleotide units, of the nucleic acid chain. In the light of this knowledge, it is apparent that the induction of penicillin-resistance by penicillin would mean that penicillin, or a closely related metabolic substance, would have to react specifically with one or more nucleic acids in particular positions on the long genic array and change them to other specific nucleic acids. Such reactions appear unlikely. The more complex cases in rats, chickens, ducks, and amphibians that we have mentioned appear even less likely.

XVIII *A Closer Look at Selection*

In many fields of biology, research tends to become quantitative. After the discovery of a new phenomenon or the presentation of a new hypothesis, subsequent work consists of finding something to measure, performing experiments that give a measurable answer, and making numerical calculations. This is true of the theory of evolution by selection.

The essential requirement for an evolutionary process is the existence of entities capable of being inherited, of reproducing variation, and of being selected. The process can be thought of as differential reproduction. These properties were responsible for the evolution of simple atoms and molecules into the complex features of man. They can be thought of as the very definition of life. Science fiction writers can speculate upon the peculiar systems that might fill these requirements and thus evolve toward the complexity we call life.

In life as we know it on earth the unit of variation is the mutating gene. It reproduces an exact copy of itself and it occasionally assumes a variant form which also reproduces exact copies. The unit of selection is more complex. The most obvious object which comes to mind is the individual animal or plant. This is what Darwin undoubtedly had in mind. The individual is the most obvious unit of reproduction. A man either reproduces or he does not. He reproduces more or he reproduces less, according to his fitness. A particular gene does not reproduce at a faster or slower rate than the other genes in a cell. Selection, as we have indicated, is intimately related to reproduction, and for this reason one might be led to take the individual as the unit of selection. But a little thought blurs the picture. There is the question of sex; can males and females be lumped together as one entity in the study of evolution? What about haploid selection—sperm, or eggs, that are favored because of their genotype? And should we think in terms of a whole population, race, species, or genus competing with and undergoing selection in relation to another such population? Some aspects of these questions will be examined below, and some of the features of variation and selection that have been found amenable to quantitative treatment will be described in the next chapter.

Let us consider first some of the difficulties of evolutionary theory which we run into when considering particular situations. The first difficulty, which has occurred to many people, concerns the evolution of complex organs such as wings and eyes. It would appear that such organs are advantageous only when perfected. The steps leading to their perfection would not seem, in many cases, to provide any advantage. Half a wing is of no more use than the smaller half of a dollar bill. A retina without a lens is no more advantageous than a film without a camera.

Social insects, ants and bees, are remarkable on account of the specialization of workers. Among ants, workers may be of several highly specialized types. These types arose, we might assume, because they were a fitter type than the unspecialized insects, a type that survived longer and left more offspring.

But we assume erroneously, for among both ants and bees the workers are sterile; they leave no offspring, whatever their fitness status. Specialization has reached such a degree of refinement that reproduction itself is monopolized by a special type. To understand how a situation like this could fit into the Darwinian picture, we must think in terms of the population, not the individual. Instead of comparing the fitness of worker to nonworker, we must consider the fitness of a colony of insects which has specialized workers compared to that of a colony which does not specialize, or specializes differently. We must estimate which colony will do better in the long run. The fitter colony will expand in numbers. Instead of thinking of the struggle of one individual with another for existence, we must think in terms of the struggle of a population with another population. The population having the fitter structure, in terms of its individuals, will be less likely to become extinct in competition with other populations.

The same argument holds for any altruistic trait on the part of an individual; it may be actually detrimental to the individual, but if it benefits the population, that population may survive, and the altruistic trait will survive with it. Let us consider, somewhat facetiously, the evolution of feminine beauty in human populations. Unusually beautiful women may tend to become film or stage actresses. By and large, these professions do not encourage the production of large families; a large family may even be a handicap to a film star. Does this then imply that the evolutionary process favors homeliness? If we think in terms of populations, we may well find that although film stars themselves do not reproduce more than average women, yet a population that includes exceptionally beautiful women and has the opportunity of spending evenings watching them on the screen, may reproduce at a higher rate than another population not so privileged. Celibate priesthoods and courageous warriors who die young come to mind in this connection.

The converse is true. Dishonesty and egotism may be an advantage to the individual. He may tend to grow rich and have a larger than average family. As a population contains more and more dishonest individuals, however, it will as a whole be at a disadvantage compared to a population of honest people. The dishonest individuals will also have less of an advantage as they become more numerous.

Selection may assume subtle forms and vary according to circumstances. In many butterflies and other insects one species resembles another which is poisonous or distasteful. The first species, called the mimic, gains an advantage because enemies who have learned from sad experience to avoid the poisonous insect, innocently avoid the mimic as well. This process works so long as the mimic is in a minority. As soon as there are a large number of mimics around, the enemy unlearns his prudence and begins to eat this type again. So when a population takes up mimicry, it had better not overdo it. It had better have only a proportion of its members mimic any one type. Again, we can think in terms of the evolution of a whole population or species.

We can also think of this sort of situation in another way. Let us have in mind that fitness and selection depend upon the environment. A heavy insulating layer of fat and fur may have considerable selective advantage in the Arctic, but will have none in central Africa. When we consider one individual, then the other individuals of the same species can be looked upon as the environment. Returning to our example of mimics, an environment consisting of 90 per cent mimics will be different from an environment of 10 per cent mimics. The mimic character may have an advantage in the latter but not in the former environment. Its contribution to fitness will depend upon its frequency in the population.

In some species of butterflies only the females are mimics.

Since one male can fertilize several females, males need not be as numerous as females in a population and the occasional loss of a male for lack of mimic protection is not so important as the loss of a female.

Another case where selective advantage will depend upon the frequency of a character is pugilistic proficiency in males. If bucks fight among themselves for the privilege of females, then one extra-large and powerful buck will have a considerable advantage over his weaker adversaries. He will presumably leave more progeny, and the characters large size and pugilistic skill will have a strong selective advantage. But if this character becomes frequent, so that most bucks are large and powerful, then the advantage will be diminished. It is an example of the law of diminishing returns. We can add a further factor. Let us assume that whatever gene or genes make for large size and prowess in combat also have an effect on fertility—that they lower fertility. The large animals will be less fertile than small ones. In such a situation the correlated characters may increase in frequency until most individuals are large, but the fertility of so many males will be so low that the population as a whole will have a good chance of becoming extinct.

In mice an interesting gene which has a recessive lethal allele has been studied by L. C. Dunn at Columbia University. The heterozygote (t^+t) is quite normal, like the wild type (t^+t^+), but the recessive homozygote (tt) dies in an embryonic stage. Most of the mouse populations in the United States, whether house mice or country mice, have been found to have t alleles. Here then is an allele which seems to cause unadulterated harm. The double dose is lethal and in the single dose no virtue can be detected. Why is this allele not eliminated by the process of natural selection? The mutation rate $t^+ \rightarrow t$ is not particularly high, certainly not high enough to maintain the t allele in the population against strong selection. The answer to this puzzle is curious. Sperm carrying the allele t

are found to be about 95 per cent more successful in fertilizing eggs than sperm carrying wild-type t^+ alleles. This was found by crossing heterozygous t^+t male mice to appropriate female mice which carried other genes such that offspring resulting from eggs fertilized by t^+ could be distinguished from those fertilized by *t* sperm. The ratio of the two kinds of offspring was 5:95. This is a case of gametic or haploid selection. It is difficult to know how prevalent this kind of selection is, but the case is a reminder that selection can act in curious ways and at any time throughout the life cycle.

One final evolutionary peculiarity which deserves attention is polymorphism. A population that is polymorphic is one that consists of two or more sharply defined types. The most obvious polymorphic trait is sex, upon which we need not dwell. Human populations are polymorphic for blood groups. Species of butterflies with mimics represent another case of polymorphism, and we have seen that a polymorphic species may do better than one with no mimics or one in which there are too many mimics of a single type. It is common to find more than one kind of mimic in a species, so there may be three or more distinct types of butterfly all belonging to the same species. We have also mentioned the social insects, which have not only functional male and female types, but also several distinct sterile types of individual in a colony. This is also a form of polymorphism, but in this case the difference between fertile females and workers is usually not genetic but physiological. It results from specific chemicals in the food, which switch development from queen to worker.

One other cause of polymorphism is worthy of mention because it may be of more general significance. Most species of animal or plant inhabit areas of land or sea which present opportunities for many different ways of life. The technical term for a particular way of life is a "niche." Various individuals of a population may be more or less well adapted to live on a certain food or in a certain peculiar local environment where they cannot be seen by enemies or cannot easily be captured. Now, each particular niche may be able to accommodate only a fraction of the whole population and so the species which is polymorphic and continually produces individuals of different types adapted to different niches will do better than one which is not.

The relative advantages of species which specialize and become rigidly adapted to a narrow niche, those which do not specialize but are jacks-of-all-trades, and those which are polymorphic and specialize in several directions, is an interesting subject which can and has been investigated abstractly, algebraically. The genetic basis of polymorphism is of particular interest. The melanic forms of the peppered moth previously mentioned can be considered a sort of polymorphism in time because these moths seem to have developed the capacity to change rapidly from a mostly pale population to a population of mostly very black moths. To introduce this change as an example of evolution, as was done in Chapter XVI, is therefore a bit unfair. There has probably been a long history of evolution toward dominance of a gene, or category of genes, that determines melanic forms. It is known that during the last hundred years or so the melanic form of moth has become blacker than it was. It is also known that the gene for melanic form is dominant only in English peppered moths. When the gene is introduced, through crossing, to Canadian peppered moths, the dominance breaks down and all kinds of intermediate kinds of blackness are found in heterozygotes. There must have been an evolution, in English moths, of a background of minor genes—polygenes—which had the effect of making a major gene for black color dominant so that a population could change rapidly from white to black. This evolution most probably started before the Industrial Revolution, but proved providential when the black clouds of England's ambitious factories swept parts of the countryside. Mutation of a gene from black to pale must sometimes occur, but populations need not wait for mutations to provide the pale allele, for in the black populations, even after a hundred and twenty years of evolution in the sooty neighborhood of Manchester, the pale allele has a frequency of some 10 or 15 per cent, which means, as we shall see in the next chapter, that 1 or 2 per cent of the individuals are of the persecuted pale type. It would be interesting to know why they are not eliminated altogether; presumably there is some advantage in being a heterozygous rather than a homozygous black even if this means producing 1 or 2 per cent of the unfit pale moths.

The familiar ladybug beetles are polymorphic for the number and pattern of black or yellow dots on their smooth, shiny backs. These delightful insects feed on aphids and other undesirable creatures and are therefore beneficial to man. In 1889 the citrus industry in California was in danger of being completely wiped out by an Australian scale insect. Ladybug beetles were introduced from the country in which the pest had originated, and within a year and a half the industry was permanently rid of this threat. Ladybug beetles protect themselves from enemies not by camouflage, like the peppered moth, but by warning coloration. They taste bad to their enemies and are brilliantly and distinctively colored so as to be easily recognized and avoided. The genetic control of their color pattern was studied by a Chinese investigator, C. C. Tan, while he was at Columbia University. He has since returned to China, and it is not easy in the Western world to follow his latest researches. He found that the pattern of spots is controlled by no less than fifteen alleles of a single gene. The patterns do not fall into any obvious order that might reflect gradients of temperature or chemical concentration. Dominance is such that heterozygotes are black in areas that are black in either parent. The number of different heterozygotes that can be formed from fifteen alleles is large, and the number of different patterns found in nature is also large—two hundred different color patterns have been found. Each color pattern occurs in only one geographic region, and the population of each region can be described in terms of the relative frequencies of the color patterns found in it. Presumably there are special features in each region that favor particular patterns.

This work presents an interesting problem in morphogenesis. In the framework of contemporary ideas one has to imagine the large number of patterns as due to different amino acid substitutions in a protein, an enzyme. It is not at all obvious how this could be achieved.

The actual course of evolution in a large number of plants and animals has been studied in detail. The fossil record is not all we could wish it to be because the coincidence of conditions that must occur to produce a good fossil is rare, but fossil hunters have reaped some rich harvests. From a study of fossils from different geological periods, together with contemporary species, an outline of the ancestral forms can be put together.

If we take a look at the evolution of various groups from a very general view, certain features are prominent. Perhaps the most striking feature is that some organisms evolve rapidly and some hardly at all. Examples of very slowly evolving animals are provided by *Triops cancriformis*, a fresh- or brackish-water crustacean whose head and thorax are covered with an oval shell, which has not changed beyond the limits of a species for 170,000,000 years, and *Lingula*, a marine bivalve, which has fossil ancestors classified in the same genus which lived some 400,000,000 years ago. Among the rapid evolvers there are some monkeys, the green monkeys *Cercopithecus aethiops* on the island of St. Kitts in the Caribbean, which have changed distinctly in the last 300 years. Most rates of evolution fall between these extremes. The evolution of the horse has been particularly well studied. The most primitive ancestor of the horse was a small mammal whose fossil remains were found in the southeast corner of England in strata which are probably some 60,000,000 years old. Subsequent evolution of the horse took place on land which is now the United States. The direct line went through some eight genera. The older forms were browsers, but later forms became specialized for grazing. They also increased in size and became specialized for speed. A notable change was the elongation of leg bones and toes. They gradually evolved from three-toed to one-toed animals. Several side branches, which have become extinct, are known. The horse finally disappeared from the American continent, to be reintroduced by Cortez with disastrous results for the indigenous human population. The rate of evolution was 0.13 genera per million years, or 7,500,000 years for a change of genus.

A rough estimate of the rate of change in the length of bones and teeth has been made by J. B. S. Haldane to the effect that evolution can increase size from 1 per cent to 10 per cent every million years. An estimate of man's evolution goes from *Australopithecus africanus*, 1,750,000 years ago; to *Homo erectus*, 1,100,000 years ago; and finally to *Homo sapiens*, 250,000 years ago. This is a rate of one species change every million years or so.

The evolution of the horse represents a line with a fairly definite trend; there were some branches and some exploration of different types, but in general, there was a smooth evolution toward speed.

The evolution of finches, often referred to as "Darwin's finches," on the Galápagos Islands is another well-studied subject. In this case, the remarkable feature is the variety of different species which rapidly evolved from a single type. This radiating kind of evolution appears to take place when a species is suddenly presented with several new and vacant environments. The Galápagos Islands most probably arose out of the sea and were slowly colonized by plants and animals from the American mainland that were able somehow to bridge the watery gap. When the ancestral finches arrived on the various islands, they found a rich variety of ways of life and few natural enemies. Several variant finches could multiply and fill various niches; from these, other new variants might arise and would again have a good chance of finding a hospitable environment. Thus, new species and genera would be formed on the various islands. The same sort of thing must have happened on a grand scale when the first fishlike creature was able to survive on land and when the first reptilelike creature was sufficiently different from his ancestors to be airborne.

Sometimes a change in environment—a change in rainfall or temperature, for instance—can present new ways of life and eliminate the old. When the environment is both uniform and constant, as it would appear to be on the ocean bed, we expect evolution to proceed at a leisurely pace. This uniformity characterizes the environment of *Lingula,* which has been mentioned as an example of slow evolution. In some cases the environment changes seasonally and drastically. Freshwater algae, such as *Chlamydomonas,* living in a small pond may find conditions very different in summer and in winter. Each summer may present different environments in various small ponds or in parts of a larger pond. It would be an advantage to fill these niches as rapidly as possible. *Chlamydomonas,* like its allied types, seems well designed for this mode of life. It forms a resistant zygote which can survive the cold winter and perhaps be blown about to other regions. When the zygote germinates in the spring it produces a variety of genotypes, the numerous recombinations of genes for which the zygotes were heterozygous. Some of these types will be just what is needed to live in a particular environment. In order to fill a particular environment, the fit *Chlamydomonas* should multiply their type as rapidly as possible without producing more zygotes and the variety of segregants that would result. As we have seen in Chapter III, *Chlamydomonas* can do just this; it can multiply in the haploid state asexually.

Longevity itself must be considered a factor of evolutionary significance. The optimum time from one generation to the next depends on many factors. One can imagine that a species living in a rapidly and constantly changing environment had better have a short life-span in order to evolve rapidly enough to keep up with the environment. But we must remember that life-span is only one of the factors which determine the speed of evolutionary change.

Reference has already been made to the fact that although selection is usually thought of as referring to individuals, it may take place at the level of populations. A whole species may die out, while another lives and expands. The extinction of species is, in fact, the rule rather than the exception. In the particular case of the Mesozoic tetrapods, 99 per cent are estimated to have become extinct and only 1 per cent have left living descendants. The extinction of species is, nevertheless, something of a puzzle. Why, for instance, did the giant reptiles that dominated the earth about 150,000,000 years ago become extinct, while the mammals rose to occupy the dominant role? Opinions on these topics are based largely on guesswork. Each biologist is entitled to his opinion, and there is no experimental result or conclusive fossil evidence that will exact, by persuasion, one unanimous opinion. At one time most biologists thought that the giant reptiles died out because the emergence of the mammals confronted them with overwhelming competition. Today, most biologists would reverse cause and effect to say that the extinction of giant reptiles left a host of vacant environments, causing the radiant evolution of mammals to fill these environments. This focuses attention on the problem of why the reptiles became extinct. Some think that it was due to the increasing coldness of the climate—that their large size and physiological makeup left them unable to cope with the cold. A few think quite the opposite, that it was due to the heat—and for a peculiar reason. It is well known that in mammals the formation of sperm in the testicles is very sensitive to heat and that at a temperature very close to body temperature functional sperm are not formed. The external position of testicles in many mammals, including man, is probably an adaptation to this fact. The giant reptiles, according to this train of thought, could not cool off enough to be fertile. This rather wild guess assumes that the giant reptiles were like mammals in this respect, a doubtful assumption.

Some species appear to have become extinct because they became ill-adapted, which seems an anomaly. An example is *Megaceros*, an animal that evolved toward larger size, presumably an advantage, but also evolved monstrously large antlers, which must have been a fatal disadvantage.

It is very plausible that the genes which make for greater size of the whole animal should also produce a much greater increase in the size of the antlers. As larger-sized animals were selected so, willy-nilly, large and cumbersome antlers were produced.[1] This partly explains the extinction of such animals, but it must be admitted that it is not quite clear in any particular case why evolution in a certain direction did not stop when disadvantage overbalanced advantage.

In the majority of cases of extinction of species, we have no idea of the details of the process. We can give a general description of what happened, but we do not know how to describe it formally: whether to consider the situation as an evolution due to internal selection of individuals of a species, or whether to formulate it in terms of selection of the species as a whole in competition with other species or with the environment.

[1] I am informed by a kind reader that *Megaceros* only produced oversized antlers in old age, when most of his reproductive years were over. This would put a new complexion on this particular problem.

XIX *Quantity to Quality: The Biometric Approach*

Taxonomists classify animals and plants into a hierarchy ot groups within groups, according to their similarities. Kingdoms, subkingdoms, phyla, classes, orders, families, genera, species, subspecies, races, and varieties are the categories. But most taxonomists are agreed that there is something special about the species. Darwin called his book *The Origin of Species* for good reasons. Other categories are somewhat arbitrary and a matter of convenience, but the species stands out as an objective category upon which, in most cases, taxonomists can agree.

This makes sense genetically, for a species consists of an interbreeding population and has been so defined by geneticists. To a geneticist a species is not a collection of herbarium specimens or museum specimens of insects or bones which have rather similar characters; it is a living group of interbreeding individuals. In fact, according to this point of view, it would be impossible to classify a dead specimen except by inference. A species, considered as an interbreeding population, is a group of individuals who are going through the cycle of passing on half of their genes to a new generation and themselves dying (see Appendix 3). No individual reproduces itself exactly except in asexual organisms, where the category of species is, in any case, less definitive. In order to develop a quantitative theory of evolution some unit which can be measured must be found. The individual, whose constitution is inevitably broken up, leaving only a packet of genes that has been passed on to the next generation, is obviously not a good unit.

The gene, on the other hand, or rather the frequency of a particular gene in a population, is something that can be measured. We could, in theory, describe a population by specifying the frequency of each allele in it. If the population was constant, was not evolving, these gene frequencies would remain more or less constant, although the individuals in the population would look different. In other words, the population would always consist of the same assortment of genes, although it might be rare that two individuals would be found having exactly the same collection of genes. Imagine a collection of a million colored marbles in an enormous bag; divide these into a hundred packets, with ten thousand marbles in each packet. It will be unlikely that any of these packets will contain identical assortments of marbles. Throw them all back in the bag and pick again and there will be another hundred packets, again all different. This analogy is not very good because genes are assorted with some method—only one allele from each locus from each of two parents is picked to form an individual—but the process remains comparable.

In evolutionary, or population, genetics the frequency of a gene in a population is taken as the basic unit. But the diploid individual cannot be ignored. We can imagine a population in which, if we consider only one locus, there are 70 per cent of allele A and 30 per cent of allele *a*. The individuals in this population can be of three genotypes, AA, *Aa*, or *aa*, and the question arises, What will the frequency of these three genotypes be? How many individuals will be AA, how many *Aa*, and how many *aa*?

EQUILIBRIUM

The answer to this question was given independently by two people, whose names are perpetuated in the Hardy-Weinberg law, the basis of all theorems in population genetics. G. H. Hardy was a mathematician and the author of the well-known text *Pure Mathematics*. He was a fellow of Trinity College, Cambridge, and later of New College, Oxford. His paper was published in 1908, the year in which the German physician W. Weinberg published his formulation of the law. Hardy's paper is very short and is interesting on account of its somewhat disdainful flavor. Pure mathematicians are apt to be impatient with less rigorous disciplines—sometimes to good effect, as in the case of Hardy; sometimes wrongly, as in the case of the mathematician A. H. Trow, also in England, who ridiculed the whole theory of crossing-over and linkage and hoped that scientists would no longer be misled by the erroneous but persistent views of T. H. Morgan and his colleagues in America! Some lines from Hardy's paper, which has become a classic, deserve quotation:

> I am reluctant to intrude in a discussion concerning matters of which I have no expert knowledge, and I should have expected the very simple point which I wish to make to have been familiar to biologists. . . .
>
> Suppose that *Aa* is a pair of Mendelian characters, A being dominant, and that in any given generation the numbers of pure dominants (*AA*), heterozygotes (*Aa*), and pure recessives (*aa*) are as p:2q:r. Finally suppose that the numbers are fairly large, so that the mating may be regarded as random, that the sexes are evenly distributed among the three varieties,

and that all are equally fertile. A little mathematics of the multiplication table type is enough to show that in the next generation the numbers will be as $(p+p)^2 : 2(p+q)(q+r) : (q+r)^2$ or as $p_1:2q_1:q_1$, say.

The interesting question is: in what circumstances will this distribution be the same as that in the generation before? It is easy to see that the condition for this is $q^2 = pr$. And since $q_1{}^2 = p_1r_1$, whatever the values of p, q and r may be, the distribution will, in any case, continue unchanged after the second generation.

The "very simple point" may escape the reader. When a mathematician writes, "It is easy to see," the word "easy" is often relative. However, we will leave this as an exercise in algebraical manipulation and will only offer the reminder that if $A:B:C = D:E:F$ then $A/B = D/E$. Hardy, naturally, did not quite see the problem from a biological standpoint and we will explain the same idea using a different notation, which is in common use today, because it reflects a biological reality. We will suppose that the ratio of three genotypes AA:*Aa*:*aa* is as $p^2:2pq:q^2$, and that $p + q = 1$. We will calculate the ratio of the next generation in these terms.

The proportions of the next generation are shown in Table 17. Remember that where the two parents are AA and *Aa*, there are two ways of making the mating, these cases have, therefore, been doubled in the table.

Remember, also, from Chapter VI, that AA x AA parents have only AA offspring and that *Aa* x *Aa* parents, for instance, have children in the proportion 1/4 AA:1/2 *Aa*:1/4 *aa*. The sum of the columns may not be immediately clear. The first column, when p^2 is taken outside brackets, comes to $p^2 (p^2 + 2pq + q^2)$. But since $p^2 + 2pq + q^2$ equals $(p + q)^2$ and $p + q = 1$, the sum of column 1 reduces to p^2. The same sort of manipulation produces the sums of the other two columns. We have demonstrated the same thing as Hardy did, using a different notation. We have shown that if the three genotypes at any generation are in the proportion $p^2:2pq:q^2$, then in the next generation the three genotypes will be in the same proportion. The reader may verify this in a numerical example by taking the frequency of the three genotypes in the original population as .36:.48:.16 (36%:48%:16%).

TABLE 17

Mating	Next Generation		
	AA	*Aa*	*aa*
AA(p^2) x AA(p^2)	p^4		
AA(p^2) x *Aa*(^2pq)	$p^2(2pq)$	$p^2(2pq)$	
AA(p^2) x *aa*(q^2)		$2p^2q^2$	
Aa($2pq$) x *Aa*($2pq$)	$1/4(2pq)^2$	$1/2(2pq)^2$	$1/4(2pq)^2$
Aa($2pq$) x *aa*(q^2)		$q^2(2pq)$	$q^2(2pq)$
aa(q^2) x *aa*(q^2)			q^4
	p^2	$2pq$	q^2

The Hardy-Weinberg equilibrium. The three genotypes AA, *Aa*, and *aa* are taken to be in the proportion $p^2:2pq:q^2$. With random mating all six pairs of mates listed in the left-hand column will appear. The frequency of genotypes in the next generation is shown in the body of the table; these frequencies are obtained by multiplying together the frequencies of the parents. In lines 2, 3, and 5, the frequencies in the next generation have been doubled.

The significance of this notation is that it uses only two symbols, p and q, which can represent the frequency of the two alleles A and *a*. If there are only these two alleles at this locus in the population, then $p + q = 1$. The relation between gene frequencies and equilibrium genotype frequencies is given by the ratios $p^2:2pq:q^2$. If we imagine a generation as the pairing together of all the genes in the population, then an A allele whose proportion is p has p x p chance of pairing off with another A allele. An *a* allele will pair with another *a* allele with a frequency of q^2 and an A will pair with an *a*, or vice versa, with a frequency 2pq. Algebraically we can represent this as $(p + q)^2 = p^2 + 2pq + q^2$. When the pairs come apart again, then the number of A alleles will be $2p^2 + 2pq$, and the number of *a* alleles, $2q^2 + 2pq$. These can be written $2p(p + q)$ and $2q(p + q)$ and since $p + q = 1$, the frequencies reduce to 2p and 2q. These are the gene frequencies back again; they are doubled because we considered the pairs or diploid genotypes to produce two genes each, but if we are considering frequencies in an infinite population, we should consider the p^2 AA individuals as producing p^2 A genes and the 2pq *Aa* individuals as producing pq A and pq *a* genes and similarly for the *aa* individuals. We can go through as many generations as we like and the genotype frequencies will remain as $p^2{:}2pq{:}q^2$. This is an equilibrium ratio. If, for some reason, the equilibrium is disturbed and we have some other ratio, then the population will return to the equilibrium ratio in one generation. Let us take a numerical example and see the process. Suppose that for some reason we have no homozygous dominants at all and the population consists of 0.6 heterozygotes *Aa* and 0.4 homozygotes *aa*. There are three possible kinds of mating and they will occur with the frequencies shown in Table 18, where the frequencies of the three types of progeny are also shown.

TABLE 18

Matings	*Frequency of Matings*	AA	*Progeny* *Aa*	*aa*
Aa(.6) x *Aa*(.6)	.36	.09	.18	.09
Aa(.6) x *aa*(.4)	2 × .24		.24	.24
aa(.4) x *aa*(.4)	.16			.16
	Totals	.09	.42	.49

The totals of the three genotypes are as .09:.42:.49; the gene frequencies are, therefore, .3 and .7, and .09:.42:.49 equals $p^2:2pq:q^2$. Note that this equilibrium ratio was reached in one generation. Equilibrium is always reached in one generation for autosomal genes in a large random mating population. For sex-linked genes the equilibrium ratio may be approached more slowly. If there are three alleles at the locus, then the equilibrium genotypes are given by the successive terms of the expansion of $(p + q + r)^2$ and equilibrium will again be established in one generation.

The equilibrium ratios that we have considered were for a single gene; a real population would be described by treating all genes in this way and this introduces one new feature. Equilibrium for each gene separately is reached in one generation, but equilibria between genes develop more gradually. With two genes there are nine different genotypes:

AABB	AABb	AAbb
AaBB	AaBb	Aabb
aaBB	aaBb	aabb

The three sums of the rows give the ratio of AA:Aa:aa and the three sums of the columns give the ratio of BB:Bb:bb. Each of these equilibria will be established after one generation, but that does not mean that all nine items in the matrix will be at their equilibrium values. With a little algebraical work it can be shown that the actual equilibrium values of the nine items are:

p^2u^2	$2p^2uv$	p^2v^2
$2pqu^2$	$4pquv$	$2pqv^2$
q^2u^2	$2q^2uv$	p^2v^2

where p and q represent the frequencies of the gene pair A, *a*, and u, and v represent the frequencies of the *B*, *b* gene pair.

In the case of combinations of independent genes, complete equilibrium will be reached very quickly; deviation from equilibrium will be halved at every generation. For linked genes equilibrium will be reached more slowly; the deviation will be reduced by the cross-over value at each generation. Closely linked genes will take some time to reach equilibrium; two genes having 1 per cent crossing-over between them will take some sixty-nine generations to halve their deviations from equilibrium.

MUTATION

The next step in developing a general theory is to investigate the effects of mutation, selection, and other factors on the gene frequencies and to ascertain under what conditions any stable equilibrium is reached. The easiest factor to formulate is a recurrent mutation: mutation from a wild-type allele a^+ to what we will call the mutant allele a, which takes place in a certain proportion of the a^+ alleles at every generation. Perhaps 1 in 100,000 a^+ alleles mutates to a in each generation, or in general terms, let us call the proportion μ. If the frequency of a^+ alleles in the population is p_n in any generation, then the frequency of new mutants in the next generation, p_{n+1}, will be $p_n\mu$. The frequency of the mutant gene a will be increased by this amount in the next generation. If the frequency of a was q_n in the initial generation, it will be $q_n + \mu p_n$ in the next. In algebraical notation $q_{n+1} = q_n + \mu p_n$. To give an example of how fast the usual sort of mutation rate will change the frequency of a gene: if $\mu = 10^{-5}$ (1 in 100,000), then it will take 11,780 generations for the gene frequency to increase from 0.1 to 0.2.

If mutation only goes one way, from a^+ to a, then eventually the population will contain only a genes, even though it may take a very long time. This shows, incidentally, the weakness of calling one of the alleles wild type, a^+, and another mutant. This nomenclature is useful, but one must always remember that "wild type" is a relative term.

A more realistic picture of the effect of mutation will take into account the fact that recurrent gene mutations usually back-mutate to the original allele or to something that looks exactly like the original. The forward- and the back-mutation rates are usually different, and are written μ and ν. We have seen that for forward mutations $q_{n+1} = q_n + \mu p_n$; this means that the change in frequency, $q_{n+1} - q_n$, is $q_n + \mu p_n - q_n$, or μp_n. This increase in frequency per generation is usually written Δq, so $\Delta q = \mu p$. For the back mutation exactly the same applies, so $\Delta p = \nu q$, but gain in the frequency p represents a loss in frequency of q, so $\Delta q_{(loss)} = \nu q$ and putting the two together, $\Delta q_{(gain)} - \Delta q_{(loss)} = \mu p - \nu q$. We can call the net change in frequency $\Delta q_{(net)}$, so $\Delta q_{(net)} = \mu p - \nu q$. In a population which starts off with almost all individuals having the allele of a gene a^+ and very few with *a*, p will be much greater than q, and the change at first will be in the direction of *a*, since μp will be greater than νq; but as the frequency of *a* increases, the rate of change will slow down and an equilibrium frequency will eventually be reached. At the equilibrium frequency, the change in frequency is zero, so $\Delta q = 0 = \mu p - \nu q$. In other words, $\mu \hat{p} = \nu \hat{q}$, the little hats over p and q indicating equilibrium frequencies. Remembering that $p + q = 1$ we can write:

$$
\begin{aligned}
\mu(1 - \hat{q}) &= \nu\hat{q} \\
\therefore \mu - \mu\hat{q} &= \nu\hat{q} \\
\therefore \mu &= \nu\hat{q} + \mu\hat{q} \\
\therefore \mu &= \hat{q}(\nu + \mu) \\
\text{or} \quad \hat{q} &= \frac{\mu}{\nu + \mu}
\end{aligned}
$$

If, for instance, the forward-mutation rate is 3×10^{-5} and the back-mutation rate is 2×10^{-5}, then $\hat{q} = \frac{3 \times 10^{-5}}{(3+2) \times 10^{-5}} =$

3/5, which means that after a large number of generations, 3/5 of the genes, or 0.6, will be a^+ and 0.4 will be *a*. Notice that the equilibrium depends only on the forward- and back-mutation rates, not on the initial frequencies. We could start with a population consisting of all, or nearly all, *a* alleles and the same equilibrium of 0.6 a^+ and 0.4 *a* would be reached. The ratio of a^+:*a* (0.6:0.4) at equilibrium is the same as the ratio of mutation rates (3:2) and this may seem intuitively obvious. The algebra may seem superfluous or even confusing, but the obvious result is sometimes wrong in such cases.

SELECTION

The most interesting, but also one of the most complex of the factors altering gene frequencies is, of course, selection. In the preceding discussion about mutation, it was assumed that there was no selection; or rather, selection, as well as all other factors except mutation, was neglected.

The simplest kind of selection acts at the level of the gene. This occurs where the gamete (*e.g.* sperm) or haploid organism of a certain genotype has a selective advantage over those of other genotypes. Consider again a single gene with two alleles, A and *a*, and suppose that p and q, and the relative frequencies of the two alleles in the population at a given time, add up to 1 ($p + q = 1$). Selection is represented by s in such a way that the relative proportion of the two alleles in the next generation is as $1:(1 - s)$. In other terms, $p_{n+1} : q_{n+1} = p_n : q(1 - s)$. The expression $1 - s$, sometimes written w, represents fitness. If $w = 1$, then the gamete or haploid organism has average fitness; if $w < 1$ (is less than 1), then it has a selective disadvantage; if $w > 1$ (is greater than 1) it has an advantage. If s is a positive number, then the total will be smaller than before and will no longer equal 1. It is simpler to keep the two proportions such that their total always equals 1. This

can be done by dividing both amounts by the total of the two which is $p + q(1 - s)$, or $1 - sq$. The new proportions, which are comparable to the original ones, are $\frac{p}{1 - sq}$ $\frac{q(1 - s)}{1 - sq}$.
This means that after one generation of selection, p becomes $\frac{p}{1 - sq}$ and q becomes $\frac{q(1 - s)}{1 - sq}$. Note that they add up to 1.

The same method, with a little more algebra, can be used in the more usual case where selection acts on the diploid organism, *i.e.* where certain diploid organisms reproduce more than other diploid organisms. The change brought about by selection can still be measured in terms of gene frequencies, but a complication is introduced because there are three different genotypes for any pair of alleles. For the allele pair A, *a* the genotypes are AA, A*a*, and *aa*. In any given generation the frequencies of genotypes at equilibrium will be as $p^2{:}2pq{:}q^2$ where p and q, as before, are the frequencies of alleles A and *a*. Let us again represent a coefficient of selection by s and let selection be against the recessive homozygote such that the *aa* individuals contribute $q^2(1 - s)$ gametes to the next generation.

The frequencies of the three genotypes, after selection has eliminated some of the *aa* genotypes, will be as follows:

Genotypes	*AA*	*Aa*	*aa*
Initial frequencies	p^2	$2pq$	q^2
Fitness (w)	1	1	$1 - s$
Frequencies after selection	p^2	$2pq$	$q^2(1 - s)$

As before, there is the problem of keeping the frequencies so that they add up to 1, and again this is accomplished by dividing by the total which, in this case is $1 - sq^2$. The new frequencies are therefore:

AA	$\frac{p^2}{1 - sq^2}$
Aa	$\frac{2pq}{1 - sq^2}$
aa	$\frac{p^2\,(1 - s)}{1 - sq^2}$

These are the frequencies of diploid organisms after selection has done its work. These organisms will provide the gametes for the next generation. The gene frequencies in these gametes can easily be found. The frequency of *a*, which we call q, will be half the heterozygotes *Aa* plus all the homozygotes *aa*, which is:

$$q_1 \text{ (after selection)} = \frac{pq}{1 - sq^2} + \frac{q^2\,(1 - s)}{1 - sq^2} = \frac{q\,(1 - sq)}{1 - sq^2} \qquad (1)$$

A simple but instructive case is the one where selection is total ($s = 1$). This would be the case of a recessive lethal. Writing the initial q as q_0 and the q after one generation of selection as q_1, we have

$$q_1 = \frac{q_0(1 - 1q_0)}{1 - 1q_0^2}$$

$$= \frac{q_0\,(1 - q_0)}{(1 + q_0)\,(1 - q_0)}$$

$$= \frac{q_0}{1 + q_0}$$

The calculation of the effects of one generation of selection may seem, and in truth should seem, rather weak stuff with which to study evolution. In this particular example it is easy to proceed further.

After a second generation of the same selection, the frequency in terms of q_1 would be:

$$q_2 = \frac{q_1}{1 + q_1} \tag{2}$$

but
$$q_1 = \frac{q_0}{1 + q_0}$$

so, substituting for q_1 in (2), $q_2 = \dfrac{\dfrac{q_0}{1 + q_0}}{1 + \dfrac{q_0}{1 + q_0}}$

$$= \frac{q_0}{1 + 2q_0}$$

The reader may guess, or may verify by repeating the previous operation, that the frequency after three generations,

$$q_3 = \frac{q_0}{1 + 3q_0}$$

and, in fact after any number, n, of generations

$$q_n = \frac{q_0}{1 + nq_0} \tag{3}$$

The successive terms constitute what is known in algebra as a harmonic progression. In succeeding generations, the frequency of *a* alleles gets smaller and smaller, until they disappear from the population altogether. To get an idea of how fast q diminishes, let $nq_0 = 1$. When we do this we find, from the above formula (3), that $q_n = \frac{q_0}{2}$ so that q is diminished by a half when $nq_0 = 1$, which is to say, when the number of generations equals $\frac{1}{q_0}$.

We have seen how the mutation rate affects gene frequency and also how selection against the recessive affects it; the obvious calculation to make next is the effect of both together. This can be done by taking the changes in gene frequency over one generation, Δq, due to mutation and due to selection, and putting them together in the same formula. The change due to mutation rate $A \rightarrow a$ has been shown on page 276 to be $\Delta q = \mu p$. For selection, if the original gene frequency is q, the frequency after one generation of selection was found (1) to be $\frac{q(1 - sq)}{1 - sq^2}$.

We have already mentioned that the quantity $1 - s$ can be thought of as representing the fitness of a particular genotype. In the same way, the sum of the fitnesses of the three genotypes, which in the present case is $1 - sq^2$, can be thought of as representing the total fitness for that gene. This quantity can be written $\overline{w}$, which simplifies the formulae somewhat, and we can write for the effects of selection:

$$\Delta q = \frac{q - q(1-sq)}{\overline{w}}$$

$$= \frac{q(1-sq^2)-q(1-sq)}{\overline{w}}$$

$$= \frac{sq^2(1-q)}{\overline{w}}$$

$$= \frac{spq^2}{\overline{w}} \qquad \text{(since } 1 - q = p\text{)}$$

If mutation acts after selection when the frequency of A is $\frac{p}{\overline{w}}$ then the change in q will be $\frac{\mu p}{\overline{w}}$ rather than μp. The overall change in q, due to a decrease by selection and an increase by mutation, is given by $\Delta q = \frac{-spq^2}{\overline{w}} + \frac{\mu p}{\overline{w}}$. At equilibrium, if there be such, the change will be zero, so

$$\Delta q = 0 \text{ and } \frac{\mu p}{\bar{\bar{W}}} - \frac{spq^2}{\bar{\bar{W}}} = 0$$

$$\therefore \frac{\mu p}{\bar{\bar{W}}} = \frac{spq^2}{\bar{\bar{W}}}$$

$$\mu = sq^2$$

$$q^2 = \frac{\mu}{s}$$

$$q = \sqrt{\frac{\mu}{s}}$$

These calculations show the way in which selection and mutation can be, and have been, formulated quantitatively. We have taken only one case, that of a recessive gene with a constant deleterious effect, but cases in which the heterozygote is intermediate between the two homozygotes, or cases where the heterozygote is superior or inferior to both homozygotes, can be dealt with in a similar way. Selection can also vary; it can be a function, for instance, of the frequency of the allele in the population, a situation we have described in Chapter XVIII; this relationship can easily be incorporated into the formulae. Readers with a mathematical bent will get some pleasure from these formulae and will wish to pursue them to greater length, or height. Other readers may exclaim, "So what?" This question may indicate a kind of boredom with life in general: What is the use of doing anything? But we will assume that any reader who has stayed with us so far means something different. He means that he gets no pleasure out of the algebra and he does not see how the formulae help at all in understanding the process of evolution. This objection is a real one, but is not altogether valid. In what might be called applied genetics, calculations of this sort can lead to useful information in some cases. This is especially true in human genetics, where some of the parameters may be known very accurately.

This approach has also clarified the evolutionary picture somewhat. It has provided further weight to the belief that selection is more important in evolution than mutation. It has also helped to fill in a larger picture, mainly through the work of Sewall Wright, who was for many years at the University of Chicago.

We have already used the symbol $\overline{w}$ to represent the sum of the fitnesses of the three genotypes of a particular gene: $1 - sq^2$ in the case that was taken. This concept of average fitness can be expanded to cover all genes of an organism: it can represent the sum of the fitnesses of all genotypes of all genes. It will then represent a kind of fitness for a population. It is difficult to think in terms of many genes, but the case of two genes can be readily pictured. Imagine a landscape, a relief map with mountain peaks and valleys. Think of the map as a sheet of graph paper in which the two sides represent the frequencies of two genes, A and *B* (Fig. 42).

FIGURE 42

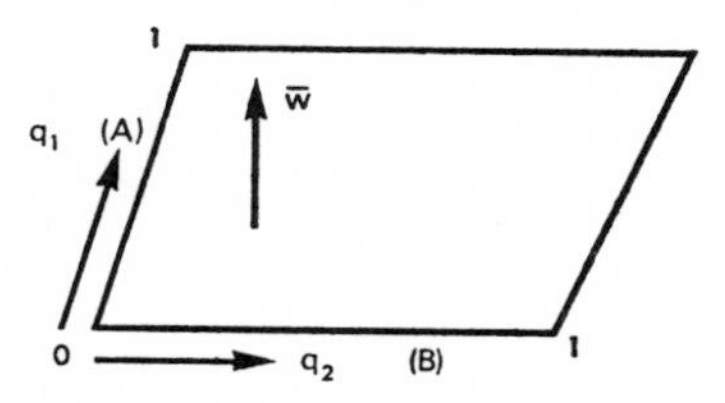

The height at a particular point would represent $\overline{w}$ for the values of q_1 and q_2 intersecting at that point. It would represent the average fitness of a population having gene *A* at a frequency of q_1 and gene *B* at a frequency of q_2. The higher the peak the greater the $\overline{w}$, and assuming that populations are getting fitter by evolution, they would act like mountain climbers and constantly rise until a peak was reached. The peaks and valleys are drawn for imaginary populations; real populations move around and occupy particular peaks and valleys. In Figure 43 an imaginary fitness landscape has been con-

FIGURE 43

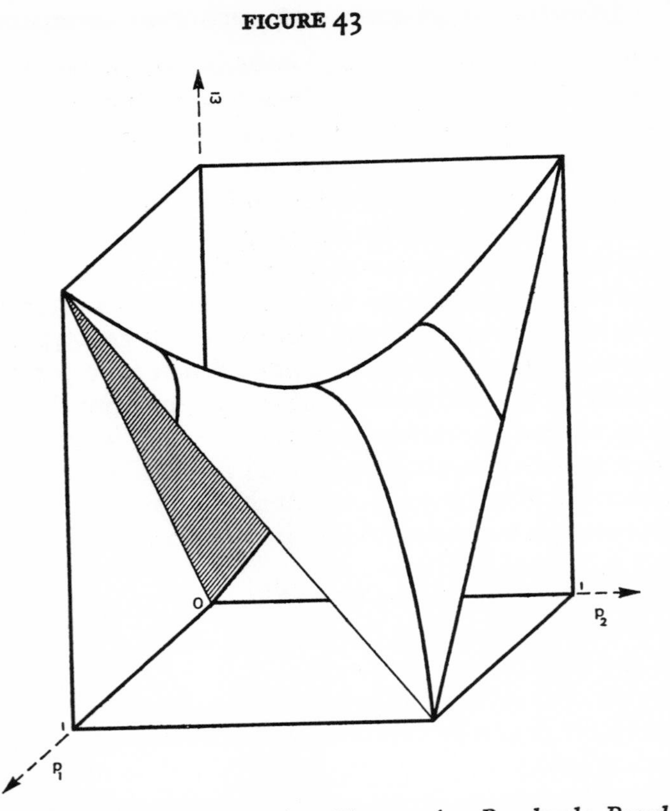

A Topographic Map Representing Fitness of a Randomly Breeding Population. Only two genes with two alleles each are considered. There are thus four positive alleles, each of which, it is assumed, adds an equal quantity to some character—each positive allele may be thought to add one inch to stature. Individuals that are too tall or too short are not so fit as those of middle height; in fact, the fittest genotypes are considered to be those with two positive alleles, namely *AAbb*, *aaBB*, and *AaBb*. The p_1 axis on the map represents the frequency of one allele, say A, and p_2 the frequency of the other allele, say *B*. The height on the saddle-shaped surface at any point represents the fitness, $\overline{w}$, of a population having the particular frequencies of A and *B* that correspond to the p_1 and p_2 coordinates at that point. The fittest populations will be seen to be those represented by points at the two corners where $p_1 = 1$, $p_2 = 0$ and $p_1 = 0$, $p_2 = 1$. These are the points where the genotypes are fixed and all individuals have the same genotype—

AAbb at one corner, *aaBB* at the other. The least fit populations are those in the other two corners, where $p_1 = 0$, $p_2 = 0$ and $p_1 = 1$, $p_2 = 1$. The genotypes are also fixed here, and they are *aabb* and *AABB*, much too short and much too tall.

structed for a case in which a medium height is fitter than tallness or shortness. This picture of a genetic landscape is useful in visualizing evolution, but when we consider more than two genes, visualization becomes more difficult. For three genes, four dimensions would be required, and for 1,000 genes, a 1,001-dimensional space would be required! But returning to a simple two-gene situation, the problem arises of how a population, once at the summit of a small hill, can ever get to a higher peak, for it will have to go down before it can go up higher. This is a technical aspect of the problem of how complex organs like eyes and wings can evolve if each intermediate stage is not more fit than its predecessor. The problem has received some thought and has given rise to considerable discussion concerning both the technical aspect considered here and the wider evolutionary field.

The first thing that can be said is that the landscape is continually changing. As the environment changes because of climatic and geological variation or changes in other forms of life, so the relative fitness of various proportions of the two genes will vary. If the climate gets colder, or if for some reason the caveman finds caves with a lower ceiling, then short men may be fitter than men of medium height. Thus the peaks and valleys are not constant, but are continually moving up and down, so that a population that continually climbs upward has a good chance of reaching higher and higher peaks.

There is another factor, the importance of which has led to intense debate among experts. This concerns the size of the population. In small populations there is an element of chance in the determination of what the next generation will be. Each generation is formed from a random sample of gametes of the previous generation. If the numbers are large, this sample will fairly represent the composition of the whole population, but if the numbers are small, then it will not, and samples will vary. Thus, although populations will be pushed by selection up to the very top of a peak they will, if small, wander around a bit through the accidents of random sampling. This drift, due to chance, prevents a small population from being as fit as it might be, but on the other hand, it may enable it to wander off to the uphill slope of a higher peak and then, by selection, climb to new heights of fitness. Sewall Wright has come to the conclusion that the best population structure may consist of a large population subdivided into several smaller populations. All subpopulations—races or varieties—would be interfertile, but individuals would usually breed among others of their subpopulation. In this way each subpopulation would, through the random chance of selection from small numbers and also perhaps through differences in environment, differ from the others. Where one subpopulation found a favorable combination of gene frequencies, it would increase in numbers and migrate to other subgroups. The population as a whole would then move in that direction. The picture of an amoeba comes to mind. Amoebae continually put out little buds of protoplasm. Some come to nothing; others grow, and protoplasm flows to them from the whole amoeba until the body moves to a new position. Calculations of the effects of small populations are too complex to be described here, but it is of interest that one of the fundamental formulae happens to be a solution of an equation in physics known as the Fokker-Planck equation. The genetic implications of the Fokker-Planck equation were published in 1935 by the great Russian mathematician A. N. Kolmogorov.

It is unfortunate that the parameters of the numerous formulae that population geneticists have derived cannot be measured. Except for studies of microorganisms, mutation rates have been measured for only a handful of genes in two or three animals. Even less is known about selection coefficients, and of course, nothing is known of either mutation rates or selection coefficients in any of the extinct species—in many instances just the species about whose evolution something is known. Furthermore, most calculations apply to a population of fixed size. A fit population, one with a high $\bar{w}$, situated on a mountain peak, is not considered to be growing in numbers. This conflicts a little with the usual view of evolution, according to which fit species grow in numbers at the expense of unfit ones and most species become extinct.

Another question which cannot yet be answered concerns the extent to which selection acts at different levels: How important is selection at the level of the diploid individual, which is what most calculations are concerned with, compared to selection at the family level and the species level?

An important feature of interbreeding populations which is receiving increasing attention is the breeding structure. The simple model of a randomly breeding population, where every individual has an equal chance of mating with any other individual, is obviously unrealistic for animal, plant, and human populations. Where breeding is not random, there is an increase in the proportion of inbreeding, in which mates are related more closely than they need be. Inbreeding disturbs the Hardy-Weinberg equilibrium; it increases the frequency of homozygotes and decreases the frequency of heterozygotes. Harmful recessives are more likely to appear in children whose parents are cousins than in children whose parents are unrelated. The effects of inbreeding are somewhat complicated, but it is easy and amusing to define a measure of inbreeding.

The closest inbreeding is self-fertilization as practiced by many plants, especially when they are unsuccessful in capturing extraneous pollen in a reasonable period of time. Marriages of double first cousins, cousins, or more distant relatives result in diminishing degrees of inbreeding. The most useful measure of inbreeding is known as the coefficient of inbreeding, F, and is defined as the chance that a child will inherit identical alleles because they come from a common ancestor of both parents. Take the case of the mating of a half brother and a half sister, represented in Figure 44.

FIGURE 44

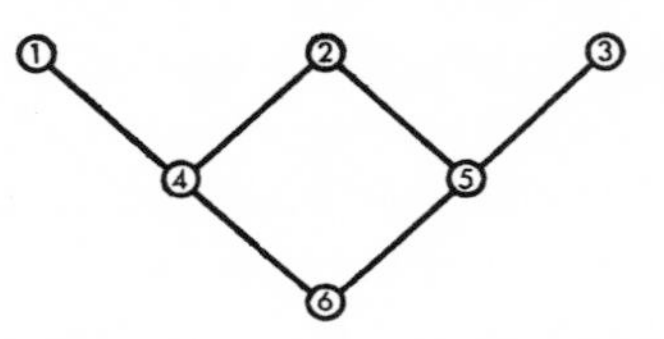

Number 2 may be thought of as the mother who had a son (4) by one husband (1) and a daughter (5) by another husband (3). The half siblings marry to produce a child (6). The coefficient of inbreeding will give the probability that 4 and 5 inherit duplicates of the same gene from some common ancestor. The only common ancestor to both 4 and 5 is 2. If the allele in question is A^1, then the chance that 4 will get A^1 is 1 in 2, or ½, and the chance that 5 will also get A^1 is ½. So the chance that both 4 and 5 will have a copy of A^1 is $\frac{1}{2} \times \frac{1}{2}$, or ¼. Again, the chance that 4 will pass this on to 6 is ½, and the chance that 5 will pass it on to 6 is ½, so in all, the chance that 6 will get both of the A^1 alleles is $\frac{1}{4} \times \frac{1}{2} \times \frac{1}{2}$, or 1/16. But all this could also be said of the other allele, A^2, of the gene that 2 had. Either allele will satisfy the definition, so $F = 1/16 + 1/16$, or 1/8.

A short-cut way of arriving at the same figure is to count the individuals from one parent back to the common ancestor and then down again to the other parent, and calculate ½ to this power. In the example given there are three, namely, 4, 2, and 5, so $F = (\frac{1}{2})^3$, or 1/8. In another example, that of marriage between double first cousins, the relationship would be as shown in Figure 45.

FIGURE 45

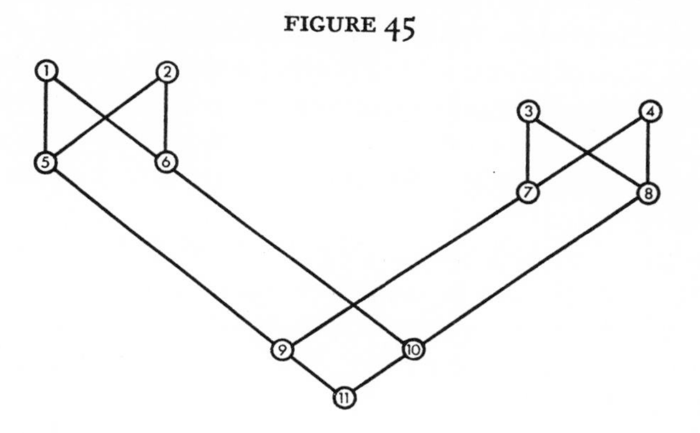

Here the parents have four common ancestors—*1*, *2*, *3*, and *4*—and we can count back to each of them. Counting to *1*, the individuals are five—*9*, *5*, *1*, *6*, and *10*—which gives $(\frac{1}{2})^5$; counting back to the other three common ancestors also gives $(\frac{1}{2})^5$ in each instance. In such a case the rule is to add the figures together, so $F = (\frac{1}{2})^5 + (\frac{1}{2})^5 + (\frac{1}{2})^5 + (\frac{1}{2})^5$, or $\frac{1}{8}$. Intuitively, one might guess that marriage between a half brother and a half sister would result in closer inbreeding than marriage between double first cousins, but genetically one would be wrong.

MULTIPLE-FACTOR INHERITANCE

Many common characters, such as weight or height or the amount of milk produced by a cow, must be recorded in terms of measurements rather than qualitative distinctions. Such characters, as was mentioned in Chapter VII, are controlled by several genes rather than single genes. This situation involves another aspect of gene frequencies which lends itself to a mathematical, or rather a statistical, treatment.

The simplest model of the way in which several genes control a character such as height is one in which each allele may add a unit—say, one inch to height. The genotype *aa* will add zero inches, *Aa* one inch, and AA two inches. Genes *B, C, D, E,* and so on, will add other inches. Genes *a, b, c, d, e,* and so on, will not increase height. In this model it is assumed that there is no dominance, no interaction of any kind between genes, and that the several alleles have a linear additive effect.

With only one gene there will be three kinds of individual possible, AA, A*a*, and *aa*, and they will be χ, $\chi + 1$, and $\chi + 2$ inches tall, where χ represents a basic minimal height outside the control of the height genes. This can be represented by a histogram (Fig. 46).

FIGURE 46

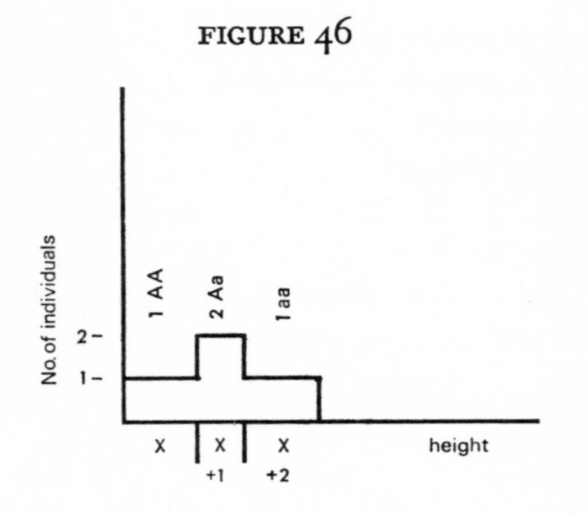

The ratio of the frequencies of the three genotypes in the F_2 generation, or in any generation of a randomly breeding population, is 1:2:1. This is the familiar Mendelian F_2 ratio and also the Hardy-Weinberg equilibrium when $p = q$, for then $p^2:2pq:q^2$ is $p^2:2p^2:p^2$, or 1:2:1. The histogram shows this pictorially. It shows that there are 1 (or 100, or 1,000, . . .) individuals χ feet (or inches, or what have you) tall, 2 individuals

$x + 1$ feet tall, and 1 individual $x + 2$ feet tall. With two genes, each of the three genotypes with regard to A can also be found in combination with each of the three genotypes with regard to *B*. They can be tabulated as shown in Table 19. This result is produced by expanding the binomial $(\frac{1}{2} + \frac{1}{2})^4$ (Fig. 47).

The general formula for finding the numbers to make such histograms is $(\frac{1}{2} + \frac{1}{2})^{2n}$ where n is the number of allele pairs. If there is dominance the formula becomes $(\frac{3}{4} + \frac{1}{4})^n$. When n is large, more than about 10, both of these formulae give histograms which look rather similar and begin to fit what

TABLE 19

	1/4 *BB* = 1/16 *AABB*	1/16	(4 capital letters)
1/4 AA	2/4 *Bb* = 2/16 *AABb*		
	1/4 *bb* = 1/16 *AAbb*	4/16	(3 capital letters)
	1/4 *BB* = 2/16 *AaBB*		
2/4 Aa	2/4 *Bb* = 4/16 *AaBb*	6/16	(2 capital letters)
	1/4 *bb* = 2/16 *Aabb*		
	1/4 *BB* = 1/16 *aaBB*	4/16	(1 capital letter)
1/4 aa	2/4 *Bb* = 2/16 *aaBb*		
	1/4 bb = 1/16 *aabb*	1/16	(0 capital letters)

is known as the normal distribution, which is a bell-shaped curve (Fig. 48).

This distribution, also known as the Gaussian curve or the curve of error, is of very great importance in statistics and is the basis of nearly all statistical calculations. A considerable amount of statistical machinery can be used once it is known that we are dealing with a normal distribution.

A normal distribution is obtained when an object is subject to a large number of small random effects. A man throw-

FIGURE 47

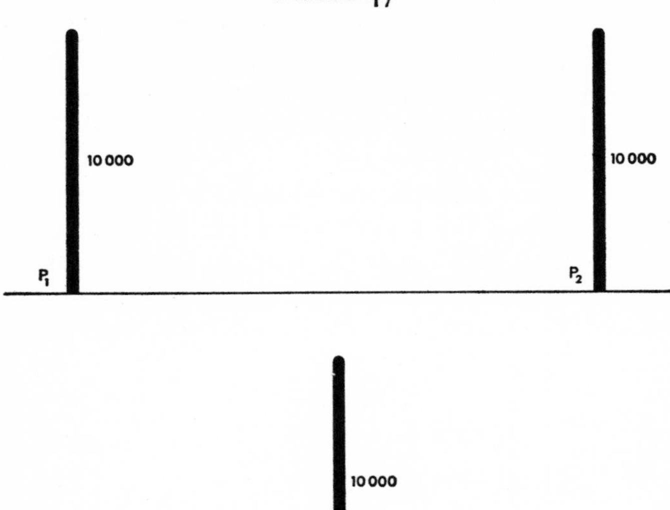

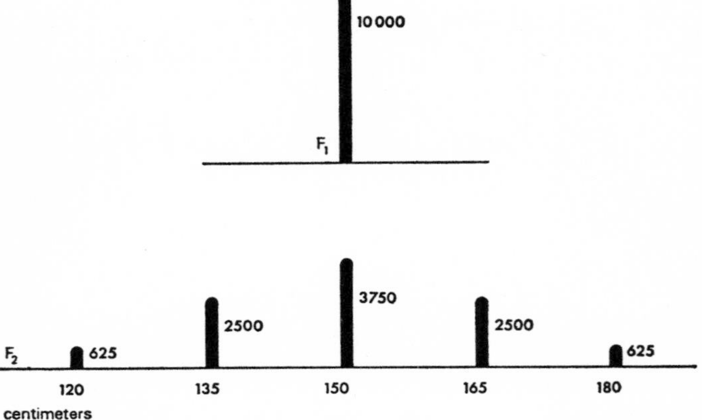

F2
625
2500
3750
2500
625
120
135
150
165
180
centimeters

Binomial Distribution for a Cross between 10,000 Plants with a Mean Height of 120 cms. and 10,000 Plants with a Mean Height 180 cms. Two pairs of genes control height, each alleleadding 15 cms. The F_2 distribution is given by the expansion of the binomial $(1/2 + 1/2)^4$.

ing darts at the bull's-eye of a target will achieve varying degrees of success. Because of small errors of muscular control, currents of wind, imperfections in the darts, and the like, many

FIGURE 48

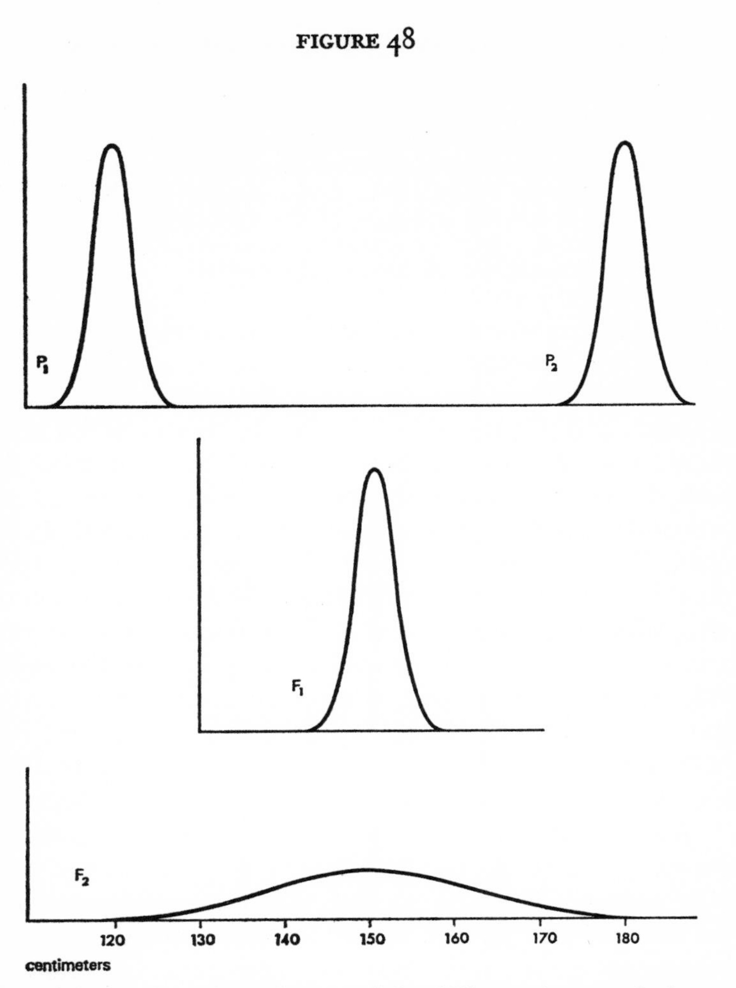

Normal Curves for a Cross between Inbred Plants of 120 and 180 cms. Mean Height Respectively. This is similar to Figure 47 except that fifteen pairs of genes control height, each allele adding 2 cms. Variance (symbolized by σ^2) due to environment is taken as 1 cm., so the P_1, P_2, and F_1 curves have $\sigma^2 = 1$ cm. and the F_2 curve has $\sigma^2 = (1/2 \times 1/2 \times 30 \times 2^2) + 1$ cm. $= 31$ cms. Only $(1/2)^{30}$, less than one in a billion (American and French, 10^9), of the F_2 will be expected to be as tall or as short as the grandparents, so the F_2 curve barely overlaps the P_1 and P_2 curves.

With random mating, successive generations will be identical to the F_2. With close inbreeding the several pure lines having $\sigma^2 = 1$ cm. will be obtained, including—if several billion individuals are involved—populations with mean heights of 120 cms. and 160 cms. like P_1 and P_2.

In Figure 47 the height of the bars represents numbers of individuals of a given height; in Figure 48 the area under the curve between two values on the abscissa represents the number or frequency of individuals whose heights lie between those values.

darts will fall outside the bull's-eye. If we tabulate how many darts are at the center (*i.e.* 0 inches from it), and how many are 1 inch, 2 inches, 3 inches, and so on, from either side of the center, and plot them on graph paper, we will have a more or less perfect normal distribution curve. The more darts, the better the fit. There will be more darts near the center and fewer and fewer darts at greater and greater distances from the center. The value corresponding to the peak of the curve is called the mean or, in loose language, the average. An important quality of a normal curve is the variance, which gives a measure of how much the measurements vary from the mean. Under the most favorable conditions most darts will be very close to the center, the frequency curve will be steep and narrow in the center, and the variance will be small. On the other hand, when many throws are wild, the variance will be large.

If the height of a few hundred soldiers or corn plants is measured, it is quite easy, by means of formulae which need not be mentioned here, to calculate the mean and the variance. The variance will be due to two main factors, genetic and environmental. One of the most useful properties of variance is that different variances are additive, so that the total variance (V_T) is equal to the variance due to genetic differences (V_G) plus the variance due to environmental factors (V_E). This property of variance provides a tool with which to separate environmental and genetic factors. Imagine a highly inbred, and therefore genetically pure, population of 100 very tall corn plants. Let us assume that they have nothing but tallness genes, perhaps 15 of them, which can be considered a large number. Another inbred population may have small plants with genes (denoted by small letters) which determine that there will be no height above the minimum. The means of the two populations may be 180 centimeters and 120 centimeters, respectively. If the two populations are crossed, the hybrid (F_1) population will have a mean height of 150 centimeters if all 30 alleles act uniformly, independently, and additively. If this population inbreeds at random, the mean of the F_2 generation will be about the same as that of the F_1. What of the variances? The two parental populations, we said, are genetically pure, so their small variances must be due to the environment. The same will be true of the F_1. In the F_2 all the different genotypes, representing 31 different sizes, will appear. The variance of the F_2 will be composed of $V_E + V_G$, whereas the variances of the parental and F_1 generations will be represented by V_E. If we subtract the parental, or F_1, variance from the total variance of the F_2, we will get the variance of the F_2 which is due to genetic factors alone, and this will tell us something about the number of genes controlling height. The frequency curves of these populations are shown in Figure 48.

If the variance of each of the three upper curves is about 1 centimeter and that of the F_2 curve 31 centimeters, then the variance due to genetic factors in the F_2 will be $31 - 1$, or 30. In the F_2 only one in $(1/2)^{30}$ will be as large as the large parent (180 centimeters), or as small as the small parent (120 centimeters), so these extremes are not likely to turn up in a sample of 100. This can be seen in Figure 48.

In real examples the conditions that we have set are not realized. Genes do interact; there are varying degrees of dominance, and some genes have a greater effect than others. Nevertheless, more complex and sophisticated statistical analyses of this sort can tell us something of the genetics of quantitative characters.

We described in Chapter III how Mendel's laws were rediscovered about the turn of the century by three men, one of whom was Bateson. Opposition to his ideas was mentioned. That opposition came from quantitative geneticists, the best known of whom was Karl Pearson.

Statistical methods were being devised which measured similarities in height between fathers and sons or between brothers. In this work Pearson assumed that heredity was continuous rather than discrete, and he attempted to formulate the similarity, due to heredity, of various relationships. Pearson founded the school of biometry, and with W. F. R. Weldon, the journal *Biometrica.* He is quoted as claiming that biometry would eventually reduce biology to a branch of mathematics. It is unfortunate that the difference in opinion between Pearson and Bateson was not the amiable and productive dialectic that one pictures as occurring between scientists. Karl Pearson went so far as to use his influence, with success, in preventing Bateson's papers concerning Mendelian segregation from being published. Even the British journal *Nature,* perhaps the best-known scientific journal in the world, refused to publish a letter of Bateson's on the subject of Mendel's principles of heredity. Bateson privately printed one paper, which was refused by *Biometrica,* in a format identical to that of *Biometrica.*

It is curious that neither antagonist could see that the discrete nature of heredity, so beautifully revealed by Mendel's kind of experiment, added a valuable ingredient to biometric machinery.

XX *The Special Genetics of* H. Sapiens

Boire sans soif et faire l'amour en tout temps, madame, il n'y a que cela qui nous distingue des autres bêtes. So said Beaumarchais, and he hit upon two of the main features of human genetics and evolution. As regards breeding, we are the most widespread of interbreeding populations with the possible exception of microorganisms. This is not to say that we are a randomly breeding population; we are not. Only in exceptional circumstances does a Pygmy girl from equatorial Africa marry a boy from Brooklyn. As regards activities, we are the only species that has achieved such complete dominance over other animals and such success in the struggle for food and shelter that we can indulge in what, for lack of a better word, we must call cultural activities. This introduces a new dimension to the picture of evolution, about which we will speculate in due course. It is unnecessary to dwell on the fact that *Homo sapiens* is a genuine species. All human beings are fertile with one another and not fertile with the higher apes; this statement is perhaps not based on sufficient evidence, but it is unlikely to be denied. When we come to smaller taxonomic categories, authoritative opinion is by no means unanimous. The terms *subspecies, race, variety, deme,* and so on, are loaded with prejudice when applied to plants; they are a hundred times more so, and dangerously, when applied to man. But a large part of the difficulty lies in words alone and the substitution of "ethnic group" for "race" or "variety" facilitates discussion. Webster's first definition of *ethnic,* "relating to the Gentiles," is unfortunate, but not widely known.

Within the large species of *Homo sapiens* there are many subgroups; in fact, there is a hierarchy of subgroups. The species can be subdivided into biological or genetic groups, cultural groups, and national groups. The three classifications do not coincide. From the biological point of view there are three main groups of humans, which we will call races, and two or three smaller groups which are sometimes given equivalent rank (Table 20).

TABLE 20

Caucasoid	Nordic Alpine Mediterranean Armenoid
Mongoloid	Tibetan, Chinese, Japanese, Eastern U. S. S. R. Malaysian Eskimo and American Indian
Negroid	African Melanesian
Bushmen and Hottentots	
Australian aborigines	

This broad classification is taken from Philip Tobias at the University of the Witwatersrand, Johannesburg; other authorities may disagree about the details, but the three main groups are obvious to all. The layman will probably think in terms of facial features. The human face is curiously important; it is the largest part of the body exposed in well-clothed people, and by its features we can easily recognize sex, age, health, humor, and race. The anthropologist can add more criteria of race in terms of the dimensions of facial bones and of other parts of the skeleton. These criteria agree pretty well with the more superficial facial characters. Finally, anthropologists are paying more and more attention to gene frequencies, or the frequencies of characters known to be controlled by single genes—such characters as the numerous blood groups and the ability or inability to taste phenylthiocarbamide, as well as certain other chemicals. The latter criteria also coincide rather well with the classical anthropological measurements, and they illustrate an important point about subdivisions of the human species or, indeed, of any other species. The boundaries between these various subdivisions are vague; that is to say, no particular man can be definitely classified as a member of a certain race or subdivision of a race. This is not an all-or-none classification like nationality, where one is legally a citizen of the U.S., of the U.S.S.R., or of some lesser power, and woe betide the man who does not have his papers in order, identifying him with some recognized nationality.

Racial groups are definite enough; they may be characterized by particular frequencies of blood groups and tasters and by a range of skeletal measurements, but there is an overlap in the measurements and gene frequencies are rarely either 0 or 1. Among American whites, for instance, the percentage of people who can taste phenylthiocarbamide ranges, in different localities, from 65 per cent to 75 per cent. Among African Negroes it ranges from 91 per cent to 97 per cent. The frequency of the I^B gene, for the B blood group, is 10 per cent to 20 per cent among Negroids and 5 per cent to 20 per cent among Caucasoids, excluding the Basques. One of the Rhesus-factor alleles (R^o) is found in about 1 per cent of the Basques and ranges from 1 per cent to 5 per cent among other Caucasoids and from 40 per cent to 70 per cent among the very dark Negroes south of the Sahara. If a certain individual cannot taste phenylthiocarbamide, is not of blood-group B, and does not have the R^o allele, is he Negroid or Caucasoid? Obviously one cannot decide for sure. All that can be said is that there is a certain probability that he belongs to the Caucasoid rather than the Negroid race.

The frequencies of some genes are closely correlated with environment. A high frequency of the sickle-cell gene is commonly found in areas where malaria is prevalent, in parts of India and Africa and around the Mediterranean. This is not surprising since heterozygotes for sickle cell are fitter in a malarious environment. Dark skin color and curly hair are common in tropical areas, and it would be a good guess that these characters also have a selective advantage in that environment. It may be that Caucasoid and Mongoloid populations living in South America are evolving toward a dark skin and that African Negroes transplanted to North America a few generations ago are evolving toward a lighter skin color.

It is indeed difficult to find characters that we can confidently say are neutral. The A, B, O blood groups a few years ago were thought to constitute such characters, but more recently there is evidence that even here there are correlations between certain blood groups and other traits that have an effect on fitness.

An interesting taxonomic character that is gaining some attention is the DNA molecule, to which earlier chapters were devoted. A technique has been developed which will tell how similar, in terms of a percentage, the base sequences in DNA of two animals are. Confidence in this technique developed when it showed that for mouse DNA and man DNA the similarity is 20–25 per cent, for green monkey and man the similarity is 85–90 per cent, and for the bacterium *E. coli* and man there is no similarity.

On the basis of anthropological measurements and the frequencies of certain traits, the human species can be subdivided into smaller and smaller subgroups until we reach the level of local populations in urban or rural districts. Any group of people who tend to breed among themselves is likely to be slightly different from other groups. Such a group may not be localized perfectly, but may belong to an interbreeding religion or caste, like those found in India. An ardent taxonomist might claim that geneticists represent a subgroup because they tend to marry each other. He might find some peculiar characters prevalent among geneticists. It is a question of how far one wants to go. In any case, caution must be used to be sure that the traits concerned are genetic. Many characters are obviously caused by the environment in each generation, and can be called cultural. An observer on some beaches in the south of France might be inclined to define a separate type or race of very dark-skinned people, but this skin color is actually a cultural trait. The same can be said of variously shaped heads among African Negroes.

In general, we can say that the human species is very far from being a homogeneous, randomly breeding species, but on the other hand, the races and different subgroups into which it can be divided are vague and continually changing.

If we look at the fossil record we find several types which are either manlike apes or apelike men. These have been found in Java, South Africa, China, Germany, Algeria, and other areas. Whether a certain type should be included in the genus *Homo* or in the species *Homo sapiens* is always a matter of controversy, and the decision is arbitrary. It is of interest to trace the ancestry of man, but the name one gives to a fossil type is not of great interest.

Several criteria are used to define the human status. The use of tools is often taken as a good indication, and cannibalism, curiously, may be correlated with the evolution of intelligence.

Our present knowledge is not sufficient to enable us to decide whether the species had a single origin, perhaps the *Australopithecus africanus* from South Africa, or whether it had many widely spread origins. One authority claims that the present three main races originated from types whose fossils are found in Europe, Java, and Africa, respectively, but this is probably not the opinion of the majority. Most students would probably agree that pure races did not exist among the very earliest manlike populations of half a million or more years ago. These early men migrated, interbred with other populations, and mixed their genes.

Subsequent to the early evolution of man there must have been a rather long period of human history during which races of man developed in relative isolation in the continents of the world. The isolation of the peoples of Africa from those of Europe is obvious when we remember that up to the end of the fifteenth century the vast majority of Europeans had never seen, much less had an opportunity to marry, a Negro. The same kind of isolation can be said to have existed in regard to the peoples of China; late in the period Marco Polo established a historic contact between the Chinese and the European civilizations. During this period there was probably a great deal of mixing of populations within Europe, Africa, and Asia, but hardly any mixture between these populations. It was this isolation that allowed the marked features of the main races of mankind to evolve. Beginning with the sixteenth century the isolation broke down; there were great movements of peoples throughout the world. It has been estimated that about fifteen million Negroes were transported from Africa to the New World. Three million Spaniards emigrated to Latin America during the first 150 years after the discovery of America.

In more recent times migration and mixing of populations has increased. From 1820 to 1935 some fifty-five million people migrated from Europe to the Western Hemisphere, which made this hemisphere a gigantic melting pot of human diversity. Millions of Russian peasants have moved to the fertile plains of Asiatic Russia.

Conscious motives, political or other, have often directed changes in populations. Of these we can list the transportation of Negroes, the deportation of Jews, the expulsion of Huguenots, the exclusion of Chinese, and also the starvation of the Irish, the extermination of the American Indians, and all the laws governing immigration and emigration. All of these have an effect on the evolution and structure of the human species.

Some estimate of the amount of gene flow from one race to another can be obtained by examining the case of the Negroes transported to North America; and let me add that this episode, the excesses of the Spanish Inquisition and the French Revolution, and the extermination of Jews in Germany during Hitler's administration are, in my opinion, the most impressive deliberate atrocities committed for the least noble motives during the last five hundred years.

One of the Rhesus-factor alleles, R^o, is most useful for our purpose. The frequency of this allele among American whites is .028; among certain African Negroes, believed to be the ancestors of the American Negroes studied, its frequency is .630; and among American Negroes its frequency is .446. If we assume that intermixture began about the middle of the seventeenth century and that the frequency of R^o has not changed among African Negroes, calculations can be made which show that the flow of R^o genes from whites to Negroes in America has been at the rate of 3.58 per cent per generation and that the American Negro is, genetically speaking, 30 per cent white.

The genetic differences between men and between groups of men are of several kinds. The categories are not precise, but they may be useful in thinking about human evolution. First, there are the rare traits, such as hemophilia (13 in 100,000 males, recessive), juvenile amaurotic idiocy (1 in 40,000, recessive), albinism (1 in 20,000, recessive), white forelock (dominant), and brachydactyly (dominant). Then there are the genes with several frequently appearing alleles, like those for A, B, and O blood groups, for the ability to taste certain chemicals, and for eye color; since they are frequent and not deleterious, we cannot refer to the alternative alleles as wild type and mutant. Genes of one particular class, called the histocompatibility genes, have a distinct action and can be studied in a Mendelian way, but they are so numerous that no two individuals are genetically identical for all of them. The histocompatibility genes determine whether or not a skin graft will take on another person, and it is well known that a graft will take only between identical twins and not even between close relatives such as mother and daughter or two brothers. Lastly, there are the numerous genes with effects that are very small, so small that they cannot be studied separately, but have to be treated all together, statistically. These minor genes control such characters as height, fingerprint pattern, and presumably intelligence, and they also modify the expression of major genes.

All these gene differences in men are the raw material, the variables, for evolution. As the frequencies of different alleles change through selection, so man evolves.

The future evolution of man is a difficult, and slightly disagreeable, subject to contemplate. We don't mind studying the changes in our species over the last 500,000 years, but there is a natural tendency to think of our present status as the end of the line, the final perfection. The way in which selection acts is certainly unique in man, but there is no good reason to believe that the species will not change as much in the future as it has in the past.

We are often reminded about how small the world has become. Travel is so rapid that long distances appear short. The same cannot be said of time. On the contrary, I believe we think of a generation as longer than our grandparents did. We plan for the next year or two, not for the next generation or two. It would be inconceivable to plan a building in the United States that would be completed fifty or a hundred years hence.

Since the advent of nuclear bombs and problems of the disposal of radioactive wastes, many scientists have turned their attention to the effects of radiation on future generations. Most of the studies are concerned with relatively immediate effects. They are concerned with suffering caused by an increase in lethal and deleterious alleles over the next few generations. This is no doubt as it should be, but if our outlook were different, if our ethical goal were the optimum evolution of the human species over the next ten thousand generations, say, then our conclusions might be different.

The ways in which selection has changed in modern society are clear to a certain extent. Modern hygiene and medicine have counteracted selection against certain deleterious genes. This tends to increase the frequency of such genes in the population and preserves some, perhaps, which would otherwise be eliminated completely. Consequently, we are a more highly polymorphic species for these genes. The same factors have caused a decrease in the death rate in early life, which is compensated for by a drop in live birth rates. In 1850 one-fourth of all the children born in the United States died before the age of five years. In 1959 this proportion of the population was expected to take sixty-three years to die. This change does not mean that lethality before birth has diminished. The frequency of embryonic death in man cannot be estimated, but in the case of cattle, sheep, mice, swine, and rabbits it is about 30 or 40 per cent.

Selection of children and adults is not the main evolutionary factor in technologically advanced human society. It is the birth rate that is important. Selection acting at the level of the birth rate means that some families—that is to say, some genotypes—will give rise to more births than others. An estimate of how effective selection could be, can be obtained by looking at the range of numbers of babies that women have in various populations. An estimate of this sort has been devised by James F. Crow, who calls it the "index of opportunity for selection"; it is the square of the coefficient of variability in the number of progeny per parent. It must be understood that this is a measure of variability, not of mean. A certain population may have large families, but they may all be pretty nearly the same size; another population may have a small average, or mean, size of family, but the actual number of children may vary a great deal, some families having no children and some having five or six or more. The interesting thing is that although the mean size of family has diminished in the United States, the index has risen, as is shown in Table 21.

This is only part of the story. It shows the possibilities for

TABLE 21

Population	*Mean number of children*	*Index of opportunity for selection*
Rural Quebec	9.9	0.20
Hutterite	9.0	0.17
Gold Coast, 1945	6.5	0.23
United States, born 1839	5.5	0.23
United States, aged 45–49 in 1950	2.3	1.14
Ramah Navaho Indians	2.1	1.57

selection within countries, the possibility that certain alleles, frequent in parts of the country or among classes of citizens, will increase at the expense of other alleles. In rural Quebec the index is low but the general birth rate is high; this would seem to indicate that alleles frequent in those individuals will spread beyond the province of Quebec.

In every war in history there must have been a considerable flow of genes one way or another. Whether the genes of the victors or of the vanquished have increased most is a debatable point.

Let us return to more immediate questions that have been studied in detail recently. One of these concerns the number of harmful recessive genes that each one of us carries in the heterozygous state. Every now and then two people carrying the same recessive allele will marry and each of their children will have a one-quarter chance of showing the defect, which may be slight or lethal. If close relatives marry, the chance that both of them will carry the same allele is greater and therefore the chance that their children will show some abnormality is also greater than for unrelated parents. The common belief that marriages between cousins tend to have a greater than average incidence of defective children is, indeed, valid. In a Japanese survey the number of deaths in the first eight years of life among offspring of cousin marriages was found to be 11.2 per cent, while the corresponding figure for offspring of unrelated parents was only 6.2 per cent. This shows that the cousin relationship increased the mortality rate by 5 per cent. Data such as the above can be analyzed quantitatively. Let us first estimate the number of homozygous recessive children that would be expected from random and from cousin marriages. In the case of random marriages we know from the Hardy-Weinberg law that for a particular allele with a frequency p, the frequency of afflicted persons in the population would be p^2 and this would represent the population of random marriages, or a sample of children from randomly married parents. If p were $\frac{1}{158}$, the proportion of homozygotes would be $(\frac{1}{158})^2 \cong \frac{1}{25,000}$, which is roughly the frequency of the defect known as phenylketonuria and slightly rarer than albinism $(\frac{1}{20,000})$. The inbreeding coefficient (see p. 288 for cousin parents is $F = \frac{1}{16}$ and the proportion of homozygotes from cousin marriages is $p^2(1 - F) + pF$, which is, in our example, $(\frac{1}{158})^2(1 - \frac{1}{16}) + \frac{1}{158}(\frac{1}{16}) \cong \frac{11}{25,000}$. Thus, for a gene of this frequency, cousin marriage would increase the chances of children having the defect about 11 times. For marriages between double first cousins, half brothers and sisters, $F = \frac{1}{8}$ and $p^2(1 - F) + pF = \frac{1}{25,000}(\frac{7}{8}) + \frac{1}{158}(\frac{1}{8}) \cong \frac{21}{25,000}$. For traits that are still rarer, like alkaptonuria, which is found in about 1 in 1,000,000 individuals, the effect is relatively greater. In this case $p = \frac{1}{1000}$ and $p^2(1 - F) + pF = \frac{1}{1,000,000}(\frac{15}{16}) + \frac{1}{1000}(\frac{1}{16}) \cong \frac{63}{1,000,000}$ for cousin marriages. The frequency was increased by a factor of about 11 for phenylketonuria and albinism, but by a factor of about 63 for the rarer trait, alkaptonuria.

If we consider not one but many alleles, the frequency of children not being homozygous for any of the alleles is $\Pi\,[1 - p_i^2 - p_i(1 - p_i)F]$. If we make approximations, which are not unreasonable where p is small and F is small (as cousin marriages), then this simplifies to $1 - (\frac{31}{32})^n$ (for cousin marriages) or, still further, when p is considered small enough and other arithmetical approximations are made, it equals $\frac{n}{32}$. In other words, using these approximate shortcuts we can estimate the number of deleterious genes by taking the increase in frequency of children of cousin marriages showing the trait and multiplying by 32.

Going back to the Japanese survey, which showed that cousin marriages increased by 5 per cent the death rate before the age of eight, we can say that there could have been $.05 \times 32$, or 1.6, deleterious alleles per person in the population. We will not pursue the algebra of this subject in more detail, but only indicate what lines it takes. Instead of considering single completely lethal alleles, it has been found convenient to think in terms of lethal equivalents. One lethal equivalent may actually be two genes, each of which kills half the homozygous individuals; or it may be three genes, each killing one-third of the time, and so on. It is a unit which, on the average, because of homozygosity of the alleles, gives rise to one death. This is sometimes called the genetic load, and is found to be rather similar for the United States, Japan, and France. For equivalents that are not lethal but detrimental, the load ranges from 2 to 4 as calculated from physical and mental defects in France, Sweden, and the United States.

Our genetic load of lethals and detrimentals may be viewed with alarm by some and with complacency by others. Should we compare it to the number of children who will suffer from family misguidance and neglect; from automobile accidents, disease, poverty, and other ills that man is heir to; or does it represent a special case? Opinions may differ on this question, and geneticists have no special qualification to judge them. We can, however, agree that an important increase in the load during the next few years would be a bad thing, at least for many generations to come. An increase in the radiation that our testicles and ovaries receive would have this effect, and here the geneticist is qualified to give expert opinion on how great this effect might be.

The first thing that has to be studied is what keeps the genetic load in equilibrium. Since it is by definition lethal or harmful, why has it not been eliminated by selection? The first reason that may occur to the reader is that new mutations are keeping it in equilibrium, according to the formulas developed in the previous chapter. If this is so, then an increase in radiation will cause a proportional increase in mutation, and this will directly increase the load and the genetic deaths or malformations. Double the radiation and the number of deaths will be doubled. It can be shown that, given enough time in generations, each lethal allele in the population will eventually become homozygous and cause the death of one person.

There is another way in which the load could be maintained which we have also mentioned in the previous chapter. It may be that although these alleles are lethal or detrimental in the homozygous state, they may, like the sickle-cell allele, have a slight advantage in the heterozygous state. Genes which act in a quantitative way, like those discussed on page 289, might be expected to belong to this category; for a homozygote may be too short of stature and for that reason at a disadvantage, but the heterozygote may be of medium height, which is better than being too tall. In the cases in which the load is maintained by superiority of the heterozygote, it can be shown that an increase in mutation rate will have a very small effect in increasing the load. The two kinds of loads which may be kept in the population are referred to as mutational load and segregational load. It is, unfortunately, very difficult to estimate how important one or the other is in human populations. Both undoubtedly exist and there is some evidence that the mutational load is the more important. With more data, better estimates will no doubt be made, and we will then be able to say more precisely what the effects of radiation will be. Segregational load is frustrating to contemplate because the evil of the homozygote is inevitably coupled to the good of the heterozygote. Reducing the segregational load would not be an unmixed blessing. In general, we can say that any increase in radiation will increase the load and that the effect is irreversible, so that once we receive an additional dose of radiation there is no way of preventing or reversing the mutant alleles.

EUGENICS

The idea of improving the human species by selective breeding is an old one. It was given serious thought in modern times by Francis Galton, who coined the term *eugenics* in 1884. Eugenics societies sprang up in several countries and began publication of some valuable journals, still in existence today. In its more or less innocuous form, the eugenic ambition is to diminish the genetic load of lethal and deleterious genes by advising or dissuading affected couples from having children. The appeal to the parents can be on a personal basis, for they will be preventing their own grief at having abnormal children.

If such marriage counseling is entirely on a personal basis, it will not lessen the load of harmful genes as much as possible, for the following reason. A child can have a recessive blemish only if both parents have an allele for that particular blemish. Thus, if one parent were known to be homozygous wild type for a particular gene and the other parent were known to be heterozygous or even homozygous for a deleterious allele of that gene, a counselor considering the parents' immediate happiness would advise them to have children; but if the genetic load in the population were considered then they, or at least the affected parent, would have to be advised not to take part in procreation. There is an argument for allowing procreation of such a couple even if we consider the wider genetic good: genetic load is considered an evil only because it produces blemished children; the genes themselves cannot be considered evil, so if we find a way of eliminating the blemish while maintaining the genes, the desired result will be achieved. In addition, genetic variability in the population will be maintained.

A danger inherent even in a seemingly innocuous form of eugenics is that we cannot know for sure what alleles are an unmitigated evil under all circumstances. A practical difficulty in the application of eugenics is that in the case of recessive alleles it is often impossible to distinguish carriers, and preventing recessives from reproducing will eliminate the gene only very slowly. We have seen in Chapter XIX how slowly recessive alleles diminish when only homozygotes are selected against; in the case of phenylketonuria, if all persons having the complaint were prevented from reproducing, the frequency of the disease would be reduced by only one-half of 1 per cent in the next generation. Sometimes the heterozygote can be recognized, either because the allele is not completely recessive and can be detected by refined clinical tests, or because a study of the incidence of the trait in other members of the family indicates the probability of its presence. If heterozygotes can be distinguished and are prevented from having children, the effect will be much more efficient. If persons heterozygous for phenylketonuria were persuaded to have only half the number of children they normally would have, the gene frequency would be reduced to one-half of what it is and the incidence of the disease to about one-quarter. Dominant traits are those in which the heterozygote is as conspicuous as the homozygote, and these could be reduced in a more efficient way.

Genetic counseling is concerned with diagnosing a trait as genetic or nongenetic, studying the family history, and advising parents about the probability that their children will have a certain abnormality. The parents may be glad to have this advice, and the eugenicists will be happy that the population as a whole may be improved.

In the 1962 *Report of the United Nations Scientific Committee on the Effects of Atomic Radiation,*[1] a rough analysis of traits known or suspected to be genetically determined is given. About 1 per cent of live-born persons are afflicted with traits known to be determined by single genes. Several hundred different traits fall into this category, of which some 70 per cent are due to dominant genes, 25 per cent to autosomal recessive genes, and 5 per cent to sex-linked recessives. The majority of those due to dominant genes are mild in their effects: polydactyly, hammer toe, and bent little finger are examples. The recessive traits are, on the contrary, mostly severe in their effects.

Another 1 per cent of the live-born suffer from traits due to chromosome aberrations. These consist of abnormal numbers of sex chromosomes or autosomes, as well as chromosomal rearrangements. They can probably all be regarded as belonging to the mutational rather than the segregational load.

At least half of the deleterious traits which are known to be determined to a large extent by genetic factors are due to more complicated and less understood varieties of genetic control. Some of these may involve several genes or genes with low penetrance.

From genetic counseling and advice to parents for their own benefit, we move to the compulsory sterilization of those

[1] General Assembly Official Records, Seventeenth Session, Supplement No. 16 (A/5216).

considered genetically unfit. Laws allowing this exist in twenty-eight states in the United States. The motive behind this practice is not so much personal benefit to the parents as benefit to the population. Sterilization is far more drastic than genetic counseling, and it involves political dangers because some authority must decide which characters are undesirable. The question of whether the benefits outbalance the dangers is a political one, and geneticists can only provide technical details which contribute to a decision.

So far, we have been discussing the negative aspects of eugenics. A far more exhilarating but also more perilous topic is positive eugenics, the improvement of the human species. In the first case, we are trying to eliminate a known trait; in the second, we are trying to move human evolution in a favorable direction, which must be, in reality, unknown.

The traits of the ideal man may seem to us obvious. He should be intelligent, creative, tall and handsome, athletic, emotionally stable, perhaps appreciative of the arts, able to make rapid and wise decisions. All, or at any rate most, of us would like our children to have these qualities and might look favorably on a scheme to breed the human race in these directions. But the course of evolution in the past shows that we must be humble in our predictions. The evolution of man's intelligence certainly opened up a vast new niche, a new environment to fill. But we know almost nothing of how this evolutionary step came about. One authority believes it was due to the eating of meat, for the fossils that this authority believes to be the direct ancestors of man had teeth designed for this purpose. He believes that tools were then desirable to catch animals and cut them up. Another authority believes that man's bad taste or smell was an important factor, for he claims that lions in Africa will eat a man only for lack of something better, or when age and decrepitude prevent them from catching a tastier meal. Thus, man was protected and able to flourish at the expense of other primates.

It is curious that custom or law has often had an influence tending to reduce the perpetuation of traits considered desirable. At a period when talents of a devout religious life were prized above pure intellect, those having such qualities—priests and monks—did not reproduce. The chivalrous, equally prized, indulged in combats which must have restricted their reproductive potential. In later days, when wealth was considered a criterion of virtue, governments were apt to enact laws which had the effect of encouraging poor parents to have more children.

It is obvious that our ideas of desirable qualities have been changing throughout history and vary from culture to culture. How are we to judge what man should be like a thousand, five thousand, or a million years hence? Should he be larger, smaller, more intelligent, more telepathic (if there be such a quality), more resistant to radiation, able to survive in space, where no gravity holds his organs in place? Should he be more submissive or more authoritative, or should the species be polymorphic in this respect, with a nice balance between authoritative and submissive types? Underlying these questions is the assumption that there is, in fact, an important genetic component in all these qualities. When one is sure of what one wants, evolution can be directed to that end: a cow toward better milk production, a chicken toward more egg-laying; but note that a cow cannot run nor a chicken fly as well as its ancestors. Techniques other than killing or sterilizing the undesirables could probably be developed in the near future to alter the course of evolution considerably. Artificial insemination in humans is already practiced on a considerable scale, and there is no insuperable obstacle to keeping testicles alive in artificial culture many years after the decease of their proper owner. One desirable male could then have many thousand times as many children during his lifetime as he normally would and could continue to procreate after his death. Very recently it has been claimed that human cells in tissue culture can be transformed by DNA in the same way as pneumococcus and other bacterial cells. The process is very inefficient, only one in a million or so cells is transformed, but if this could be applied to sperm cells it would be a means of producing a directed mutation. The techniques are already available and new ones will undoubtedly be developed, but their use is more than questionable.

The simple technique of killing off a selected group of humans, either before or during their reproductive age, has been applied, no doubt, in numerous instances. Both the Greeks and the Carthaginians are reputed to have practiced infanticide. Their motives were different; the Carthaginians were of a religious turn of mind and sacrificed their healthiest and strongest specimens to the gods. The Greeks, being more rational, left babies exposed to such conditions as would kill off the weak ones.

The major attempt at changing the course of evolution in our times is now rightly condemned almost universally. The attempt to "purify the Nordic race" was intended to improve not the human species as a whole, but a subgroup of that species, at the expense of others. It was based, in any case, on erroneous genetic ideas.

A geneticist cannot claim to have a special prerogative to decide what is or is not a desirable human quality, but his occupation does give him a certain outlook and philosophy, which he is entitled to expound. The present writer can see only one principle which is safe to adopt. The human species should be prevented from reaching a dead end in evolution, like *Lingula* or the dinosaurs. In other words, the best conditions for evolution should be encouraged. The first requirement for this is that there should be a large reservoir of variability: we should maintain polymorphism. In this connection the extinction of Tasmanians and the situation among the Bushmen in Africa should be viewed with alarm.

We have already mentioned that a large population subdivided into many smaller populations, between which there is not too little and not too much interbreeding, probably provides the most favorable structure for evolution. The history of man must have been one of interbreeding groups consisting of only a few families. During historic times the aristocracy, as well as conquering soldiers, may have reproduced over a large area, but the majority bred within their own nation or district. In modern times, with the increased opportunities for travel, interbreeding over large areas seems to have reached the masses, but this may be offset to some extent by preferential mating within professional, religious, or cultural groups.

Population structure, in the sense of preferential mating habits, is certainly an important evolutionary factor. Another important factor is population size. Is the world overpopulated or underpopulated? Should the population fluctuate or should it be stable? These are questions which are being discussed with renewed vigor today. The geneticist can contribute one technical item to the discussion. Fertility is certainly genetic to some extent; to what extent we do not know. We do not even have reliable estimates of involuntarily sterile marriages in human populations. There must, however, be some selection for higher or lower fertility. We do alter the effect of selection for this factor by law, for the institution of monogamy ensures that the fertility of any marriage is controlled by the fertility of its least fertile partner.

We are thus affecting the course of our own evolution by legislation. We will most probably do so more and more consciously in the future. This is one of the outcomes of the evolution of conscience. A geneticist can only say that his way of thinking leads him to conclude that the desirable qualities in a future man cannot be known; that there are many pitfalls in trying to reach a defined goal, and that the wisest course is to ensure a wide pool of genetic variability. If some enthusiasts insist on improving the race, then let theirs be local projects so that different groups will be bred for different qualities.

In concluding let us say a word about cultural evolution. In many ways this resembles genetic evolution. A culture is transmitted from one generation to the next: changes or mutations occur and are passed on. The highly evolved construction of a sailing vessel or violin can be traced through many stages of small improvements. The unfit novelties are eliminated by selection and the fit ones survive and multiply. An important difference is that cultural mutations are not quite random; we can perhaps say that in the case of culture there is an inheritance of acquired characteristics.

If the similarity between genetic and cultural evolution is at all valid, may it not be that the best conditions for cultural evolution too are supplied by a subdivided population? This would mean that we should not aim at a uniform culture over a large area, but should, on the contrary, preserve and encourage small cultural groups between which there is some, but not too much, exchange. I think it is important that unpopular groups should be included. Perhaps we could go so far as to say that the more unpopular a thought or way of behaving is, the more important it is not to extinguish it.

The language barriers in Europe and other parts of the world may well have contributed to rapid evolution. The anticipated extinction of Bushman culture would, from this point of view, be most unfortunate. The large continental and in some ways homogeneous cultures which are dominant today would seem also to be undesirable in this connection, but here again it may be that the subdivisions are professional, religious, and social rather than geographical.

The evolution of culture depends on the brain. The evolution of higher centers of the brain and of thought introduces what we vaguely call conscience. Acquisition of the faculty of thinking about oneself is a drastic step in evolution. One aspect of this faculty is that it contains a peculiar feedback system. As soon as a man can think about himself, he may become disgusted with his life; he may decide life is not worth living, and since he can both think and act on that thought, he may actually commit suicide. With conscience, however, comes knowledge of God and the afterlife. This enables man to complete a life which might otherwise appear intolerable. For those rational minds who have difficulty in following a theological argument, the course of evolution, both genetic and cultural, can serve the same function. The biologist is made aware of the interrelationships between men. One cell, the gamete, will survive him physically. One molecule of DNA will survive many generations intact. This is admittedly a small part of a man, but it is an important part. On another plane, every action of a man—every sentence he writes, every painting he paints, piece of music he composes, or word he speaks, will affect to some degree the evolutionary course of culture.

Bibliography ♀/♂

The following books represent, in the author's opinion, the best available on various aspects of genetics. They are all more or less specialized and together cover the whole area of genetics in its widest sense.

The order of listing corresponds roughly to the order in which the subjects are discussed in the text.

White, M. J. D., *The Chromosomes.* Methuen's Monographs on Biological Subjects, London. 5th ed., 1961. A concise and authoritative account of the chromosomes from a morphological rather than a genetic or biochemical point of view.

Loewy, A. G., and Siekevitz, P., *Cell Structure and Function.* Holt, Rinehart and Winston, New York, 1963. An up-to-date account of chemical (molecular) genetics showing relations to cell anatomy. (Paperback.)

Watson, J. D., *Molecular Biology of the Gene.* W. A. Benjamin, Inc., New York and Amsterdam. 1965. A fairly advanced text, but written in an easy dogmatic style.

Wagner, R. P., and Mitchell, H. K., *Genetics and Metabolism.* John Wiley & Sons, New York. 2nd ed., 1964. A comprehensive and advanced text on physiological genetics. The only up-to-date text covering the field.

Hayes, W., *The Genetics of Bacteria and Their Viruses.* Blackwell, Oxford. 1964. A large and comprehensive book which does not require an extensive background but is nevertheless an advanced text.

Stent, G. S., *Molecular Biology of Bacterial Viruses.* Freeman & Co., San Francisco. 1963. An enjoyable account of the subject, with an interesting historical chapter.

Lack, D., *Darwin's Finches.* Harper Torchbooks, New York. 1961. This book and the following one, by Simpson, are both very readable and of high scholarship. They represent the best writing, perhaps, on evolutionary trends.

Simpson, G. G., *Horses.* Doubleday Anchor Books, Garden City, New York. 1961. A well-illustrated and fascinating story of the evolution of horses.

Li, C. C., *Human Genetics.* McGraw-Hill, New York. 1961. One of the more readable texts for the outsider covering the algebraical aspect of population genetics.

Stern, C., *Human Genetics.* Freeman & Co., San Francisco. 2nd ed., 1960. Comprehensive and not too specialized, this book includes an account of elementary genetic principles.

Medawar, P. B., *The Future of Man*. Methuen & Co., Ltd., London. First published in 1960. A series of lectures delivered over the British Broadcasting Corporation network. Well written and intellectually entertaining, the book covers problems of human genetics and population trends.

Lush, J. L., *Animal Breeding Plans*. Iowa State University Press, Ames. 3rd ed., 1945. A description of a specialized field of applied genetics. Covers subjects which have been mostly omitted in the present volume.

Allard, R. W., *Principles of Plant Breeding*. John Wiley & Sons, New York. 1960. Another specialized and applied aspect of the subject.

Peters, J. A., ed., *Classic Papers in Genetics*. Prentice-Hall, Englewood Cliffs, New Jersey. 1959. These represent a well-chosen selection of original papers by well-known geneticists. It is nearly always preferable to learn something directly from its original source rather than from a secondary or tertiary source.

Taylor, J. H., ed., *Selected Papers on Molecular Genetics*. Academic Press, New York. 1965. A collection of papers more recent and more technical than those included in the above.

Glossary ♀/♂

ACTIVATING ENZYME. An enzyme which plays a part in translating the genetic code. Each activating enzyme attaches itself to a specific amino acid and also to the appropriate transfer RNA.

ALLELE. An abbreviation, used by American and some British writers, of "allelomorph." An allele is one particular state of a gene. The gene controlling eye color, for instance, has two alleles; one producing brown eyes, the other blue eyes.

ASEXUAL REPRODUCTION. Reproduction and cell division in which no sexual mating or fusion of gametes is involved. The chromosomes in asexual reproduction divide by mitosis. Also called vegetative reproduction.

BLASTULA STAGE. A stage in the development of an animal from fertilized egg, or zygote, into the fully formed organism, in which the embryo consists of a microscopic hollow ball whose wall is formed by a single layer of cells. It is followed by a gastrula stage.

CELL. The unit of structure of all life, except that viruses are usually regarded as noncellular. The typical cell of higher organisms consists of an outer membrane, a region of cytoplasm containing ribosomes, mitochondria, and other structures, a nucleus surrounded by a membrane, and chromosomes within the nucleus.

CHARACTER. Any structure, behavior, or process that can be defined and studied genetically.

CHROMOSOME. One of the threadlike structures in the nucleus of cells which stain deeply and are clearly visible under a microscope. They are seen only in dividing cells, and the evidence that they represent the structures along which genes lie is overwhelming.

CODE, CODON. "Genetic code" is a general term covering the nature of the way in which DNA contains the information for producing peptide chains and hence proteins. A "codon" is the particular code, believed to consist of three nucleotides, for an amino acid.

CONVERSION. At meiosis alleles normally segregate in a ratio of exactly 2:2. Thus a cell whose alleles are A and *a* will give rise to two cells having the A allele and two having the *a* allele. When alleles segregate in a ratio of 3:1 or 4:0 or, in later divisions, 5:3; 6:2, 7:1, or 8:0, the phenomenon is known by some as conversion.

CYTOPLASM. That part of a cell which is not nucleus. It consists mainly of proteins in the form of enzymes, simple chemicals in solution, and various particles such as mitochondria, ribosomes, and chloroplasts. It may be permeated by an extensive folded membrane, the endoreticulum, and it is bounded on the inside by the nuclear membrane and on the outside by a cytoplasmic membrane.

DIFFERENTIATION. The process by which cells change as the fertilized egg, or zygote, divides repeatedly to form all the various types of cells in the different tissues of the body.

DIPLOID. Having two sets of chomosomes and genes, one set being derived from each parent.

DNA. Deoxyribose nucleic acid. A special form of nucleic acid which constitutes the hereditary substance of the chromosomes. Its detailed structure consists of a double helix as proposed by Watson and Crick. See *RNA*.

DOMINANT. In a heterozygote, where two different alleles are present, one allele often masks the other; the former is then known as dominant. The allele for brown eye is dominant over that for blue, which is recessive. If *B* represents the dominant allele for brown eyes and *b* the recessive for blue, then the genotypes *BB* and *Bb* will appear equally brown-eyed and *bb* will appear blue-eyed.

ELECTRON MICROSCOPE. An electronic device which focuses an electron beam onto the object being examined and then on to a fluorescent screen for immediate viewing, or onto a photographic plate. Whereas the limit of resolution of a light microscope is about .2 μ, the electron microscope can resolve down to about 5 Å. One micron (μ) equals $\frac{1}{1{,}000}$ mm. One Angstrom unit (Å) equals $\frac{1}{10{,}000}$ μ.

ENZYME. A substance, consisting of large protein molecules made up of one or more peptide chains, which promotes specific chemical reactions.

EPISTASIS. The domination of one gene by another. Not to be confused with "dominance," which concerns domination of one allele over another allele of the same gene.

EVOLUTION. The idea, associated with Charles Darwin, that species of animals and plants, including man, have changed slowly throughout the ages, the main trend being progressive—from simple to more complex organisms. This idea, or theory, is now accepted by the vast majority of professional biologists. See *Natural Selection.*

EXPRESSIVITY. The degree to which a gene expresses itself in individuals having the gene. When the expressivity of a gene is low, the hereditary contribution is only marginal and is greatly influenced by environmental or random factors.

GAMETE. A cell that joins with another in sexual mating. Sperm and eggs are gametes.

GASTRULA STAGE. A stage of animal development, following the blastula stage, in which half of the blastula is folded into the other half. After some further cell movement and growth, this produces a hollow ball whose wall consists of a double layer of cells with a hole in it.

GENE. A unit of heredity transmitted by the germ cells. The term is used somewhat ambiguously in that it may include all the alternative types (thus becoming synonymous with "locus"), or it may mean only one type (thus becoming synonymous with "allele.")

GENETIC LOAD. A term which is supposed to designate the sum total of bad genes, especially recessive alleles, carried by a population. For a more complete discussion, see Chapter XX.

GENOTYPE. The total gene content of an organism.

HAPLOID. Having one set of chromosomes and genes.

HETEROCHROMATIN. Parts of the chromosomes which stain differently, probably because of the way in which the DNA thread is coiled up in these regions.

HETEROKARYON. A cell containing two or more different nuclei, or an organism consisting of such cells.

HETEROZYGOUS. A diploid cell or organism is heterozygous for a gene if it contains two different alleles of that gene. If the two alleles are similar, the organism is homozygous. Heterozygous individuals do not breed true.

HOMOZYGOUS. See *Heterozygous.*

INHIBITOR. A substance which blocks the function of an enzyme. It is usually a metabolite which blocks enzymes in the metabolic sequence that leads to its own synthesis.

LINKAGE MAP. A representation of a linear array of genes with appropriate distances between them. Linkage maps are usually constructed from the proportions of different types of offspring from a cross.

LOCUS. The particular place on a linkage map occupied by a gene or allele. The chromosomes are the visible, material structures which correspond to linkage maps derived indirectly from breeding experiments.

LYSOGENY. The potential ability to lyse, or dissolve. Lysogenic bacteria are bacteria which carry a virus (phage) in a latent state which, upon provocation, may become virulent, kill the cell, and dissolve most of it. In the lysogenic bacteria, phage multiply in a controlled way, in step with the host bacteria to whose chromosomes they are, in fact, attached.

MATERNAL. From the mother. Some characters, for various reasons, tend to follow a matrilineal inheritance; these are known as maternal characters.

MEIOSIS. Special division of the chromosomes which occurs, in higher animals, just before the formation of germ cells (sperm and eggs). Meiosis consists of two divisions, and each of the resulting four cells has half as many chromosomes as the original cell.

MESSENGER RNA. A particular species of RNA which appears to take information from a gene and convey it to the ribosome, where the information is translated into a protein molecule.

MITOSIS. Division of the chromosomes in ordinary tissues of plants and animals. Each chromosome duplicates exactly, and the two resulting nuclei are identical to each other and to the original nucleus.

MUTANT. A gene that has mutated. There is some ambiguity here since all genes have probably mutated sometime in their history. Generally, the most common allele of the gene is known as wild type, and the rarer allele is regarded as the mutant.

MUTATION. The alteration of a gene. This rare event can be made more frequent by treatment with radiation or certain chemicals; the mutation is then an induced mutation; otherwise it is known as a spontaneous mutation.

NATURAL SELECTION. A theory which attempts to explain the mechanism by which evolution takes place. Like the theory of evolution, it is associated with Charles Darwin. It is an idea which deserves a great deal more attention than may seem to be called for at first glance. Briefly and superficially, it says that species will become fitter and fitter because the fittest individual of each generation will leave more children than the unfit and the children of the fit will tend to resemble their parents.

NEUROSPORA. A fungus belonging to the Ascomycetes, which include the molds, yeasts, and many plant parasites. It is a favorable organism for research because it grows quickly under laboratory conditions and requires no complex substances in the growth medium except biotin, and because its sexually produced spores are arranged in packets of eight, representing twin products of the four cells of a meiotic division.

NUCLEOTIDE. The structural unit of DNA and RNA. It is made up of a base, a sugar, and phosphate grouping. The important nucleotides, their corresponding bases and nucleosides (base and sugar, but no phosphate), and playing-card symbols used in the text are:

Base	*Nucleosides*	*Nucleotides*	*Symbol*
adenine	adenosine	adenosine phosphate	♡
guanine	guanosine	guanosine phosphate	◇
cytosine	cytidine	cytidine phosphate	♣
thymine	thymidine	thymidine phosphate	♠
uracil	uridine	uridine phosphate	♠

NUCLEUS. The part of a cell, surrounded by a membrane, which contains chromosomes.

PATERNAL. From the father. See *Maternal*.

PENETRANCE. A gene has low penetrance when only a small percentage of the individuals having the gene show the character (see

Chapter VII). Those who do show the character, however, show it to the full extent. This phenomenon adds confusion to the genetic analysis of such character. (See *Expressivity.*)

PETRI DISH. A round glass dish about five inches in diameter, with a similar but larger glass top. The dish is filled with a gelatin, or more commonly an agar, nutrient medium, and organisms can be grown under sterile conditions on the surface of this solid medium. Single microorganisms will thus produce single visible colonies.

PHAGE. A virus that attacks bacteria, more properly called a bacteriophage.

PHENOTYPE. The appearance of an organism. It may or may not have a one-to-one relation with the genotype.

POLYMORPHISM. The existence of several well-defined types in a population.

RECESSIVE. An allele masked by the dominant allele is known as recessive. An individual heterozygous for a gene for hemophilia, for instance, will not be a hemophiliac because the hemophilia allele is masked by the normal allele; such a person is often called a carrier.

REPRESSOR GENE. A gene which produces a hypothetical repressor substance which prevents the formation of an enzyme. The repressor gene may or may not be closely linked to the structural gene of the enzyme or enzymes concerned.

RIBOSOME. New name for a microsome—one of the particles, found in the cytoplasm of cells, which are now known to consist mainly of RNA and protein and to be intimately concerned with protein synthesis.

RNA. Ribose nucleic acid, another form of nucleic acid. It differs from DNA in the sugar portion of the molecule and in the substitution of uracil for thymine among the bases. RNA is found in the ribosomes, which lie mostly in the cytoplasm of the cells, and is believed to have several different functions in translating the genes into the enzymes they determine. (See *Messenger RNA, transfer RNA.*)

SEGREGATION. The sorting out of parental characters in offspring.

SUPPRESSOR GENE. A gene which suppresses the effect (phenotype) of another mutant gene. An organism carrying the original mutation and a suppressor mutation will then appear wild type and may, at first sight, be taken for a back mutation of the original gene. Suppressors are not necessarily linked to the gene or genes they suppress.

TAPE. Synonymous with "messenger RNA" and going out of common usage. It was presumably coined to suggest an analogy with the magnetic tape which stores musical information for use in tape recorders.

TEMPERATE PHAGE. A phage that is not virulent. Lysogenic bacteria carry temperate phage. Temperate phage may become virulent upon provocation.

TRANSFER RNA. A form of RNA which plays a part in translating the genetic code. It is sometimes referred to as soluble RNA (s-RNA) or adaptor RNA.

TRANSFORMATION. The genetic modification of bacteria induced by the incorporation of DNA. Attempts to transform higher organisms are, up to the present, dubious.

VEGETATIVE REPRODUCTION. See *Asexual Reproduction.*

VIRUS. The smallest living organism. Viruses are invisible to ordinary light microscopes, and they cannot live outside the living cells of some other organism.

WILD TYPE. A vague but nevertheless useful term. It refers to the majority or conforming type of a character, thus contradicting the colloquial meaning. It is symbolized by a "+" superscript or a + in a particular position among other symbols representing alleles.

ZYGOTE. The fertilized egg or the cell that results from the fusion of male and female gametes.

Appendices ♀/♂

Appendix 1

Unit	Length	Number of Base pairs	Number of Combinations	Properties
Base pair	3·4 Å	4	4	Ultimate unit of recombination and mutation
Codon	10 Å	3	64	Determines one amino acid
Gene	0·3μ	1000	10^{200}	Determines one polypeptide chain for an enzyme
(Operon)	1μ	1000-5000	–	Unit of control of polypeptide synthesis
Chromosome				Unit of independent assortment
Large phage	53μ-90μ	$2·7 \times 10^5$	10^{81}	
E. coli	1 cm	10^7	$10^{30,000}$	
Man	4 cms	$1·3 \times 10^9$	$10^{3,000,000}$	
Total DNA per cell				Unit of genetic control of cell
Large phage	53μ-90μ	$2·7 \times 10^5$	10^{81}	
PPLO*	25μ	$7·5 \times 10^4$	$10^{2,000}$	
E. coli	1 cm	10^7	$10^{30,000}$	
Jellyfish	10 cms	3×10^8	$10^{1,000,000}$	
Man	1 meter	3×10^9	$10^{10,000,000}$	

Phenotypes (2 alleles per locus)

10,000Å=1μ 1,000μ=1mm Diameter of ribosome = 200 Å Diameter of nucleus (liver cell) 5μ Diameter of cell (liver) 20μ

* 1) Pleuropneumonia-like organism, the smallest living organism able to live outside living cells.

Appendix 2

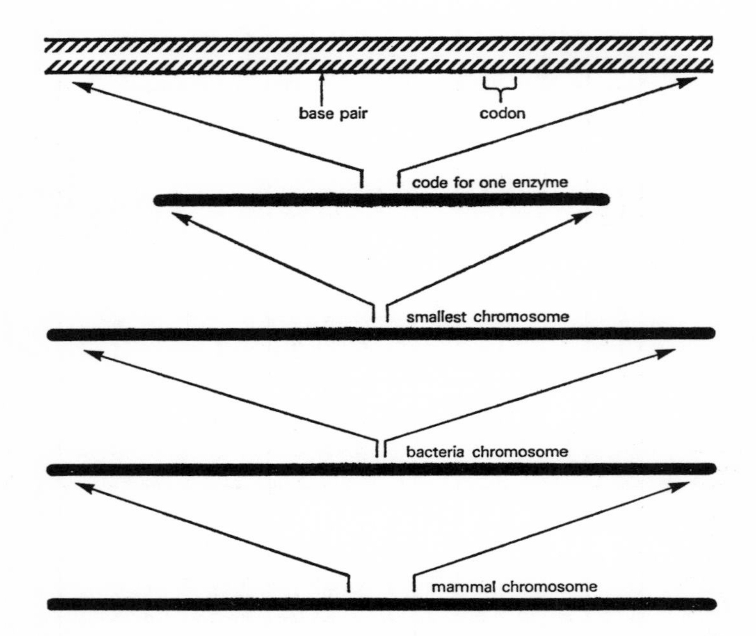

Approximate Sizes of Various Units—Illustrated. This is a rough graphical illustration giving an idea of the magnitude of some of the units discussed throughout the book and tabulated in Appendix 1.

Appendix 3

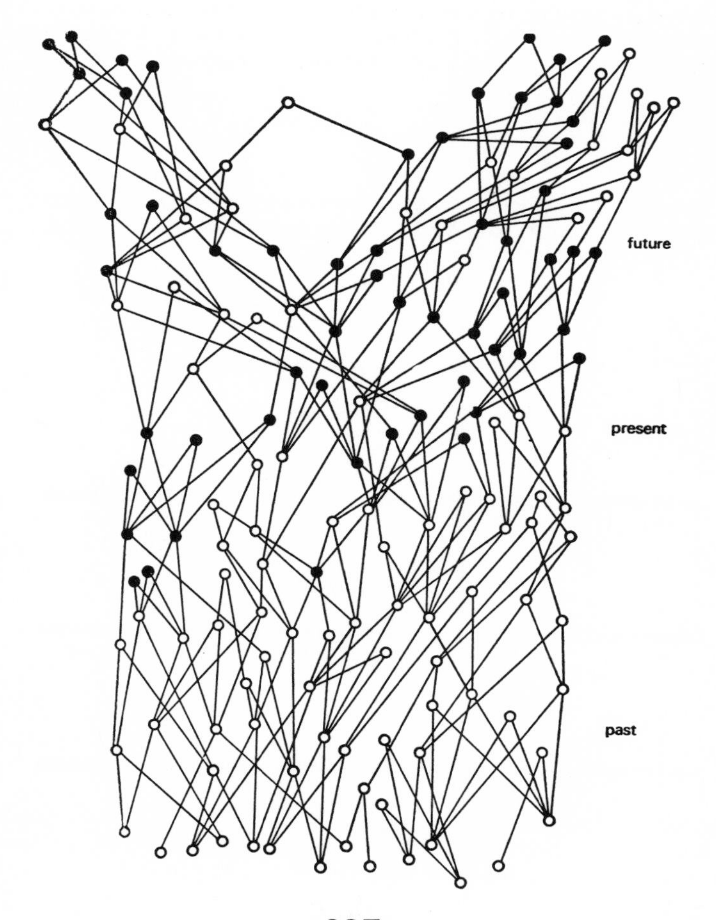

Diagram of a Randomly Breeding Population. About seven generations are represented. Mating is monogamous, with occasional individuals mating twice. Population number is about twenty. With such a small population, inbreeding is inevitable; there are several cousin matings, the offspring of which are indicated by black circles. In the last two or three generations the population splits up into two smaller populations which hardly ever interbreed. Each circle is a diploid individual, and each line represents a haploid set of chromosomes in a gamete. Each circle has two lines entering it from the south, the egg and sperm, and any number leaving it from the north, eggs or sperm. The diagram is thus not an accurate representation of the situation in mammals, where fertilization is internal. Evolutionary selection can be envisaged as eliminating the circles and hence the lines emanating from them.

Appendix 4

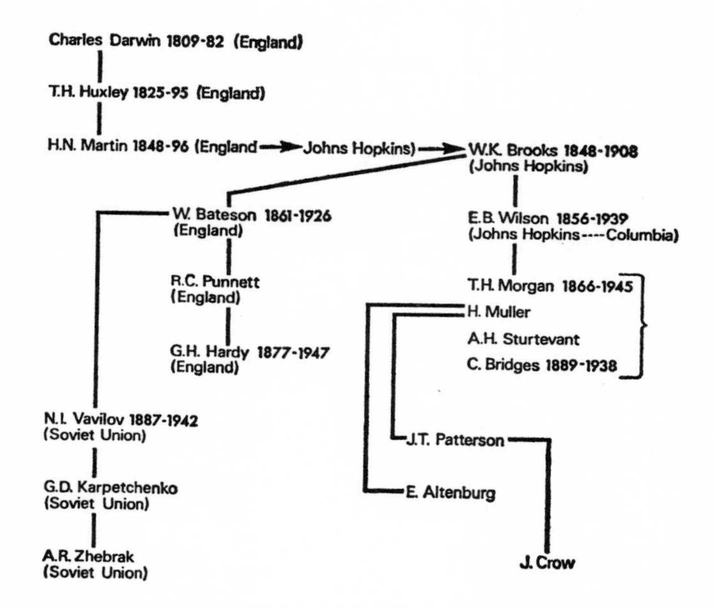

Relationships of Influence Among Some Geneticists. For several reasons this tree has been included with some hesitation. The few names in it have been rather arbitrarily chosen to show the influences on and from the Columbia group of *Drosophila* geneticists (Morgan, Muller,

Sturtevant, Bridges), and many worthy members of this group have been omitted for reasons of space. Individuals mentioned in the book have been given preference. Relationships are generally based on proximity; two or more people working in the same institution are presumed to have influenced each other and generally the older is (perhaps erroneously) believed to have influenced the younger more than vice versa. The contact of a young man with a brilliant established scientist is undoubtedly an important factor in the development of scientists and science, but the relationship is often complex and difficult to describe. Sometimes the relationship is simple; in the case of Hardy and Punnett the bond was the game of cricket and proximity on a committee at Cambridge University to retain Greek in the Previous Examination. Punnett, a geneticist, had been asked, following an address at the Royal Society, why the population was not getting increasingly brown-eyed, since brown eyes are dominant over blue. Punnett put this question in an abstract form to his mathematical friend Hardy, who knew no genetics at all but soon answered with the classical Hardy (now Hardy-Weinberg) law.

Two other streams of genetic thought have been equally influential in the United States. One of these has concentrated on mammals, and includes C. B. Davenport, W. E. Castle, Sewell Wright, L. C. Dunn, H. S. Jennings, and T. M. Sonneborn. The other has developed corn as a genetic subject, and includes R. A. Emerson, E. M. East, G. W. Beadle, and most of the contemporary corn geneticists.

A notable feature of recent years has been the influx of men trained in the nongenetic fields of physics and chemistry.

Index ♀/♂